LINEAR TRANSFORMATIONS
in *n*-dimensional vector space

LINEAR TRANSFORMATIONS
in *n*-dimensional vector space

AN INTRODUCTION TO THE THEORY OF HILBERT SPACE

BY

H. L. HAMBURGER
Professor in the University of Cologne

AND

M. E. GRIMSHAW
Fellow of Newnham College, Cambridge

CAMBRIDGE
AT THE UNIVERSITY PRESS
1956

PUBLISHED BY
THE SYNDICS OF THE CAMBRIDGE UNIVERSITY PRESS
London Office: Bentley House, N.W.1
American Branch: New York
Agents for Canada, India, and Pakistan: Macmillan

First edition 1951
Reprinted 1956

First printed in Great Britain at the University Press, Cambridge
Reprinted by offset-litho by
Jarrold and Sons Ltd., Norwich

PREFACE

In this book we introduce the ideas and methods of the theory of linear transformations in Hilbert space by using them to present the elements of the theory in a finite dimensional vector space. We discuss problems fundamental in the study of general abstract linear spaces and use the powerful methods appropriate to the consideration of these spaces; both problems and methods, however, are simplified by our restriction to an n-dimensional space.

Some particular features of the presentation may be mentioned. The main results in the theory of linear transformations, namely, the spectral representations of Hermitian transformations, and the canonical representations and commutativity properties of general linear transformations, are developed here without the use of determinants because determinants can be used in Hilbert space only in very special cases. A concrete vector space has been chosen in preference to an abstract space so that the ideas may be more readily grasped, but the coordinates of vectors and the elements of matrices occur only exceptionally in the proofs; most of them could be applied unchanged for an abstract space. By defining the scalar product at the start instead of developing first the descriptive properties of linear manifolds and transformations (an alternative course with some obvious advantages, followed in the books by G. Julia [V]* and P. R. Halmos [III]) we can introduce the Schmidt orthogonalization process at an early stage and take advantage of its appeal to geometrical intuition; for instance, we obtain a natural geometrical illustration of the problem of the solution of a system of homogeneous linear equations. The resulting development on geometrical lines of the calculus of linear manifolds replaces the familiar and more formal calculus of matrices.

We use only orthogonal coordinate systems because the use of oblique coordinates would lead to difficulties in later generalizations to Hilbert space. This means that we consider general linear transformations only as mappings of the space on itself, while we interpret unitary transformations both as congruent mappings of the space on itself and also as transformations of coordinate systems.

* Numbers in square brackets refer to the list of references at the end of the book. Roman numbers are used for books and arabic numbers for papers.

Finally, although we deal with algebraical problems, we have not excluded analytical methods in view of their importance for certain problems in Hilbert space, and we use them to obtain the spectral representations of Hermitian transformations.

The book presents a self-contained account of the theory of linear transformations in finite dimensional vector space. Chapter I contains the elementary general properties of linear manifolds and linear transformations. Chapter II introduces the algebraical treatment of the normal transformations (with the Hermitian and unitary transformations as special examples) and of general and orthogonal projectors. In Chapter III the spectral representations of Hermitian and normal transformations are obtained by the analytical methods due to Hilbert and based on the property of the eigen-values of a Hermitian form as its maxima in certain closed sets of the vector space. The methods are developed further to give inequalities for the eigen-values that have proved of value in recent computational work. The chapter closes with a discussion of the functional calculus for Hermitian and normal transformations. In Chapter IV we return to algebraical methods in dealing with the more complicated problem of the reduction of a general linear transformation to the Jordan canonical form. The existence of eigen-values is established here, without the introduction of determinants, by the use of arguments contained in recent papers by N. Dunford and one of the present authors ([16] and [23]). The spectral representations of normal transformations are obtained again, this time as special examples of the representations of linear transformations with simple elementary divisors, and the chapter ends with a discussion of the commutativity properties of general linear transformations. These results include a series of theorems for linear transformations with simple elementary divisors, and a formulation, in terms of the complete reduction of the linear transformation A, of the commutativity properties of the polynomials $p(A)$, for which we have found no reference. The theme of Chapter III is taken up again in Chapter V, which is concerned with the spectral representation of the pencil $H-\lambda G$, where H and G are Hermitian transformations of which G is positive definite; a familiar problem with various applications in mathematical physics. The application to the dynamical theory of small oscillations is dealt with in detail in order to illustrate the significance of the inequalities of Chapter III. The introduction, in Chapter V, of a generalized n-dimensional vector space in which the scalar product is defined by a positive definite Hermitian form foreshadows some of our later work on abstract spaces and provides a link between this work and the elementary approach of Chapter I. Moreover, it leads to the theorem given towards the end of Chapter V, that every linear transformation with simple elementary divisors can be considered as a normal transformation in a vector space in which the scalar product is suitably defined.

The notes at the end of the book give references for the main results. They are selected somewhat arbitrarily and make no claim to completeness. No references to the notes are made in the text; they are meant to be consulted after the reading of each chapter.

H. L. H.
M. E. G.

CAMBRIDGE
September 1947

ACKNOWLEDGEMENTS

The authors wish to record their indebtedness to Dr N. Aronszajn for permission to publish the proof of his inequalities which appears in Chapter III.

They also wish to thank Miss S. M. Edmonds, Miss N. Walls and Dr J. D. Weston for assistance in proof correction and for much valuable criticism.

H. L. H.
M. E. G.

CONTENTS

CHAPTER I

LINEAR MANIFOLDS AND LINEAR TRANSFORMATIONS IN $\mathfrak{B}_n$

§ 1. Vectors and operations on vectors

1·0. In these first four chapters we deal for the most part with well-known algebraical problems which we describe in geometrical terms and interpret in a space of n-dimensional complex vectors (an n-dimensional vector space). Our object is to introduce the ideas and technique that are characteristic of the theory of Hilbert space, and so we give the proofs as far as possible without using the coordinates of vectors or the elements of matrices; most of them would have taken the same form if we had defined the vector space, as Hilbert space is defined, in terms of its abstract properties. We illustrate the applications of the general theory by considering for n-dimensional vector space such familiar problems as those of the solution of systems of homogeneous and non-homogeneous linear equations and of the transformation of a Hermitian form to principal axes, but we do not give the familiar arguments using determinants because they are not in keeping with our development of the theory and cannot be generalized for Hilbert space. Indeed, we have deliberately avoided the use of determinants throughout the book.

It will be seen that we define a metric form for the space at a very early stage in the discussion, and that this leads us at once to the idea of orthogonality and to the introduction of Schmidt's orthogonalization process which plays an essential part in the theory of bounded linear transformations in Hilbert space.

1·1. Definition of a vector. *We define a vector x as an ordered system of n complex numbers $x_1, x_2, \ldots, x_n$,* called the *coordinates* of the vector, and we write $x=(x_1, x_2, \ldots, x_n)$. We define the *zero vector* as $0=(0, 0, \ldots, 0)$.

A system of n complex numbers may also be called a *point,* and the point $(0, 0, \ldots, 0)$ may be called the *origin.*

When $x'=(x'_1, x'_2, \ldots, x'_n)$ we write $x=x'$ if, and only if, $x_\nu=x'_\nu$ for $\nu = 1, 2, \ldots, n$. We write $\bar{x} = (\bar{x}_1, \bar{x}_2, \ldots, \bar{x}_n)$, where $\bar{x}_\nu$ denotes the number conjugate to x_ν, and we say that the vector $\bar{x}$ is conjugate to x. We say that x is real if $x = \bar{x}$; that is, if the n coordinates x_ν are all real.

Throughout the book vectors are represented by letters of the same types as those representing complex numbers, but in the case of vectors suffixes are raised. Thus, $x^1, x^2, \ldots, x^n$ denotes a set of n vectors, while n numbers (for example, the coordinates of a vector) are denoted by $x_1, x_2, \ldots, x_n$.

The set of all vectors x defined by n coordinates forms the n-dimensional vector space which we denote by $\mathfrak{V}_n$. We write $x \in \mathfrak{V}_n$ to mean that x is an element of $\mathfrak{V}_n$ and, more generally, we write $x \in \mathfrak{X}$ if x is an element of any set $\mathfrak{X}$ of vectors.

Sets of vectors are denoted by German capital letters; sets in the plane of complex numbers, such as curves and domains, are denoted by small German letters.

1·2. Multiplication of a vector by a number. If x is any vector, $x = (x_1, x_2, \ldots, x_n)$, and if α is any complex number, then x multiplied by α is defined as the vector $(\alpha x_1, \alpha x_2, \ldots, \alpha x_n)$ and is written as αx. In particular, we write $-x$ for αx when $\alpha = -1$.

The vector αx coincides with x if $\alpha = 1$; it is the zero vector if, and only if, either $\alpha = 0$ or $x = 0$. We see at once that $\overline{\alpha x} = \bar{\alpha}\bar{x}$, and that, if β is any complex number, then $\alpha(\beta x) = \beta(\alpha x) = \alpha\beta x$.

1·3. Addition of vectors. If

$$x = (x_1, x_2, \ldots, x_n) \quad \text{and} \quad y = (y_1, y_2, \ldots, y_n),$$

then the sum of x and y is defined as the vector

$$x + y = (x_1 + y_1,\ x_2 + y_2,\ \ldots,\ x_n + y_n).$$

We write $x - y$ for $x + (-y)$. We see that $x - x = 0$.

1·31. The commutative, associative and distributive laws of addition all hold, since we obtain at once, for vectors x, y, z and any numbers α, β,

$$x + y = y + x, \quad (x + y) + z = x + (y + z)$$

and

$$\alpha(x + y) = \alpha x + \alpha y, \quad (\alpha + \beta)x = \alpha x + \beta x.$$

If $x + y = x + z$, then $y = z$.

1·32. For any non-real vector z there are two real vectors x and y such that $z = x + iy$; they are

$$x = \tfrac{1}{2}(z + \bar{z}), \quad y = \frac{1}{2i}(z - \bar{z}).$$

1·33. The vectors

$$u^1 = (1, 0, \ldots, 0), \quad u^2 = (0, 1, 0, \ldots, 0), \quad \ldots, \quad u^n = (0, 0, \ldots, 0, 1)$$

are called the *coordinate vectors*. We have, for any vector x,

$$x = \sum_{\nu=1}^{n} x_\nu u^\nu. \tag{1·33·1}$$

1·4. Definition of the scalar product of two vectors. The *scalar product* of two vectors x and y is a complex number associated with the vectors. We denote it by (x, y) and define it so that it shall satisfy the following three conditions for any vectors x, y, z and any number α:

$$\text{(i) } (\alpha x, y) = \alpha(x, y), \quad \text{(ii) } (x+y, z) = (x, z) + (y, z),$$

$$\text{(iii) } (y, x) = \overline{(x, y)} = (\bar{x}, \bar{y}).$$

The conditions (i) and (iii) imply that

$$(x, \alpha y) = \overline{(\alpha y, x)} = \bar{\alpha}\overline{(y, x)} = \bar{\alpha}(x, y), \tag{1·4·1}$$

and (ii) and (iii) imply that

$$(x, y+z) = \overline{(y+z, \bar{x})} = \overline{(y, x)} + \overline{(z, x)} = (x, y) + (x, z). \tag{1·4·2}$$

We now add the definition of the special scalar products of the coordinate vectors u^ν by writing

$$\text{(iv) } (u^\mu, u^\nu) = \delta_{\mu\nu} \quad (\mu, \nu = 1, 2, \ldots, n),$$

where here, and throughout the book, $\delta_{\mu\nu}$ is the Kronecker symbol with the interpretation

$$\delta_{\mu\nu} = 0 \quad (\mu \neq \nu), \qquad \delta_{\mu\nu} = 1 \quad (\mu = \nu).$$

Writing $x = \sum_{\nu=1}^{n} x_\nu u^\nu$, $y = \sum_{\nu=1}^{n} y_\nu u^\nu$ we see by (i), (ii) and (iv) that $(x, u^\nu) = x_\nu$ and hence, by (1·33·1), that $x = \sum_{\nu=1}^{n} (x, u^\nu) u^\nu$. We also obtain the analytical expression for the scalar product

$$(x, y) = \sum_{\nu=1}^{n} \sum_{\mu=1}^{n} x_\nu \overline{y_\mu} (u^\nu, u^\mu) = \sum_{\nu=1}^{n} \sum_{\mu=1}^{n} x_\nu \overline{y_\mu} \delta_{\mu\nu}$$

$$= \sum_{\nu=1}^{n} x_\nu \overline{y_\nu}, \tag{1·4·3}$$

which could have been used for the definition. Had we defined the scalar product by (1·4·3) we should have deduced at once the conditions (i), (ii), (iii) and (iv).

We deduce at once from the condition (iii) that (x, y) is real if x and y are both real and that $(y, x) = 0$ if $(x, y) = 0$.

1·41. Definition of the absolute value of a vector. *The absolute value, or norm, of a vector x is defined as the non-negative real number*

$$\| x \| = (x, x)^{\frac{1}{2}} = \left(\sum_{\nu=1}^{n} | x_\nu |^2 \right)^{\frac{1}{2}}.$$

We also call $\| x \|$ the *length* of the vector x. We see that $\| x \| = 0$ if and only if $x = 0$. If $\| x \| = 1$ we say that x is a *unit vector*; the coordinate vectors are unit vectors. The absolute value $\| x-y \|$ is called the *distance* between the points, or vectors, x and y. Clearly, $\| x-y \| = \| y-x \|$.

By **1·4** (i) and (1·4·1), we have

$$\| \alpha x \|^2 = (\alpha x, \alpha x) = \alpha\bar{\alpha}(x, x) = | \alpha |^2 \| x \|^2,$$

and hence

$$\| \alpha x \| = | \alpha | \, \| x \|. \tag{1·41·1}$$

We notice that this proof of (1·41·1) is independent of the special condition **1·4** (iv) for the scalar product.

1·42. For any vectors x and y and any number λ we have

$$\begin{aligned} \| x+\lambda y \|^2 &= (x+\lambda y, x+\lambda y) \\ &= \| x \|^2 + \lambda(y, x) + \bar{\lambda}(x, y) + \lambda\bar{\lambda} \| y \|^2 \\ &\geqslant 0, \end{aligned}$$

with equality if, and only if, $x+\lambda y = 0$. Taking $\| y \| \neq 0$ and $\lambda \| y \|^2 = -(x, y)$, we obtain

$$\| x \|^2 \| y \|^2 - | (x, y) |^2 \geqslant 0,$$

and we deduce that

$$| (x, y) | \leqslant \| x \| \, \| y \|, \tag{1·42·1}$$

with equality if, and only if, one of the vectors x and y is zero or is a numerical multiple of the other.

The inequality (1·42·1) follows from the conditions (i), (ii) and (iii) of **1·4** for the scalar product. If condition (iv) is also used, (1·42·1) follows from (1·4·3) by the Cauchy inequality.

If neither x nor y is zero, and if we write

$$\frac{(x, y)}{\| x \| \, \| y \|} = \cos\theta, \tag{1·42·2}$$

θ is real so long as (x, y) is real, and we can then interpret it as the angle between the vectors x and y. Thus the scalar product defines both length and angle; it is the metric form in $\mathfrak{V}_n$.

If $(x, y) = 0$ we say that the vectors x and y are *orthogonal*. Thus, condition (iv) of **1·4** means that any two of the coordinate vectors u^ν are orthogonal. If $x = \alpha y \neq 0$ we say that x and y are *parallel*.

1·43. The absolute value satisfies the 'triangle inequality'

$$\| x+y \| \leqslant \| x \| + \| y \|,$$

since, by (1·42·1),

$$\begin{aligned}\| x+y \|^2 &= (x+y, x+y) = (x,x)+(x,y)+\overline{(x,y)}+(y,y)\\ &\leqslant \| x \|^2 + 2\,|(x,y)| + \| y \|^2 \leqslant \| x \|^2 + 2\| x \| \, \| y \| + \| y \|^2\\ &= (\| x \| + \| y \|)^2.\end{aligned}$$

When x and y are orthogonal vectors we obtain the Theorem of Pythagoras

$$\| x+y \|^2 = \| x \|^2 + \| y \|^2.$$

1·5. We now prove that the space $\mathfrak{V}_n$ is complete and separable. We shall not again refer explicitly to these properties of n-dimensional vector space. We introduce them here in preparation for the discussion of the same important properties of Hilbert vector space.

1·51. Definition of a limit vector of a sequence. We say that the vector $\mathring{x}$ of $\mathfrak{V}_n$ is the *limit vector of the sequence* $\{x^m\}$ of vectors of $\mathfrak{V}_n$, and we write $\lim\limits_{m\to\infty} x^m = \mathring{x}$, if $\lim\limits_{m\to\infty} \| x^m - \mathring{x} \| = 0$.

It follows from **1·43** that a sequence cannot have two distinct limit vectors. For suppose that $\mathring{x}$ and $\mathring{y}$ are both limit vectors of the sequence $\{x^m\}$. Then, for any integer m,

$$\| \mathring{x} - \mathring{y} \| \leqslant \| \mathring{x} - x^m \| + \| x^m - \mathring{y} \| \to 0$$

as $m \to \infty$, so that $\| \mathring{x} - \mathring{y} \| = 0$ and $\mathring{y}$ coincides with $\mathring{x}$.

1·52. THEOREM. *Let* $\lim\limits_{m\to\infty} x^m = \mathring{x}$ *and let* y *be any vector of* $\mathfrak{V}_n$. *Then* $\lim\limits_{m\to\infty} (x^m, y) = (\mathring{x}, y)$.

PROOF. We have, by **1·4** (ii) and (1·42·1),

$$|(x^m, y) - (\mathring{x}, y)| = |(x^m - \mathring{x}, y)| \leqslant \| x^m - \mathring{x} \| \, \| y \| \to 0$$

as $m \to \infty$.

1·53. THEOREM. *The space* $\mathfrak{V}_n$ *is complete; that is, if a sequence* $\{x^m\}$ *of vectors of* $\mathfrak{V}_n$ *satisfies the condition that there corresponds to any positive number* ϵ *an integer* m_0 *such that* $\| x^p - x^q \| < \epsilon$ *for* $p, q \geqslant m_0(\epsilon)$, *then there exists a vector* $\mathring{x}$ *of* $\mathfrak{V}_n$ *which is the limit vector of the sequence.*

PROOF. Let $x^m = \sum\limits_{\nu=1}^{n} x_{m\nu} u^\nu$. Then

$$\begin{aligned}|x_{p\nu} - x_{q\nu}| &\leqslant \left(\sum_{\nu=1}^{n} |x_{p\nu} - x_{q\nu}|^2 \right)^{\frac{1}{2}}\\ &= \| x^p - x^q \| < \epsilon \quad (p, q \geqslant m_0),\end{aligned}$$

and so $\lim_{m\to\infty} x_{m\nu}$ exists; denote it by $\mathring{x}_\nu$ and write $\mathring{x} = \sum_{\nu=1}^{n} \mathring{x}_\nu u^\nu$. We obtain

$$\|\mathring{x}-x^m\| = \left(\sum_{\nu=1}^{n} |\mathring{x}_\nu - x_{m\nu}|^2\right)^{\frac{1}{2}} \to 0$$

as $m\to\infty$, and this gives the desired result.

A sequence that satisfies the condition of Theorem **1·53** is said to be *convergent*. We readily see that a sequence that has a limit vector $\mathring{x}$ is convergent and we say that it *converges to* $\mathring{x}$.

1·6. Definition of the closure of a set of vectors, of a closed set and of an everywhere dense subset. Let $\mathfrak{S}$ be any set of vectors of $\mathfrak{V}_n$. The set obtained by *adding all those limit vectors of sequences of elements of* $\mathfrak{S}$ *that do not belong to* $\mathfrak{S}$ is called *the closure of* $\mathfrak{S}$; we denote it by $\bar{\mathfrak{S}}$. If $\bar{\mathfrak{S}}$ coincides with $\mathfrak{S}$ we say that $\mathfrak{S}$ is *closed*.

Let $\mathfrak{C}$ be any set of vectors of $\mathfrak{V}_n$ and let $\mathfrak{S}$ be a subset of $\mathfrak{C}$. If $\mathfrak{C}$ is contained in $\bar{\mathfrak{S}}$ we say that $\mathfrak{S}$ *is everywhere dense in* $\mathfrak{C}$.

A necessary and sufficient condition that $\mathfrak{S}$ is everywhere dense in $\mathfrak{C}$ is that there corresponds to any element x of $\mathfrak{C}$ and any positive number ϵ an element s of $\mathfrak{S}$ such that $\|x-s\|<\epsilon$, for this condition is equivalent to the condition that x is either an element of $\mathfrak{S}$ or else the limit vector of a sequence of elements of $\mathfrak{S}$.

1·61. Theorem. *The space* $\mathfrak{V}_n$ *is separable; that is, there exists a denumerably infinite set* $\mathfrak{S}$ *of vectors of* $\mathfrak{V}_n$ *that is everywhere dense in* $\mathfrak{V}_n$.

Proof. Consider the set $\mathfrak{S}$ of all vectors s of $\mathfrak{V}_n$ of which the coordinates $s_\nu = \sigma_\nu + i\tau_\nu$ are formed from rational numbers σ_ν and τ_ν. Now the set of rational numbers is denumerable and so is the set of ordered pairs of rationals. Thus the set of the numbers s_ν is denumerable. The elements of $\mathfrak{S}$ may be regarded as ordered sets of n numbers s_ν, so that $\mathfrak{S}$ is also denumerable. Further, since we can express any complex number as the limit of a sequence of numbers s_ν, it follows that we can express any vector of $\mathfrak{V}_n$ that is not a vector of $\mathfrak{S}$ as the limit vector of a sequence of vectors of $\mathfrak{S}$. Thus the set $\mathfrak{S}$ fulfils the requirements of the theorem.

§2. Linear Manifolds

2·0. Definition of a linear manifold. *A set* $\mathfrak{M}$ *of vectors of* $\mathfrak{V}_n$ *is called a linear manifold* (denoted by the abbreviation L.M.) *if, whenever* $a\in\mathfrak{M}$ *and* $b\in\mathfrak{M}$, *then also* $\alpha a\in\mathfrak{M}$ *and* $a+b\in\mathfrak{M}$, where α is any complex number.

If $a^1, a^2, \ldots, a^r$ are any vectors of $\mathfrak{V}_n$ and $\alpha_1, \alpha_2, \ldots, \alpha_r$ any complex numbers, then the vector $\alpha_1 a^1 + \alpha_2 a^2 + \ldots + \alpha_r a^r$ is said to be a *linear combination* of the vectors $a^1, a^2, \ldots, a^r$. It follows immediately from Definition **2·0** that, if $a^1, a^2, \ldots, a^r$ are contained in the L.M. $\mathfrak{M}$, then so is any linear combination of these vectors. In particular, any L.M. contains the zero vector.

If the L.M. $\mathfrak{M}$ consists of all linear combinations of the vectors $a^1, a^2, \ldots, a^r$ we write it as $\mathfrak{M} = [a^1, a^2, \ldots, a^r]$ and we say that $\mathfrak{M}$ is *spanned* by the vectors $a^1, a^2, \ldots, a^r$. The space $\mathfrak{B}_n$ is the L.M. spanned by the coordinate vectors, so that $\mathfrak{B}_n = [u^1, u^2, \ldots, u^n]$. The zero vector constitutes a L.M. which we denote by $\mathfrak{M} = \mathfrak{O}$.

If $\mathfrak{M}$ and $\mathfrak{M}'$ are L.M.'s such that every vector of each is contained in the other we write $\mathfrak{M}' = \mathfrak{M}$; if every vector of $\mathfrak{M}'$ is contained in $\mathfrak{M}$ we write $\mathfrak{M}' \subseteq \mathfrak{M}$ and $\mathfrak{M} \supseteq \mathfrak{M}'$. If there is a vector of $\mathfrak{M}$ that is not contained in $\mathfrak{M}'$ while every vector of $\mathfrak{M}'$ is contained in $\mathfrak{M}$ we write $\mathfrak{M}' \subset \mathfrak{M}$ and $\mathfrak{M} \supset \mathfrak{M}'$. Plainly, the L.M. $\mathfrak{O}$ is contained in every L.M. $\mathfrak{M}$ so that we always have $\mathfrak{M} \supseteq \mathfrak{O}$.

2·1. Definition of linear dependence and linear independence of vectors. The vector x is said to be *linearly dependent* on the vectors $a^1, a^2, \ldots, a^r$ if it is a linear combination of these vectors; that is, if there exist numerical coefficients α_ν such that $x = \sum_{\nu=1}^{r} \alpha_\nu a^\nu$. The vectors $a^1, a^2, \ldots, a^r$ are said to be linearly dependent, or to form a *linearly dependent set*, if there exist numerical coefficients α_ν, not all zero, such that

$$\sum_{\nu=1}^{r} \alpha_\nu a^\nu = 0. \qquad (2\cdot1\cdot1)$$

The vectors $a^1, a^2, \ldots, a^r$ are said to be *linearly independent*, or to form a *linearly independent set*, if a relation (2·1·1) implies that all the coefficients α_ν are zero.

It follows at once that any subset of a linearly independent set of vectors is a linearly independent set. We also see that a linearly independent set cannot contain the zero vector, since the relation $\alpha 0 = 0$ does not imply that $\alpha = 0$. An example of a linearly independent set of n vectors is the set of coordinate vectors $u^1, u^2, \ldots, u^n$.

2·11. The vectors $\overline{a^1}, \overline{a^2}, \ldots, \overline{a^r}$ are linearly dependent or linearly independent according as $a^1, a^2, \ldots, a^r$ are linearly dependent or linearly independent.

2·12. Let $\mathfrak{M}$ be a L.M. in $\mathfrak{B}_n$, and let $\overline{\mathfrak{M}}$ denote the set of all vectors conjugate to vectors of $\mathfrak{M}$. Then $\overline{\mathfrak{M}}$ is also a L.M. for, if $\bar{a} \in \overline{\mathfrak{M}}$ and $\bar{b} \in \overline{\mathfrak{M}}$, then $\alpha a \in \mathfrak{M}$ and $a + b \in \mathfrak{M}$ for every number α, and so $\overline{\alpha a} \in \overline{\mathfrak{M}}$ and $\bar{a} + \bar{b} \in \overline{\mathfrak{M}}$.

If $\mathfrak{M} = [a^1, a^2, \ldots, a^r]$ then, clearly, $\overline{\mathfrak{M}} = [\overline{a^1}, \overline{a^2}, \ldots, \overline{a^r}]$. We say that the L.M.'s $\mathfrak{M}$ and $\overline{\mathfrak{M}}$ are conjugate to one another.

2·2. Definition of a basis of a L.M. The set of vectors $a^1, a^2, \ldots, a^r$ is called a *basis* of the L.M. $\mathfrak{M}$ if the following two conditions are satisfied:

(i) *the vectors* $a^1, a^2, \ldots, a^r$ *are linearly independent,*

(ii) $\mathfrak{M} = [a^1, a^2, \ldots, a^r]$.

The set of coordinate vectors u^ν is a basis of the L.M. $\mathfrak{V}_n$.

2·21. We prove by the next two theorems that every L.M. in $\mathfrak{V}_n$ has a basis of not more than n elements, but we need first the following lemma.

LEMMA. *If the set of vectors* $a^1, a^2, \ldots, a^r$ *is a basis of* $\mathfrak{M}$, *and if*

$$b = \beta_1 a^1 + \beta_2 a^2 + \ldots + \beta_r a^r,$$

where β_ν *is not zero, then the set of vectors* $a^1, a^2, \ldots, a^{\nu-1}, b, a^{\nu+1}, \ldots, a^r$ *is also a basis of* $\mathfrak{M}$.

PROOF. Without loss of generality we may take $\nu = 1$ and $\beta_1 \neq 0$. We first show that if there exists a relation

$$\alpha_1 b + \alpha_2 a^2 + \ldots + \alpha_r a^r = 0$$

then all the coefficients are zero. We substitute for b in the relation and obtain

$$\alpha_1 \beta_1 a^1 + (\alpha_2 + \alpha_1 \beta_2) a^2 + \ldots + (\alpha_r + \alpha_1 \beta_r) a^r = 0.$$

But, since $a^1, a^2, \ldots, a^r$ are linearly independent, and since $\beta_1 \neq 0$, this gives successively $\alpha_1 = 0$, $\alpha_2 = 0, \ldots, \alpha_r = 0$. Thus the vectors $b, a^2, \ldots, a^r$ are linearly independent.

Now any vector linearly dependent on $b, a^2, \ldots, a^r$ belongs to $\mathfrak{M}$ and further, since every element of $\mathfrak{M}$ is linearly dependent on $a^1, a^2, \ldots, a^r$, and since

$$a^1 = \frac{1}{\beta_1}(b - \beta_2 a^2 - \ldots - \beta_r a^r),$$

it follows that every element of $\mathfrak{M}$ is linearly dependent on $b, a^2, \ldots, a^r$. Thus these vectors form a basis of $\mathfrak{M}$.

2·3 THEOREM. *Let* $\mathfrak{M}$ *be a L.M. in* $\mathfrak{V}_n$ *with a basis of* r *elements. Then any set of* r *linearly independent elements of* $\mathfrak{M}$ *is a basis of* $\mathfrak{M}$ *and any set of* $r+1$ *elements of* $\mathfrak{M}$ *is linearly dependent.*

PROOF. Let $\mathfrak{M} = [a^1, a^2, \ldots, a^r]$ and let $b^1, b^2, \ldots, b^r$ be any set of r linearly independent elements of $\mathfrak{M}$. Then

$$b^1 = \alpha_{11} a^1 + \alpha_{12} a^2 + \ldots + \alpha_{1r} a^r,$$

where at least one of the coefficients, say α_{11}, is not zero, since no element b^μ can be zero because the b's are linearly independent. Then, by Lemma **2·21**,

$$\mathfrak{M} = [a^1, a^2, \ldots, a^r] = [b^1, a^2, \ldots, a^r].$$

Suppose we have proved that

$$\mathfrak{M} = [b^1, b^2, \ldots, b^{s-1}, a^s, \ldots, a^r],$$

where $2 \leqslant s \leqslant r$. Then we have

$$b^s = \beta_{s1} b^1 + \ldots + \beta_{s,s-1} b^{s-1} + \alpha_{ss} a^s + \ldots + \alpha_{sr} a^r,$$

where the coefficients $\alpha_{s\mu}$ are not all zero since $b^1, b^2, \ldots, b^s$ are linearly independent, and we may assume $\alpha_{ss} \neq 0$. Then, by Lemma **2·21**,

$$\mathfrak{M} = [b^1, b^2, \ldots, b^s, a^{s+1}, \ldots, a^r].$$

We obtain in this way, by an induction process, $\mathfrak{M} = [b^1, b^2, \ldots, b^r]$, and we see that the elements $b^1, b^2, \ldots, b^r$ form a basis of $\mathfrak{M}$ since, by hypothesis, they are linearly independent.

It follows at once that no set of $r+1$ elements of $\mathfrak{M}$ is linearly independent.

2·31. Corollary of Theorem **2·3**. *Every set of $n+1$ vectors of $\mathfrak{V}_n$ is linearly dependent.*

Proof. The corollary follows at once from Theorem **2·3**, since the coordinate vectors $u^1, u^2, \ldots, u^n$ form a basis of $\mathfrak{V}_n$.

2·4. Theorem. *There corresponds to every L.M. $\mathfrak{M}$ in $\mathfrak{V}_n$ (with the trivial exception $\mathfrak{M} = \mathfrak{O}$) a positive integer r, where $r \leqslant n$, which is the maximum number of linearly independent elements contained in $\mathfrak{M}$. Every set of r linearly independent elements of $\mathfrak{M}$ is a basis of $\mathfrak{M}$, and every basis of $\mathfrak{M}$ has exactly r elements.*

Note. This theorem establishes the existence of a basis of at most n elements for every L.M. in $\mathfrak{V}_n$. We describe a method of constructing such a basis in **2·5**.

Proof. By Corollary **2·31**, every set of $n+1$ vectors of $\mathfrak{V}_n$ is linearly dependent so that $\mathfrak{M}$ cannot contain a linearly independent set of more than n vectors. On the other hand, any non-zero vector of $\mathfrak{M}$ constitutes a linearly independent set. Hence, if $\mathfrak{M} \neq \mathfrak{O}$, there are linearly independent subsets of $\mathfrak{M}$, and the number of elements they contain has a greatest value r, where $r \leqslant n$.

Now let $a^1, a^2, \ldots, a^r$ be any set of r linearly independent elements of $\mathfrak{M}$ and let x be any other element of $\mathfrak{M}$. The $r+1$ elements $x, a^1, a^2, \ldots, a^r$ cannot be linearly independent, and there exists therefore a relation of the form $\alpha x + \beta_1 a^1 + \ldots + \beta_r a^r = 0$ in which at least one of the coefficients is not zero. In particular, $\alpha \neq 0$, for if $\alpha = 0$ we should also have every $\beta_\mu = 0$, since the elements a^μ are linearly independent. Thus

$$x = -\frac{1}{\alpha}(\beta_1 a^1 + \beta_2 a^2 + \ldots + \beta_r a^r).$$

It follows that the set $a^1, a^2, \ldots, a^r$ is a basis of $\mathfrak{M}$.

Finally, $\mathfrak{M}$ cannot contain a basis $b^1, b^2, \ldots, b^\rho$, where $\rho < r$, since, if there were such a basis, then, by Theorem **2·3**, every set of more than ρ elements of $\mathfrak{M}$ would be linearly dependent, contrary to the fact that there are linearly independent subsets of r elements.

2·41. Definition of the rank of a L.M. The number r that is *the invariant number of elements in any basis of a L.M.* $\mathfrak{M}$ of $\mathfrak{V}_n$, where $\mathfrak{M} \neq \mathfrak{O}$, is called the *rank* of $\mathfrak{M}$. We say that the L.M. $\mathfrak{O}$ has *zero rank.*

The space $\mathfrak{V}_n$ itself has rank n, and we always have $n \geqslant r \geqslant 1$ for $\mathfrak{M} \neq \mathfrak{O}$.

It follows at once, by Theorem **2·3**, that the rank of any L.M. $\mathfrak{M}$ is the maximum number of linearly independent elements of $\mathfrak{M}$.

2·42. Corollary 1 of Theorem **2·4.** *If the L.M. $\mathfrak{M}$ in $\mathfrak{V}_n$ has rank r, then the conjugate L.M. $\overline{\mathfrak{M}}$ also has rank r.*

Proof. It follows at once from **2·12** and **2·11** that, if $a^1, a^2, \ldots, a^r$ is a basis of $\mathfrak{M}$, then $\overline{a^1}, \overline{a^2}, \ldots, \overline{a^r}$ is a basis of $\overline{\mathfrak{M}}$.

2·43. Corollary 2 of Theorem **2·4.** *If $\mathfrak{M} = [a^1, a^2, \ldots, a^m]$, and if $\mathfrak{M}$ has rank r, then $r \leqslant m$ and the set $a^1, a^2, \ldots, a^m$ contains a linearly independent set of r elements.*

Proof. By an argument similar to that of Theorem **2·4** we see that there is a greatest number s of linearly independent elements in the set $a^1, a^2, \ldots, a^m$, where $1 \leqslant s \leqslant m$, and that any linearly independent subset of s elements is such that the remaining $m-s$ elements are linearly dependent on them. Clearly, such a subset forms a basis of $\mathfrak{M}$. By Theorem **2·4**, $s = r$; thus $r \leqslant m$.

2·5. In constructing a basis of any L.M. $\mathfrak{M}$ in $\mathfrak{V}_n$, where $\mathfrak{M} \neq \mathfrak{O}$, we begin with any non-zero element a^1 of $\mathfrak{M}$ and consider the L.M. $[a^1]$. Clearly, $[a^1] \subseteq \mathfrak{M}$, and if $[a^1] = \mathfrak{M}$ then a^1 forms a basis of $\mathfrak{M}$ and $\mathfrak{M}$ has rank 1. If, however, $[a^1] \subset \mathfrak{M}$ we take any element a^2 of $\mathfrak{M}$ not contained in $[a^1]$ and consider $[a^1, a^2]$, where a^1, a^2 are linearly independent by construction. We have $[a^1, a^2] \subseteq \mathfrak{M}$, and we have again to distinguish between two cases: either $[a^1, a^2] = \mathfrak{M}$ and $\mathfrak{M}$ is of rank 2 with basis a^1, a^2; or else $[a^1, a^2] \subset \mathfrak{M}$, there is an element a^3 of $\mathfrak{M}$ not contained in $[a^1, a^2]$ and we obtain

$$[a^1, a^2, a^3] \subseteq \mathfrak{M},$$

where the elements a^1, a^2, a^3 are linearly independent by construction. We continue the process. If at any stage we have $[a^1, a^2, \ldots, a^\kappa] \subset \mathfrak{M}$, where the elements $a^1, a^2, \ldots, a^\kappa$ are linearly independent, we take an element $a^{\kappa+1}$ of $\mathfrak{M}$ not contained in $[a^1, a^2, \ldots, a^\kappa]$ and we obtain $[a^1, a^2, \ldots, a^{\kappa+1}] \subseteq \mathfrak{M}$, where the elements $a^1, a^2, \ldots, a^{\kappa+1}$ are linearly independent by construction. The process must come to an end after a finite number of steps (not more than n), by Corollary **2·31**, when we finally obtain

$$[a^1, a^2, \ldots, a^r] = \mathfrak{M},$$

where the elements $a^1, a^2, \ldots, a^r$ are linearly independent and so form a basis of $\mathfrak{M}$.

This method of construction may give rise to different bases of $\mathfrak{M}$ all with the same number r of elements.

2·6. THEOREM. *If $\mathfrak{M}'$ and $\mathfrak{M}$ have the same rank r and if $\mathfrak{M}' \subseteq \mathfrak{M}$, then $\mathfrak{M}' = \mathfrak{M}$.*

PROOF. Let the vectors $b^1, b^2, \ldots, b^r$ form a basis of $\mathfrak{M}'$. By hypothesis, the vectors b^μ are also contained in $\mathfrak{M}$ and, by Theorem **2·4**, they form a basis of $\mathfrak{M}$. Hence $\mathfrak{M} = \mathfrak{M}' = [b^1, b^2, \ldots, b^r]$.

2·61. COROLLARY OF THEOREM **2·6.** *The only L.M. in $\mathfrak{V}_n$ of rank n is $\mathfrak{V}_n$ itself.*

PROOF. In **2·41** we have remarked that $\mathfrak{V}_n$ has rank n. Any L.M. in $\mathfrak{V}_n$ of rank n must therefore coincide with $\mathfrak{V}_n$, by Theorem **2·6.**

2·7. Definition of a real L.M. We say that a L.M. $\mathfrak{M}$ is *real* if $\bar{x} \in \mathfrak{M}$ whenever $x \in \mathfrak{M}$.

Clearly $\mathfrak{M}$ is real if, and only if, $\overline{\mathfrak{M}} = \mathfrak{M}$.

2·71. THEOREM. *If a L.M. $\mathfrak{M}$ is spanned by a set of real vectors, then $\mathfrak{M}$ is real. Thus, $\mathfrak{M}$ is real if it has a basis of real elements. Conversely, if $\mathfrak{M}$ is real there is a basis of real elements.*

PROOF. (i) If $\mathfrak{M}$ is spanned by the real vectors $a^1, a^2, \ldots, a^r$, every vector x of $\mathfrak{M}$ has the form $x = \sum_{\kappa=1}^{r} \alpha_\kappa a^\kappa$, so that $\bar{x} = \sum_{\kappa=1}^{r} \overline{\alpha_\kappa} a^\kappa$ and $\bar{x} \in \mathfrak{M}$. Thus $\mathfrak{M}$ is real.

(ii) If $\mathfrak{M}$ is real and is not identical with $\mathfrak{O}$, it contains at least one non-zero vector x. Now $\bar{x} \in \mathfrak{M}$ and therefore $x+\bar{x}$ and $i(x-\bar{x})$, which cannot both be zero, are real vectors of $\mathfrak{M}$; thus $\mathfrak{M}$ contains at least one real non-zero vector. If the rank of $\mathfrak{M}$ is r, and if there is a linearly independent set of r real vectors of $\mathfrak{M}$ they will form a basis of $\mathfrak{M}$, by Theorem **2·4**, and there is nothing further to prove. Let us assume then that no linearly independent set of real vectors of $\mathfrak{M}$ contains more than ρ vectors, where $1 \leqslant \rho < r$, and that $a^1, a^2, \ldots, a^\rho$ is such a set. Then $[a^1, a^2, \ldots, a^\rho] \subset \mathfrak{M}$. Using the method described in **2·5**, we can write $\mathfrak{M} = [a^1, a^2, \ldots, a^\rho, a^{\rho+1}, \ldots, a^r]$, where $a^\nu = \alpha^\nu + i\beta^\nu$ for $\nu = \rho+1, \rho+2, \ldots, r$, and where α^ν and β^ν are real vectors with $\beta^\nu \neq 0$. Now α^ν, $\beta^\nu \in \mathfrak{M}$, since

$$\alpha^\nu = \tfrac{1}{2}(a^\nu + \overline{a^\nu}) \quad \text{and} \quad \beta^\nu = -\tfrac{1}{2}i\,(a^\nu - \overline{a^\nu}),$$

and therefore the assumption that there is no linearly independent set of more than ρ real vectors of $\mathfrak{M}$ implies that

$$\alpha^\nu = \sum_{\kappa=1}^{\rho} \alpha_{\nu\kappa} a^\kappa, \quad \beta^\nu = \sum_{\kappa=1}^{\rho} \beta_{\nu\kappa} a^\kappa,$$

where the coefficients $\alpha_{\nu\kappa}$ and $\beta_{\nu\kappa}$ are not all zero, and hence that

$$a^\nu = \sum_{\kappa=1}^{\rho} (\alpha_{\nu\kappa} + i\beta_{\nu\kappa})\, a^\kappa \quad (\nu = \rho+1, \rho+2, \ldots, r).$$

Thus, a^ν is linearly dependent on $a^1, a^2, \ldots, a^\rho$, and the set of vectors $a^1, a^2, \ldots, a^\rho, a^{\rho+1}, \ldots, a^r$ cannot be a basis of $\mathfrak{M}$. The assumption $\rho < r$ leads to a contradiction, and we therefore conclude that there is a basis of $\mathfrak{M}$ of r real elements.

§ 3. Projections; orthonormal bases of a L.M.; complete orthonormal systems

3·0. Definition of an orthonormal system. *A set of vectors $g^1, g^2, \ldots, g^r$ is said to be an orthonormal system if*

$$(g^\mu, g^\nu) = \delta_{\mu\nu}.$$

The n coordinate vectors u^ν form an orthonormal system.

3·01. Theorem. *Any r non-zero vectors $a^1, a^2, \ldots, a^r$ such that*

$$(a^\mu, a^\nu) = 0 \quad (\mu \neq \nu;\ \mu, \nu = 1, 2, \ldots, r)$$

are linearly independent.

Proof. If we had $\sum_{\mu=1}^{r} \alpha_\mu a^\mu = 0$ for a set of numbers $\alpha_1, \alpha_2, \ldots, \alpha_r$, we should have

$$\alpha_\mu (a^\mu, a^\mu) = 0 \quad (\mu = 1, 2, \ldots, r),$$

and so $\alpha_\mu = 0$ since $(a^\mu, a^\mu) \neq 0$. Thus, by Definition **2·1**, the vectors $a^1, a^2, \ldots, a^r$ are linearly independent.

3·02. By Theorem **3·01**, an orthonormal system of vectors is a linearly independent set and therefore, by Corollary **2·31**, an orthonormal system in $\mathfrak{V}_n$ cannot contain more than n vectors.

3·1. Definition of an orthonormal basis of a L.M. *A basis of a L.M. is said to be an orthonormal basis if its vectors form an orthonormal system.*

It is the aim of this section to show that every L.M. has an orthonormal basis, and to this end we introduce a new operation on vectors that we call projection.

3·2. Definition of projection. Let x be any vector of $\mathfrak{V}_n$ and $\mathfrak{M}$ any L.M. We say that the vector $p = P_{\mathfrak{M}}x$ is the *projection of* x *on* $\mathfrak{M}$ if the following two conditions are satisfied:

(i) $p \in \mathfrak{M}$,

(ii) *the vector* $q = x - p$ *is orthogonal to every element of* $\mathfrak{M}$.

We call q the *perpendicular dropped from* x *on* $\mathfrak{M}$.

We prove in **3·4** that the projection $p = P_{\mathfrak{M}}x$ always exists for any vector x on any L.M. $\mathfrak{M}$.

3·21. There cannot be two distinct vectors p and p^1 that satisfy the conditions (i) and (ii) of Definition **3·2**. For, if we could write

$$x = p + q = p^1 + q^1,$$

where $p, p^1 \in \mathfrak{M}$ and where both q and q^1 were orthogonal to every element of $\mathfrak{M}$, we should have $(p - p^1) \in \mathfrak{M}$ and $(p - p^1, q - q^1) = 0$. But this would give $(p - p^1, p - p^1) = 0$, since $p - p^1 = q^1 - q$, so that p and p^1 would coincide. It follows that $p = x$ and $q = 0$ if, and only if, $x \in \mathfrak{M}$.

3·22. If p is the projection of x on $\mathfrak{M}$ and q the perpendicular dropped from x on $\mathfrak{M}$, we obtain at once, by Definition **3·2**,

$$\| x \|^2 = (p+q, p+q) = \| p \|^2 + \| q \|^2, \qquad (3·22·1)$$

since $(p, q) = (q, p) = 0$. Thus

$$\| x \|^2 \geqslant \| p \|^2,$$

with equality if, and only if, $x \in \mathfrak{M}$.

3·3. We first consider the projection of any vector x of $\mathfrak{V}_n$ on a L.M. $\mathfrak{M}$ of rank 1. We write $\mathfrak{M} = [a]$, where the vector a is not zero, and take the vector $g = \| a \|^{-1} a$ as an orthonormal basis of $\mathfrak{M}$.

Then the projection p of x on $\mathfrak{M}$ and the perpendicular q dropped from x on $\mathfrak{M}$ are obtained as

$$p = (x,g)\,g, \quad q = x-(x,g)\,g.$$

For, plainly, $p \in \mathfrak{M}$ and, since $(q,g) = 0, q$ is orthogonal to every vector of $\mathfrak{M}$.

3·31. Now let $\mathfrak{M}$ be any L.M. of rank r, where $r > 1$, and let x be any vector of $\mathfrak{B}_n$. If we assume the existence of an orthonormal basis $g^1, g^2, \ldots, g^r$ of $\mathfrak{M}$ we obtain the projection p of x on $\mathfrak{M}$ and the perpendicular q dropped from x on $\mathfrak{M}$ as

$$p = P_{\mathfrak{M}}x = \sum_{\nu=1}^{r} (x,g^\nu)\,g^\nu, \quad q = x - \sum_{\nu=1}^{r} (x,g^\nu)\,g^\nu. \quad (3\cdot31\cdot1)$$

For, as before, $p \in \mathfrak{M}$, and q is orthogonal to every vector of $\mathfrak{M}$, since $(q,g^\mu) = 0$ for $\mu = 1, 2, \ldots, r$.

3·4. We make use of the geometrical conception of projection to establish the existence of an orthonormal basis of any L.M. We then interpret (3·31·1) as giving the projection of any vector x on any L.M. $\mathfrak{M}$.

THEOREM. *Every L.M. $\mathfrak{M}$ in $\mathfrak{B}_n$, with the trivial exception $\mathfrak{M} = \mathfrak{O}$, has an orthonormal basis.*

PROOF. We prove the theorem by induction, considering a L.M. $\mathfrak{M}$ of rank r, where $r > 1$, and assuming that the theorem is true for any L.M. of rank $r-1$. We have already verified the theorem, in **3·3**, for the case $r = 1$.

Let the vectors $a^1, a^2, \ldots, a^r$ form a basis of $\mathfrak{M}$ and consider the L.M. $\mathfrak{M}' = [a^1, a^2, \ldots, a^{r-1}]$, of rank $r-1$, which does not contain a^r. Then, by our assumption, $\mathfrak{M}'$ has an orthonormal basis $g^1, g^2, \ldots, g^{r-1}$ and, by (3·31·1), the perpendicular q^r from a^r on $\mathfrak{M}'$ is

$$q^r = a^r - \sum_{\nu=1}^{r-1} (a^r, g^\nu)\,g^\nu.$$

By a remark in **3·21**, q^r is not zero, since a^r is not contained in $\mathfrak{M}'$, and we may therefore write $g^r = \| q^r \|^{-1} q^r$. We now readily verify that the set of vectors $g^1, g^2, \ldots, g^r$ forms an orthonormal basis of $\mathfrak{M}$. Thus, the theorem is true for any L.M. of rank r.

3·41. The method described in the proof of Theorem **3·4** enables us to replace any basis $a^1, a^2, \ldots, a^r$ of a L.M. $\mathfrak{M}$ of rank r by an orthonormal basis $g^1, g^2, \ldots, g^r$ by successive steps and in such a way that

$$[a^1, a^2, \ldots, a^\mu] = [g^1, g^2, \ldots, g^\mu] \quad (\mu = 1, 2, \ldots, r).$$

The process is known as E. Schmidt's *orthogonalization process.*

It should be noted that the procedure holds, with trivial modifications, for elements $a^1, a^2, \ldots, a^m$ spanning the L.M. $\mathfrak{M}$ that are not known to be linearly independent. In this case the vector

$$q^\mu = a^\mu - \sum_{\nu=1}^{\mu-1} (a^\mu, g^\nu)\, g^\nu$$

is zero if $\quad a^\mu \in [a^1, a^2, \ldots, a^{\mu-1}] = [g^1, g^2, \ldots, g^{\mu-1}],$

and then a^μ is simply ignored.

3·5. Theorem. *Any real L.M. $\mathfrak{M}$ has an orthonormal basis of real elements.*

Proof. The L.M. $\mathfrak{M}$ has a real basis $a^1, a^2, \ldots, a^r$, by Theorem **2·71**. The formulae of **3·4** and **3·41** show that the application of Schmidt's process to these elements gives real vectors g^μ at each stage.

3·6. Definition of a complete orthonormal system. An orthonormal system of vectors $g^1, g^2, \ldots, g^r$ in $\mathfrak{B}_n$ is said to be a *complete orthonormal system* if $[g^1, g^2, \ldots, g^r] = \mathfrak{B}_n$.

The equations

$$(h, g^\mu) = 0 \quad (\mu = 1, 2, \ldots, r) \tag{3·6·1}$$

imply that $\| h \|^2 = 0$, and hence that $h = 0$, if the orthonormal system $g^1, g^2, \ldots, g^r$ is complete. If, however, the system is not complete, there exists a vector a of $\mathfrak{B}_n$ not contained in the L.M. $\mathfrak{M} = [g^1, g^2, \ldots, g^r]$, and, by Definition **3·2**, the perpendicular q from a on $\mathfrak{M}$ provides a non-zero solution $h = q$ of the equations (3·6·1). These equations define a L.M. of vectors h, since $(\alpha h^1, g^\mu) = 0$ and $(h^1 + h^2, g^\mu) = 0$ if both $(h^1, g^\mu) = 0$ and $(h^2, g^\mu) = 0$, and this L.M., which consists of all the vectors of $\mathfrak{B}_n$ orthogonal to every vector of $\mathfrak{M}$, is different from $\mathfrak{O}$ if, and only if, the orthonormal system $g^1, g^2, \ldots, g^r$ is not complete.

By Corollary **2·61**, the condition $r = n$ is necessary and sufficient for any orthonormal system of r vectors in $\mathfrak{B}_n$ to be complete. This simple criterion for the completeness of a system cannot be generalized for Hilbert space. The condition discussed above, however, that the equations $(h, g^\mu) = 0$ for $\mu = 1, 2, \ldots, r$ imply that $h = 0$, is readily generalized; we now deduce another condition that can also be generalized.

3·61. THEOREM. *An orthonormal system $g^1, g^2, \ldots, g^r$ of vectors of $\mathfrak{B}_n$ is complete if, and only if,*

$$\| x \|^2 = \sum_{\nu=1}^{r} |(x, g^\nu)|^2$$

for every vector x of $\mathfrak{B}_n$ (PARSEVAL'S THEOREM). *If the system is not complete we have, for every vector x of $\mathfrak{B}_n$,* BESSEL'S INEQUALITY

$$\| x \|^2 \geqslant \sum_{\nu=1}^{r} |(x, g^\nu)|^2,$$

and there are vectors x for which the equality sign does not hold.

PROOF. Let x be any vector of $\mathfrak{B}_n$. Drop the perpendicular h from x on the L.M. $\mathfrak{M} = [g^1, g^2, \ldots, g^r]$ and write $x = p + h$, where p is the projection of x on $\mathfrak{M}$. Then, by (3·22·1) and (3·31·1), we have

$$\| x \|^2 = \| p \|^2 + \| h \|^2,$$

$$p = \sum_{\nu=1}^{r} (x, g^\nu) g^\nu$$

and
$$\| p \|^2 = \left(\sum_{\nu=1}^{r} (x, g^\nu) g^\nu, \sum_{\mu=1}^{r} (x, g^\mu) g^\mu \right)$$

$$= \sum_{\mu, \nu=1}^{r} (x, g^\nu)(g^\nu, g^\mu)(g^\mu, x) = \sum_{\nu=1}^{r} (x, g^\nu)(g^\nu, x)$$

$$= \sum_{\nu=1}^{r} |(x, g^\nu)|^2.$$

If the system of the g^ν is complete, $x \in \mathfrak{M}$, $x = p, h = 0$ and

$$\| x \|^2 = \| p \|^2 = \sum_{\nu=1}^{r} |(x, g^\nu)|^2.$$

If the system is not complete we still have the equality above for $x \in \mathfrak{M}$. But, for vectors x of $\mathfrak{B}_n$ not belonging to $\mathfrak{M}$, $h \neq 0$ and

$$\| x \|^2 = \| p \|^2 + \| h \|^2 > \| p \|^2 = \sum_{\nu=1}^{r} |(x, g^\nu)|^2.$$

3·62. A L.M. $\mathfrak{M}$ with orthonormal basis $g^1, g^2, \ldots, g^r$ can be interpreted as an r-dimensional 'subspace $\mathfrak{B}_r$' with coordinate vectors g^ν and coordinates (x, g^ν) for any x of $\mathfrak{M}$. If $x, y \in \mathfrak{M}$ their scalar product (x, y) in $\mathfrak{B}_n$ is

$$\left(\sum_{\nu=1}^{r} (x, g^\nu) g^\nu, \sum_{\mu=1}^{r} (y, g^\mu) g^\mu \right) = \sum_{\nu=1}^{r} (x, g^\nu)(g^\mu, y)$$

which, by (1·4·3), is also their scalar product in $\mathfrak{B}_r$.

If $\mathfrak{M}$ has rank n, then $\mathfrak{M} = \mathfrak{B}_n$, any complete orthonormal system $\{g^\nu\}$ is an orthonormal basis of $\mathfrak{B}_n$ and $\{g^\nu\}$ can be interpreted as a new coordinate system. The formulae of the corresponding coordinate transformation are given in **9·52**.

§ 4. Products and sums of L.M.'s

4·0. In later chapters we make frequent use of a simple calculus of L.M.'s for which we now introduce the notation.

4·1. Let $\mathfrak{M}$ and $\mathfrak{N}$ be any two L.M.'s in $\mathfrak{B}_n$. We denote by $\mathfrak{M} . \mathfrak{N}$ the set of all vectors that are elements of both $\mathfrak{M}$ and $\mathfrak{N}$. Plainly, $\mathfrak{M} . \mathfrak{N}$ is a L.M.; we call it the product of $\mathfrak{M}$ and $\mathfrak{N}$.

It is immediate that $\mathfrak{M} . \mathfrak{N} \subseteq \mathfrak{M}$ and $\mathfrak{M} . \mathfrak{N} \subseteq \mathfrak{N}$. Further, $\mathfrak{M} . \mathfrak{N} = \mathfrak{N}$ if, and only if, $\mathfrak{N} \subseteq \mathfrak{M}$.

4·2. Let $\mathfrak{M}$ and $\mathfrak{N}$ be two L.M.'s in $\mathfrak{B}_n$ such that $\mathfrak{M} . \mathfrak{N} = \mathfrak{O}$. We denote by $\mathfrak{M} \oplus \mathfrak{N}$ the set of all vectors x of the form $x = a + b$, where $a \in \mathfrak{M}$ and $b \in \mathfrak{N}$. The set $\mathfrak{M} \oplus \mathfrak{N}$ is a L.M. and, if $\mathfrak{M} = [a^1, a^2, \ldots, a^r]$ and $\mathfrak{N} = [b^1, b^2, \ldots, b^s]$, we have

$$\mathfrak{M} \oplus \mathfrak{N} = [a^1, a^2, \ldots, a^r, b^1, b^2, \ldots, b^s].$$

The L.M. $\mathfrak{M} \oplus \mathfrak{N}$ contains both $\mathfrak{M}$ and $\mathfrak{N}$; we call it their sum. Throughout the book we restrict the use of the notation $\mathfrak{M} \oplus \mathfrak{N}$ to those cases where $\mathfrak{M} . \mathfrak{N} = \mathfrak{O}$. The restriction ensures that any vector x of $\mathfrak{M} \oplus \mathfrak{N}$ can be written as a sum $x = a + b$, where $a \in \mathfrak{M}$ and $b \in \mathfrak{N}$, in only one way.

4·21. Theorem. *Let the L.M.'s $\mathfrak{M}$ and $\mathfrak{N}$ be such that $\mathfrak{M} . \mathfrak{N} = \mathfrak{O}$. If the r vectors $a^1, a^2, \ldots, a^r$ form a basis of $\mathfrak{M}$ and the s vectors $b^1, b^2, \ldots, b^s$ form a basis of $\mathfrak{N}$, then the $r+s$ vectors*

$$a^1,\ a^2,\ \ldots,\ a^r,\quad b^1,\ b^2,\ \ldots,\ b^s$$

form a basis of $\mathfrak{M} \oplus \mathfrak{N}$. Thus, the rank of $\mathfrak{M} \oplus \mathfrak{N}$ is the sum of the ranks of $\mathfrak{M}$ and $\mathfrak{N}$.

Proof. The $r+s$ vectors $a^1, a^2, \ldots, a^r, b^1, b^2, \ldots, b^s$ are linearly independent, since a relation

$$\sum_{\kappa=1}^{r} \alpha_\kappa a^\kappa + \sum_{\kappa=1}^{s} \beta_\kappa b^\kappa = 0,$$

together with the condition $\mathfrak{M} . \mathfrak{N} = \mathfrak{O}$, would imply that each of these two sums was zero and therefore that every coefficient α_κ and every coefficient β_κ was zero, because of the linear independence of the sets of vectors a^κ and b^κ. Thus, by **4·2**, the $r+s$ vectors form a basis of $\mathfrak{M}\oplus\mathfrak{N}$. Definition **2·41** shows that $\mathfrak{M}$ and $\mathfrak{N}$ have ranks r and s respectively and that $\mathfrak{M}\oplus\mathfrak{N}$ has rank $r+s$.

4·3. THEOREM. *If $\mathfrak{M}$ and $\mathfrak{M}_1$ are L.M.'s of ranks r and r_1 respectively, and if $\mathfrak{M}\subset\mathfrak{M}_1$, then $r_1>r$ and there is a L.M. $\mathfrak{N}$ such that $\mathfrak{M}\oplus\mathfrak{N}=\mathfrak{M}_1$. Although it is not uniquely determined, $\mathfrak{N}$ always has rank r_1-r.*

PROOF. Let the set of vectors $a^1, a^2, \ldots, a^r$ be a basis of $\mathfrak{M}$. Since $\mathfrak{M}\subset\mathfrak{M}_1$, the method of **2·5** gives a basis of $\mathfrak{M}_1$ containing these vectors; let it be $a^1, a^2, \ldots, a^r, b^1, b^2, \ldots, b^s$. Then $r+s=r_1>r$. Write

$$\mathfrak{N}=[b^1, b^2, \ldots, b^s].$$

The vectors $b^1, b^2, \ldots, b^s$ are linearly independent and therefore form a basis of $\mathfrak{N}$, so that $\mathfrak{N}$ has rank s, where $s\geqslant 1$. Further, $\mathfrak{M}\,.\,\mathfrak{N}=\mathfrak{O}$, since a relation

$$\sum_{\kappa=1}^{r}\alpha_\kappa a^\kappa=\sum_{\kappa=1}^{s}\beta_\kappa b^\kappa,$$

in which the coefficients α_κ and β_κ were not all zero, would imply the linear dependence of the vectors $a^1, a^2, \ldots, a^r, b^1, b^2, \ldots, b^s$. Thus, by Theorem **4·21**, $\mathfrak{M}_1=\mathfrak{M}\oplus\mathfrak{N}$.

The basis elements b^κ of $\mathfrak{M}_1$ are not uniquely determined; hence $\mathfrak{N}$ is not uniquely determined. But, by Theorem **4·21**, if $\mathfrak{N}$ is any L.M. of rank s such that $\mathfrak{M}_1=\mathfrak{M}\oplus\mathfrak{N}$, then $s=r_1-r$, so that the rank of $\mathfrak{N}$ is uniquely determined.

4·31. THEOREM. *Let the L.M.'s $\mathfrak{M}$ and $\mathfrak{N}$ be such that $\mathfrak{M}\,.\,\mathfrak{N}=\mathfrak{O}$, and let $\mathfrak{N}$ have a basis $b^1, b^2, \ldots, b^s$. If*

$$\mathfrak{N}'=[b^1+x^1,\ b^2+x^2,\ \ldots,\ b^s+x^s],$$

where $x^1, x^2, \ldots, x^s$ are any elements of $\mathfrak{M}$ (distinct or not), then $\mathfrak{M}\,.\,\mathfrak{N}'=\mathfrak{O}$ and $\mathfrak{M}\oplus\mathfrak{N}=\mathfrak{M}\oplus\mathfrak{N}'$. Conversely, any L.M. $\mathfrak{N}'$ such that $\mathfrak{M}\,.\,\mathfrak{N}'=\mathfrak{O}$ and $\mathfrak{M}\oplus\mathfrak{N}=\mathfrak{M}\oplus\mathfrak{N}'$ is of the form

$$\mathfrak{N}'=[b^1+x^1,\ b^2+x^2,\ \ldots,\ b^s+x^s],$$

where $x^1, x^2, \ldots, x^s$ are elements of $\mathfrak{M}$. In either case, the system $\{b^\kappa+x^\kappa\}$ is a basis of $\mathfrak{N}'$.

PROOF. (i) The vectors $b^1+x^1, b^2+x^2, \ldots, b^s+x^s$, where x^κ is any element of $\mathfrak{M}$, are linearly independent. For a relation

$$\sum_{\kappa=1}^{s}\alpha_\kappa(b^\kappa+x^\kappa)=0$$

would imply that

$$-\sum_{\kappa=1}^{s}\alpha_\kappa x^\kappa=\sum_{\kappa=1}^{s}\alpha_\kappa b^\kappa=0,$$

since $\mathfrak{M}.\mathfrak{N} = \mathfrak{O}$, and therefore that $\alpha_\kappa = 0$, since the vectors b^κ are linearly independent. Thus, if $\mathfrak{N}' = [b^1+x^1, b^2+x^2, \ldots, b^s+x^s]$, the system $\{b^\kappa + x^\kappa\}$ is a basis of $\mathfrak{N}'$. Let the vectors $a^1, a^2, \ldots, a^r$ be a basis of $\mathfrak{M}$. Then the $r+s$ elements

$$a^1, a^2, \ldots, a^r, b^1+x^1, b^2+x^2, \ldots, b^s+x^s$$

are, clearly, linearly independent. But these $r+s$ elements are contained in $\mathfrak{M}\oplus\mathfrak{N}$ which has rank $r+s$, so that, by Theorem **2·4**, they form a basis of $\mathfrak{M}\oplus\mathfrak{N}$. Thus

$$\mathfrak{M}\oplus\mathfrak{N} = [a^1, a^2, \ldots, a^r, b^1+x^1, b^2+x^2, \ldots, b^s+x^s].$$

Now $\mathfrak{M}.\mathfrak{N} = \mathfrak{O}$, and it readily follows that $\mathfrak{M}.\mathfrak{N}' = \mathfrak{O}$. Therefore, by Theorem **4·21**, we have $\mathfrak{M}\oplus\mathfrak{N} = \mathfrak{M}\oplus\mathfrak{N}'$.

(ii) Let $\mathfrak{M}.\mathfrak{N}' = \mathfrak{O}$ and $\mathfrak{M}\oplus\mathfrak{N} = \mathfrak{M}\oplus\mathfrak{N}'$, so that, by Theorem **4·21**, $\mathfrak{N}'$ has rank s. Let the vectors $c^1, c^2, \ldots, c^s$ be a basis of $\mathfrak{N}'$. Then $c^\kappa \in \mathfrak{M}\oplus\mathfrak{N}$ and therefore $c^\kappa = b'^\kappa + x'^\kappa$, where $x'^\kappa \in \mathfrak{M}$ and $b'^\kappa \in \mathfrak{N}$. We prove, as in (i), that the elements $b'^\kappa = c^\kappa - x'^\kappa$ are linearly independent, since $\mathfrak{M}.\mathfrak{N}' = \mathfrak{O}$. Hence, by Theorem **2·4**, they form a basis of $\mathfrak{N}$ and we may write

$$b^\nu = \sum_{\kappa=1}^{s} \beta_{\nu\kappa} b'^\kappa \quad (\nu = 1, 2, \ldots, s).$$

Then
$$\sum_{\kappa=1}^{s} \beta_{\nu\kappa} c^\kappa = b^\nu + x^\nu,$$

where
$$x^\nu = \sum_{\kappa=1}^{s} \beta_{\nu\kappa} x'^\kappa \in \mathfrak{M}.$$

Thus, $\mathfrak{N}'$ contains the set of s elements $b^\nu + x^\nu$. Finally, we prove as in (i) that these elements are linearly independent and form a basis of $\mathfrak{N}'$.

4·4. Definition of linear independence of L.M.'s and of the sum of a finite number of L.M.'s. The m L.M.'s $\mathfrak{M}_1, \mathfrak{M}_2, \ldots, \mathfrak{M}_m$ are said to be *linearly independent* if a relation $\sum_{\mu=1}^{m} a^\mu = 0$, where $a^\mu \in \mathfrak{M}_\mu$, implies that all the vectors a^μ are zero.

It follows at once that two L.M.'s $\mathfrak{M}$ and $\mathfrak{N}$ are linearly independent if, and only if, $\mathfrak{M}.\mathfrak{N} = \mathfrak{O}$.

If the L.M.'s $\mathfrak{M}_\mu$ $(\mu = 1, 2, \ldots, m)$ are linearly independent, we write the L.M. $\mathfrak{M}$ of all vectors x of the form $x = \sum_{\mu=1}^{m} a^\mu$, where $a^\mu \in \mathfrak{M}_\mu$, as

$$\mathfrak{M} = \mathfrak{M}_1 \oplus \mathfrak{M}_2 \oplus \ldots \oplus \mathfrak{M}_m = \sum_{\mu=1}^{m} \mathfrak{M}_\mu \oplus,$$

and we call $\mathfrak{M}$ the *sum* of the L.M.'s $\mathfrak{M}_\mu$.

4·41. We readily deduce from the definition of $\mathfrak{M}$ in **4·4** that the order of the terms in the sum $\sum_{\mu=1}^{m} \mathfrak{M}_\mu \oplus$ is immaterial, and also that $\mathfrak{M}$ may be obtained by forming, for $\kappa = 1, 2, \ldots, m-1$, the L.M.'s $(\mathfrak{M}_1 \oplus \mathfrak{M}_2 \oplus \ldots \oplus \mathfrak{M}_\kappa) \oplus \mathfrak{M}_{\kappa+1}$.

4·42. If the m L.M.'s $\mathfrak{M}_\mu$ are linearly independent, and if the set of vectors $b^{\mu 1}, b^{\mu 2}, \ldots, b^{\mu r_\mu}$ is a basis of $\mathfrak{M}_\mu$, then, by successive applications of Theorem **4·21**, we see that the set

$$b^{11},\ b^{12},\ \ldots,\ b^{1r_1},\ b^{21},\ b^{22},\ \ldots,\ b^{2r_2},\ \ldots,\ b^{m1},\ b^{m2},\ \ldots,\ b^{mr_m}$$

is a basis of $\sum_{\mu=1}^{m} \mathfrak{M}_\mu \oplus$, and that the rank of this sum is the sum of the ranks r_μ of the L.M.'s $\mathfrak{M}_\mu$.

4·43. It follows at once that, if a set of vectors $b^1, b^2, \ldots, b^r$ is a basis of any L.M. $\mathfrak{M}$, then we can write

$$\mathfrak{M} = \sum_{\mu=1}^{m} \mathfrak{M}_\mu \oplus \quad (m \leqslant r),$$

where each $\mathfrak{M}_\mu$ is spanned by some of the vectors b^κ and where the r vectors b^κ are distributed over the m L.M.'s $\mathfrak{M}_\mu$ in such a way that each of them belongs to one, and only to one, $\mathfrak{M}_\mu$.

4·5. We add a theorem giving a lower bound for the rank of the product $\mathfrak{M} . \mathfrak{N}$.

THEOREM. *Let $\mathfrak{M}$ and $\mathfrak{N}$ be two L.M.'s in $\mathfrak{V}_n$ of ranks r and s respectively, and let the rank of $\mathfrak{M} . \mathfrak{N}$ be ρ. Then $\rho \geqslant r+s-n$.*

NOTE. The inequality $\rho \geqslant r+s-n$ is trivial except when $r+s > n$.

PROOF. If $\mathfrak{N} = \mathfrak{M} . \mathfrak{N} \subseteq \mathfrak{M}$, we have $s = \rho \leqslant r \leqslant n$ and there is nothing to prove. We therefore assume $\mathfrak{M} . \mathfrak{N} \subset \mathfrak{M}$ and $\mathfrak{M} . \mathfrak{N} \subset \mathfrak{N}$. By Theorem **4·3**, there exist L.M.'s $\mathfrak{M}'$ and $\mathfrak{N}'$, of ranks $r-\rho$ and $s-\rho$ respectively, such that $\mathfrak{M} . \mathfrak{N} \oplus \mathfrak{M}' = \mathfrak{M}$ and $\mathfrak{M} . \mathfrak{N} \oplus \mathfrak{N}' = \mathfrak{N}$. Then the three L.M.'s $\mathfrak{M} . \mathfrak{N}$, $\mathfrak{M}'$ and $\mathfrak{N}'$ are linearly independent. For a relation $a' + b' + c = 0$, where $a' \in \mathfrak{M}'$, $b' \in \mathfrak{N}'$ and $c \in \mathfrak{M} . \mathfrak{N}$, and where at least one of the vectors a' and b' (say a') was not zero, would imply that $a' = -b' - c$ and so that $a' \in \mathfrak{N}$, since $b' + c \in \mathfrak{N}$; but this would mean that $a' \in \mathfrak{M}$, $a' \in \mathfrak{N}$ and $a' \in \mathfrak{M}'$, contrary to the construction of $\mathfrak{M}'$. Thus there exists a L.M.

$$\mathfrak{M}_0 = \mathfrak{M} . \mathfrak{N} \oplus \mathfrak{M}' \oplus \mathfrak{N}',$$

which is of rank $\rho + (r-\rho) + (s-\rho)$, by **4·42**. Since the rank of $\mathfrak{M}_0$ is not greater than n, we obtain the inequality $r+s-\rho \leqslant n$ and hence the required inequality $\rho \geqslant r+s-n$.

§ 5. Orthogonal complements; systems of homogeneous linear equations

5·0. Definition of the orthogonal complement. Let $\mathfrak{M}$ and $\mathfrak{N}$ be two L.M.'s of $\mathfrak{B}_n$ and let $\mathfrak{N} \subset \mathfrak{M}$. Then, by Theorem **4·3**, there is an infinity of L.M.'s $\mathfrak{X}$ such that $\mathfrak{N} . \mathfrak{X} = \mathfrak{O}$ and $\mathfrak{N} \oplus \mathfrak{X} = \mathfrak{M}$. We give a unique interpretation of the subtraction symbol by defining the L.M. $\mathfrak{X}$ that we denote by $\mathfrak{M} \ominus \mathfrak{N}$ as the set of all vectors of $\mathfrak{M}$ orthogonal to every vector of $\mathfrak{N}$. We proved in **3·6** that the set $\mathfrak{B}_n \ominus \mathfrak{N}$ is a L.M., so that $\mathfrak{M} \ominus \mathfrak{N}$, which is the product $\mathfrak{M} . (\mathfrak{B}_n \ominus \mathfrak{N})$, is also a L.M. If $\mathfrak{N} = \mathfrak{M}$ we write $\mathfrak{M} \ominus \mathfrak{N} = \mathfrak{O}$.

We call the L.M. $\mathfrak{B}_n \ominus \mathfrak{N}$ the *orthogonal complement of* $\mathfrak{N}$ and, if $\mathfrak{N} \subseteq \mathfrak{M}$, we call the L.M. $\mathfrak{M} \ominus \mathfrak{N}$ the *orthogonal complement of* $\mathfrak{N}$ *with regard to* $\mathfrak{M}$.

5·01. To construct the L.M. $\mathfrak{M} \ominus \mathfrak{N}$, where $\mathfrak{N} \subset \mathfrak{M}$, we take an orthonormal basis $g^1, g^2, \ldots, g^s$ of $\mathfrak{N}$ and any basis $a^1, a^2, \ldots, a^r$ of $\mathfrak{M}$, where s and r are the ranks of $\mathfrak{N}$ and $\mathfrak{M}$ respectively; we write $\mathfrak{M} = [g^1, g^2, \ldots, g^s, a^1, a^2, \ldots, a^r]$ and apply Schmidt's process, as it is described in **3·4** and **3·41**, first taking the perpendicular h^1 dropped from a^1 on $[g^1, g^2, \ldots, g^s]$, then the perpendicular h^2 from a^2 on $[g^1, g^2, \ldots, g^s, h^1]$, and so on. In accordance with the remark of **3·41**, we ignore those vectors h that are zero. Let us assume, for simplicity, that h^1 and h^2 are not zero. We obtain

$$[g^1, g^2, \ldots, g^s, a^1] = [g^1, g^2, \ldots, g^s, h^1],$$
$$[g^1, g^2, \ldots, g^s, h^1, a^2] = [g^1, g^2, \ldots, g^s, h^1, h^2], \quad \ldots,$$

and hence, successively,

$$\begin{aligned}\mathfrak{M} &= [g^1, g^2, \ldots, g^s, a^1, a^2, \ldots, a^r] = [g^1, g^2, \ldots, g^s, h^1, a^2, \ldots, a^r] \\ &= [g^1, g^2, \ldots, g^s, h^1, h^2, a^3, \ldots, a^r] = \ldots \\ &= [g^1, g^2, \ldots, g^s, h^1, h^2, \ldots, h^{r-s}],\end{aligned} \qquad (5·01·1)$$

where the set $g^1, g^2, \ldots, g^s, h^1, h^2, \ldots, h^{r-s}$ is an orthonormal basis of $\mathfrak{M}$. It is now clear that the vectors of the form

$$\alpha_{s+1} h^1 + \alpha_{s+2} h^2 + \ldots + \alpha_r h^{r-s}$$

are the only elements of $\mathfrak{M}$ that are orthogonal to every element of $\mathfrak{N}$. Thus

$$\mathfrak{X} = \mathfrak{M} \ominus \mathfrak{N} = [h^1, h^2, \ldots, h^{r-s}]$$

and $\mathfrak{M} \ominus \mathfrak{N}$ *is therefore of rank* $r-s$. We also deduce from (5·01·1) that

$$\mathfrak{N} \oplus \mathfrak{X} = \mathfrak{N} \oplus (\mathfrak{M} \ominus \mathfrak{N}) = \mathfrak{M}$$

and that

$$\mathfrak{M} \ominus \mathfrak{X} = \mathfrak{M} \ominus (\mathfrak{M} \ominus \mathfrak{N}) = [g^1, g^2, \ldots, g^s] = \mathfrak{N}.$$

In the special case when $\mathfrak{M} = \mathfrak{B}_n$ we can take the set of coordinate vectors $\{u^\nu\}$ as the basis $\{a^\nu\}$ of $\mathfrak{B}_n$, and we then find that *the rank of* $\mathfrak{B}_n \ominus \mathfrak{N}$ *is* $n-s$, that $\mathfrak{N} \oplus (\mathfrak{B}_n \ominus \mathfrak{N}) = \mathfrak{B}_n$ and $\mathfrak{N} = \mathfrak{B}_n \ominus (\mathfrak{B}_n \ominus \mathfrak{N})$.

5·02. Definition of complementary L.M.'s in $\mathfrak{B}_n$. Whenever

$$\mathfrak{M} . \mathfrak{N} = \mathfrak{O} \quad \text{and} \quad \mathfrak{M} \oplus \mathfrak{N} = \mathfrak{B}_n,$$

we say that the L.M.'s $\mathfrak{M}$ and $\mathfrak{N}$ are *complementary*.

Theorem **4·21** shows that the sum of the ranks of any two complementary L.M.'s $\mathfrak{M}$ and $\mathfrak{N}$ in $\mathfrak{B}_n$ is n, and Definition **4·2** shows that any vector x of $\mathfrak{B}_n$ may be written uniquely as a sum $x = x^1 + x^2$, where $x^1 \in \mathfrak{M}$ and $x^2 \in \mathfrak{N}$.

We see from **5·01** that any L.M. and its orthogonal complement are complementary.

5·03. Theorem. *If $\mathfrak{N}_1$, $\mathfrak{N}_2$ and $\mathfrak{M}$ are three L.M.'s such that every element of $\mathfrak{N}_1$ is orthogonal to every element of $\mathfrak{N}_2$ and $\mathfrak{N}_1 \oplus \mathfrak{N}_2 \subset \mathfrak{M}$, then*

$$\mathfrak{M} \ominus (\mathfrak{N}_1 \oplus \mathfrak{N}_2) = (\mathfrak{M} \ominus \mathfrak{N}_1) \ominus \mathfrak{N}_2.$$

Proof. By hypothesis, $\mathfrak{M}$ contains both $\mathfrak{N}_1$ and $\mathfrak{N}_2$, and further, since $\mathfrak{N}_1$ and $\mathfrak{N}_2$ are orthogonal, $\mathfrak{N}_1 . \mathfrak{N}_2 = \mathfrak{O}$ and $\mathfrak{N}_2 \subseteq \mathfrak{M} \ominus \mathfrak{N}_1$. We readily see that each side of the equation to be established represents all elements of $\mathfrak{M}$ that are orthogonal both to all elements of $\mathfrak{N}_1$ and to all elements of $\mathfrak{N}_2$.

5·1. Theorem. *If $\mathfrak{M}$ and $\mathfrak{N}$ are real L.M.'s and if $\mathfrak{N} \subset \mathfrak{M}$, then $\mathfrak{M} \ominus \mathfrak{N}$ is also real.*

Proof. By Theorem **2·71**, $\mathfrak{N}$ has a real basis; let $b^1, b^2, \ldots, b^s$ be such a basis. Then $\mathfrak{M} \ominus \mathfrak{N}$ is the set of all elements x of $\mathfrak{M}$ such that $(x, b^\mu) = 0$ for $\mu = 1, 2, \ldots, s$. But the relation $(x, b^\mu) = 0$ implies that $(\bar{x}, b^\mu) = 0$, since b^μ is real. Moreover, $\bar{x} \in \mathfrak{M}$, since $\mathfrak{M}$ is real. Thus $\bar{x} \in \mathfrak{M} \ominus \mathfrak{N}$ whenever $x \in \mathfrak{M} \ominus \mathfrak{N}$ and therefore $\mathfrak{M} \ominus \mathfrak{N}$ is real.

5·2. Systems of homogeneous linear equations. We now apply the calculus of L.M.'s in $\mathfrak{B}_n$, as we have so far developed it, to the familiar problem of the solution of a system of homogeneous linear equations in n variables. We consider the m equations

$$\sum_{\nu=1}^{n} a_{\mu\nu} x_\nu = 0 \quad (\mu = 1, 2, \ldots, m) \qquad (5·2·1)$$

for the complex numbers x_ν. We call the rectangular array of the coefficients

$$\begin{pmatrix} a_{11} & a_{12} & \cdots & a_{1n} \\ a_{21} & a_{22} & \cdots & a_{2n} \\ \cdots & \cdots & \cdots & \cdots \\ a_{m1} & a_{m2} & \cdots & a_{mn} \end{pmatrix}$$

the matrix $(a_{\mu\nu})$ of the system of equations. Putting

$$a^{*\mu} = \sum_{\nu=1}^{n} \overline{a_{\mu\nu}}\, u^\nu, \quad x = \sum_{\nu=1}^{n} x_\nu u^\nu, \tag{5·2·2}$$

we write the equations (5·2·1) in the equivalent form

$$(x, a^{*\mu}) = 0 \quad (\mu = 1, 2, \ldots, m). \tag{5·2·3}$$

We readily see that we may interpret the problem of the solution of the equations (5·2·1) or (5·2·3) as that of finding vectors x orthogonal to all the vectors of the L.M. $[a^{*1}, a^{*2}, \ldots, a^{*m}]$, which is the L.M. conjugate to that spanned by the vectors that are defined by the rows of the matrix of the equations (5·2·1).

We notice that when the matrix $(a_{\mu\nu})$ is square, that is, when $m = n$, we can write

$$a^\mu = \sum_{\nu=1}^{n} a_{\nu\mu} u^\nu, \tag{5·2·4}$$

thereby defining by the columns of the matrix a set of vectors a^μ corresponding to the vectors $a^{*\mu}$. We shall use this notation in § **6**.

We verify at once that the zero vector is always a solution of the system of equations (5·2·3), and that the set of all solutions constitutes a L.M., since, if x^1 and x^2 are two solutions, then αx^1 and $x^1 + x^2$ are also solutions. We identify the L.M. of the solutions in the following theorem:

5·3. THEOREM. *Let the L.M.* $\mathfrak{M} = [a^{*1}, a^{*2}, \ldots, a^{*m}]$ *have rank* r. *Then the set of all solutions of the system of equations*

$$(x, a^{*\mu}) = 0 \quad (\mu = 1, 2, \ldots, m) \tag{5·3·1}$$

forms the L.M. $\mathfrak{B}_n \ominus \mathfrak{M}$ *of rank* $n - r$. *In particular, the equations* (5·3·1) *have no solution except the zero vector if, and only if,* $r = n$, *that is, if* $\mathfrak{M} = \mathfrak{B}_n$; *and the equations* (5·3·1) *are satisfied by every vector* x *of* $\mathfrak{B}_n$ *if, and only if,* $r = 0$, *that is, if* $\mathfrak{M} = \mathfrak{O}$.

PROOF. The problem of finding the set of all vectors orthogonal to every vector of $\mathfrak{M}$ has already been solved in **5·01** by the construction of the L.M. $\mathfrak{B}_n \ominus \mathfrak{M}$, and this L.M. gives the set of solutions of the equations (5·3·1). We have also proved in **5·01** that the rank of $\mathfrak{V}_n \ominus \mathfrak{M}$ is $n-r$.

5·31. Corollary of Theorem **5·3.** *If the number m of equations in the system* (5·2·1) *is less than n, there exists at least one non-zero solution* $(x_1, x_2, \ldots, x_n)$.

Proof. We consider the equivalent system of equations (5·3·1). The rank r of the L.M. $\mathfrak{M}$ of Theorem **5·3** is not greater than m, by Corollary **2·43**, so that, if $m<n$, $n-r \geqslant 1$. Thus, by Theorem **5·3**, the L.M. of the solutions of the equations (5·3·1) has rank at least 1 and there exists at least one non-zero solution.

5·4. Theorem. *If the coefficients* $a_{\mu\nu}$ *of the system of equations* (5·2·1) *are all real, and if the rank of the corresponding L.M.* $[a^{*1}, a^{*2}, \ldots, a^{*m}]$ *is r, then there exist* $n-r$ *linearly independent real solutions.*

Proof. We again consider the equivalent system of equations (5·3·1). The vectors $a^{*\mu}$, defined in **5·2**, are real, since the coefficients $a_{\mu\nu}$ are real, and the L.M. $\mathfrak{M}$ that they span is of rank r and is real, by Theorem **2·71**. Hence, the L.M. $\mathfrak{V}_n \ominus \mathfrak{M}$, which is of rank $n-r$, is also real, by Theorem **5·1**, and, by Theorem **2·71**, there is a basis consisting of $n-r$ real vectors. These vectors give a set of $n-r$ linearly independent real solutions of the equations (5·2·1).

§ 6. Linear transformations; systems of non-homogeneous linear equations

6·0. Definition of a linear transformation. Any relation $x' = Ax$ that correlates a vector x' with every vector x of $\mathfrak{V}_n$ is a *transformation of* $\mathfrak{V}_n$. The transformation $x' = Ax$ or, shortly, the transformation A, is called a *linear transformation* (denoted by the abbreviation L.T.) if the following two conditions are satisfied:

(i) $A(\alpha x) = \alpha(Ax)$ *for every vector x and every number* α,

(ii) $A(x+y) = Ax+Ay$ *for every pair of vectors x and y.*

If, in addition, Ax is a real vector whenever x is a real vector, we say that A is a *real L.T.*

Two L.T.'s A and B are said to be *identical* if $Ax = Bx$ for every vector x of $\mathfrak{V}_n$; we then write $A = B$.

6·01. We define two special L.T.'s, the zero transformation O and the identical transformation, or identity, I by the equations $Ox = 0$ and $Ix = x$, respectively, for every vector x of $\mathfrak{V}_n$.

6·02. Definition **6·0** leads at once to the analytical representation of a L.T. $x' = Ax$. Let $a^1, a^2, \ldots, a^n$ be n vectors such that

$$a^\nu = Au^\nu \quad (\nu = 1, 2, \ldots, n). \tag{6·02·1}$$

Then, writing $x = \sum_{\nu=1}^{n} x_\nu u^\nu$, we have

$$x' = Ax = \sum_{\nu=1}^{n} x_\nu a^\nu, \tag{6·02·2}$$

and we see that the vectors a^ν determine the L.T. A. Hence, two L.T.'s A and B are identical if, and only if, for $\nu = 1, 2, \ldots, n$ we have $Au^\nu = Bu^\nu$.

By writing, as in (5·2·4),

$$x' = \sum_{\mu=1}^{n} x'_\mu u^\mu, \quad a^\nu = \sum_{\mu=1}^{n} a_{\mu\nu} u^\mu, \tag{6·02·3}$$

we obtain from (6·02·1) and (6·02·3),

$$(Au^\nu, u^\mu) = (a^\nu, u^\mu) = a_{\mu\nu},$$

$$x'_\mu = (Ax, u^\mu) = \sum_{\nu=1}^{n} x_\nu (Au^\nu, u^\mu) = \sum_{\nu=1}^{n} a_{\mu\nu} x_\nu, \tag{6·02·4}$$

and in (6·02·4) we have the analytical representation of the L.T. $x' = Ax$.

The square array of n rows and n columns of the coefficients $a_{\mu\nu}$ determined by the L.T. A is called the matrix of A. We say that such a matrix of n rows and n columns is of order n. Every L.T. in $\mathfrak{B}_n$ defines a square matrix of order n and, conversely, every square matrix of order n defines a L.T. in $\mathfrak{B}_n$ by the equations (6·02·4), so that we may denote the corresponding L.T. and square matrix by the same letter. When we wish to describe the matrix in terms of its elements we write $A = (a_{\mu\nu})$, where $a_{\mu\nu}$ is the element in the μth row and νth column.

It is immediate from **6·01** that $O = (0)$ and $I = (\delta_{\mu\nu})$.

6·03. We can generalize the equations (6·02·1) that define the L.T. A by taking any set of n linearly independent vectors v^ν of $\mathfrak{B}_n$ instead of the coordinate vectors u^ν. Then, by Theorem **2·3**, the vectors v^ν form a basis of $\mathfrak{B}_n$, and we may express any x of $\mathfrak{B}_n$ as $x = \sum_{\nu=1}^{n} \alpha_\nu v^\nu$. Hence, if we write

$$Av^\nu = b^\nu, \tag{6·03·1}$$

we see that Ax is uniquely determined as $Ax = \sum_{\nu=1}^{n} \alpha_\nu b^\nu$.

6·04. The bilinear form. We obtain at once from (6·02·4) the bilinear form (Ax, y) associated with any L.T. A as

$$(Ax, y) = \sum_{\mu=1}^{n} \sum_{\nu=1}^{n} a_{\mu\nu} x_\nu \overline{y_\mu}, \tag{6·04·1}$$

where the vectors x and y are expressed as

$$x = \sum_{\nu=1}^{n} x_\nu u^\nu, \quad y = \sum_{\nu=1}^{n} y_\nu u^\nu.$$

The bilinear form (Ax, y) is determined by the L.T. A and, conversely, it determines A, since the coefficients $a_{\mu\nu}$ determine A.

6·05. We deduce from (6·02·2) that

$$\| Ax \| = \left\| \sum_{\nu=1}^{n} x_\nu a^\nu \right\| \leqslant \| x \| \sum_{\nu=1}^{n} \| a^\nu \| = M \| x \|, \tag{6·05·1}$$

where $M = \sum_{\nu=1}^{n} \| a^\nu \|$, since $| x_\nu | \leqslant \| x \|$. It follows that

$$|(Ax, y)| \leqslant \| Ax \| \, \| y \| \leqslant M \| x \| \, \| y \| \tag{6·05·2}$$

for every x and y of $\mathfrak{V}_n$.

Conversely, an inequality

$$|(Ax, y)| \leqslant M \| x \| \, \| y \|, \tag{6·05·3}$$

where M is some positive constant, implies that $\| Ax \| \leqslant M \| x \|$. For, writing $y = Ax$ in (6·05·3), we obtain

$$(Ax, Ax) = \| Ax \|^2 \leqslant M \| x \| \, . \, \| Ax \|$$

and hence $\| Ax \| \leqslant M \| x \|$.

6·06. Theorem. *If $(Ax, x) = 0$ for every x of $\mathfrak{V}_n$, then $A = O$.*

Proof. Let x and y be any vectors of $\mathfrak{V}_n$ and α and β any complex numbers. We have

$$\begin{aligned} 0 = (A(\alpha x + \beta y), \alpha x + \beta y) &= \alpha\bar{\alpha}(Ax, x) + \alpha\bar{\beta}(Ax, y) \\ &\quad + \beta\bar{\alpha}(Ay, x) + \beta\bar{\beta}(Ay, y) \\ &= \alpha\bar{\beta}(Ax, y) + \beta\bar{\alpha}(Ay, x). \end{aligned}$$

Taking first $\alpha = 1$, $\beta = 1$ and then $\alpha = i$, $\beta = 1$, we obtain

$$(Ax, y) + (Ay, x) = 0, \quad i(Ax, y) - i(Ay, x) = 0,$$

and hence $(Ax, y) = 0$ for every x and y of $\mathfrak{V}_n$. If now we write $y = Ax$ we deduce that $Ax = 0$ for every x of $\mathfrak{V}_n$.

Corollary. The last step of the preceding proof is sufficient to prove the weaker result that *the L.T. $A = O$ if $(Ax, y) = 0$ for every x and y of $\mathfrak{V}_n$.*

NOTE. We see that Theorem **6·06** does not remain true under the weaker condition that $(Ax, x) = 0$ for all real x of $\mathfrak{B}_n$. For, if the coefficients $a_{\mu\nu}$ in (6·04·1) satisfy the conditions $a_{\mu\mu} = 0$, $a_{\nu\mu} = -a_{\mu\nu}$, with some $a_{\mu\nu} \neq 0$, we have, for real x,

$$(Ax, x) = \sum_{\mu=1}^{n} \sum_{\nu=1}^{n} a_{\mu\nu} x_\mu x_\nu = \sum_{\mu=2}^{n} \sum_{\nu=1}^{\mu-1} a_{\mu\nu}(x_\mu x_\nu - x_\nu x_\mu) = 0,$$

and yet Ax does not even vanish for all real x. We still have $Ax = 0$, however, if we impose the condition that the coefficients $a_{\mu\nu}$ are real and $a_{\mu\nu} = a_{\nu\mu}$.

6·07. Definition of the conjugate L.T. We define $\bar{A}$, the *conjugate transformation* of A, by the relation $\bar{A}x = \overline{A\bar{x}}$ for every x of $\mathfrak{B}_n$. It is clear that $\bar{A}$ is a L.T. when A is a L.T.

When A is determined by the equations (6·02·2) we have

$$\bar{A}x = \sum_{\nu=1}^{n} x_\nu \overline{a^\nu}.$$

6·08. We deduce at once from Definition **6·07** that the L.T. A is real if, and only if, $A = \bar{A}$. Further, if A is real, the vectors a^ν are all real, by (6·02·1), so that the numbers $a_{\mu\nu}$ are all real. Conversely, it is clear that A is real if the $a_{\mu\nu}$ are all real.

6·1. Definition of the range of a L.T. The set of all vectors x' of $\mathfrak{B}_n$ determined by the L.T. $x' = Ax$ is called the *range of* A; we denote it by $\mathfrak{R}$.

Definition **6·0** implies that $\mathfrak{R}$ is a L.M. and, more precisely, it follows from (6·02·2) that

$$\mathfrak{R} = [a^1, a^2, \ldots, a^n]. \qquad (6·1·1)$$

We see from (6·02·3) that $\mathfrak{R}$ is spanned by the vectors defined by the columns of the matrix A. We deduce from **6·07** and **2·12** that the range of $\bar{A}$ is $\bar{\mathfrak{R}}$, where

$$\bar{\mathfrak{R}} = [\overline{a^1}, \overline{a^2}, \ldots, \overline{a^n}], \qquad (6·1·2)$$

so that $\mathfrak{R}$ is real when A is real.

6·11. Definition of the rank of a L.T. The *rank* of a L.T. A is defined as the *rank* r *of its range* $\mathfrak{R}$.

By Corollary **2·42**, $\mathfrak{R}$ and $\bar{\mathfrak{R}}$, and hence A and $\bar{A}$, have the same rank.

6·12. Definition of the null manifold and of the nullity of a L.T. The set $\mathfrak{X}$ of all vectors ξ of $\mathfrak{B}_n$ such that $A\xi = 0$ is clearly a L.M. It is called the *null manifold* $\mathfrak{X}$ of A and its rank is called the *nullity* of A.

We prove in **6·21** that the nullity of A is $n-r$ when the rank of A is r.

6·2. We need the following theorem in our subsequent work.

THEOREM. *Let A be a L.T. in $\mathfrak{V}_n$ with null manifold $\mathfrak{X}$ and let $\mathfrak{M}$ be any L.M. such that $\mathfrak{M}\,.\,\mathfrak{X} = \mathfrak{O}$. Then the set $\mathfrak{M}'$ of all vectors x' of $\mathfrak{V}_n$ corresponding to vectors x of $\mathfrak{M}$ by the L.T. $x' = Ax$ is a L.M. of the same rank as $\mathfrak{M}$, called the image of $\mathfrak{M}$ with respect to A. The L.T. A determines a one-one correspondence between the vectors of $\mathfrak{M}$ and its image $\mathfrak{M}'$.*

PROOF. Let the set of vectors $b^1, b^2, \ldots, b^\rho$ be a basis of $\mathfrak{M}$, so that $\mathfrak{M}$ has rank ρ, and write $b'^\mu = Ab^\mu$ for $\mu = 1, 2, \ldots, \rho$. Then, plainly,

$$\mathfrak{M}' = [b'^1, b'^2, \ldots, b'^\rho], \tag{6·2·1}$$

and we now show that the vectors b'^μ are linearly independent. For, a relation $\sum_{\mu=1}^{\rho} \alpha_\mu b'^\mu = 0$ implies that

$$0 = \sum_{\mu=1}^{\rho} \alpha_\mu A b^\mu = A\left(\sum_{\mu=1}^{\rho} \alpha_\mu b^\mu\right), \tag{6·2·2}$$

and if we write $\sum_{\mu=1}^{\rho} \alpha_\mu b^\mu = \xi$ we see that $\xi \in \mathfrak{M}$ and, by (6·2·2), that $\xi \in \mathfrak{X}$, so that $\xi = 0$ since $\mathfrak{M}\,.\,\mathfrak{X} = \mathfrak{O}$. Thus $\alpha_\mu = 0$ for $\mu = 1, 2, \ldots, \rho$, since the vectors b^μ are linearly independent, and therefore the vectors b'^μ are also linearly independent and form a basis of $\mathfrak{M}'$ which thus has the same rank ρ as $\mathfrak{M}$.

If x^1, x^2 are distinct elements of $\mathfrak{M}$, then $Ax^1 \neq Ax^2$, since equality would mean that both $(x^1 - x^2) \in \mathfrak{X}$ and $(x^1 - x^2) \in \mathfrak{M}$, contrary to the hypothesis $\mathfrak{M}\,.\,\mathfrak{X} = \mathfrak{O}$. Thus the correspondence determined by A between the vectors of $\mathfrak{M}$ and $\mathfrak{M}'$ is a one-one correspondence.

6·21. THEOREM. *Let $\mathfrak{X}$ be the null manifold of the L.T. A in $\mathfrak{V}_n$, let ρ be its nullity and r its rank. Then $\rho + r = n$. Hence $\mathfrak{X} = \mathfrak{O}$ if, and only if, $r = n$.*

PROOF. Let x be any vector of $\mathfrak{V}_n$ and let $\mathfrak{M}$ be any L.M. complementary to $\mathfrak{X}$. Write, in accordance with **5·02**, $x = a + \xi$, where $a \in \mathfrak{M}$ and $\xi \in \mathfrak{X}$. Then $Ax = Aa$ and therefore the range $\mathfrak{R}$ of A coincides with the image of $\mathfrak{M}$. By Theorem **6·2**, $\mathfrak{M}$ and $\mathfrak{R}$ have the same rank r which, by Definition **6·11**, is the rank of A. It follows from **5·02** that $\mathfrak{X}$ has rank $n - r$; hence $\rho + r = n$.

6·3. Definition of the adjoint transformation and of the adjoint matrix. Let A be any L.T. in $\mathfrak{V}_n$. We define a transformation A^* which we call the *adjoint transformation* of A by the relation

$$(Ax, y) = (x, A^*y) \tag{6·3·1}$$

for every x and y of $\mathfrak{V}_n$.

Now (6·3·1) is equivalent to the relation

$$(A^*y, x) = (y, Ax), \tag{6·3·2}$$

from which we deduce that A^*y is uniquely defined by (6·3·1) for every y of $\mathfrak{V}_n$ and that the transformation A^* is linear. For, if (6·3·2) is satisfied by a value A^*y for any y of $\mathfrak{V}_n$, we have

$$A^*y = \sum_{\nu=1}^{n} (A^*y, u^\nu)\, u^\nu = \sum_{\nu=1}^{n} (y, Au^\nu)\, u^\nu,$$

and therefore A^* is defined as a L.T. Conversely, this value obtained for A^*y clearly satisfies (6·3·2) and (6·3·1) for every x of $\mathfrak{V}_n$.

The equations (6·3·1) and (6·3·2) imply that the L.T. A is the adjoint of A^*, that is, that

$$(A^*)^* = A^{**} = A. \tag{6·3·3}$$

Now let the analytical form of the L.T. A^* be given by the equations corresponding to (6·02·1) and (6·02·3), namely,

$$A^*u^\mu = a^{*\mu} = \sum_{\nu=1}^{n} a^*_{\nu\mu} u^\nu. \tag{6·3·4}$$

Then the associated square matrix A^* of order n has elements $a^*_{\nu\mu}$; we call it the adjoint matrix of A.

By comparing the bilinear forms for the L.T.'s A and A^*,

$$(Ax, y) = \sum_{\mu=1}^{n} \sum_{\nu=1}^{n} a_{\mu\nu} x_\nu \overline{y_\mu},$$

$$(x, A^*y) = \sum_{\nu=1}^{n} x_\nu \left(\sum_{\mu=1}^{n} \overline{a^*_{\nu\mu} y_\mu} \right) = \sum_{\mu=1}^{n} \sum_{\nu=1}^{n} \overline{a^*_{\nu\mu}} x_\nu \overline{y_\mu}, \tag{6·3·5}$$

we obtain at once from (6·3·1) the relation

$$a^*_{\nu\mu} = \overline{a_{\mu\nu}} \tag{6·3·6}$$

between the coefficients for A and A^*.

The relation (6·3·6) shows that A^* is real if A is real; we then have $a^*_{\nu\mu} = a_{\mu\nu}$. We notice that substitution of the values of the $a^*_{\nu\mu}$ from (6·3·6) in (6·3·4) gives the same expression for $a^{*\mu}$ as (5·2·2).

6·31. We obtain the range $\mathfrak{R}^*$ of A^* from (6·1·1) and (6·3·4) as the L.M.

$$\mathfrak{R}^* = [a^{*1}, a^{*2}, \ldots, a^{*n}], \tag{6·31·1}$$

and we show in Theorem **6·4** that the rank r^* of $\mathfrak{R}^*$ equals the rank r of $\mathfrak{R}$, the range of A. We denote by $\mathfrak{Y}$ the null manifold of A^*, which is the L.M. of all vectors η of $\mathfrak{V}_n$ such that $A^*\eta = 0$.

6·4. THEOREM. *Let A be a L.T. in $\mathfrak{V}_n$ and let A^* be its adjoint. Let $\mathfrak{R}$ and $\mathfrak{R}^*$ be the ranges of A and A^* and let $\mathfrak{X}$ and $\mathfrak{Y}$ be the null manifolds. Then $\mathfrak{R} = \mathfrak{V}_n \ominus \mathfrak{Y}$ and $\mathfrak{R}^* = \mathfrak{V}_n \ominus \mathfrak{X}$; $\mathfrak{R}$ and $\mathfrak{R}^*$ have the same rank r; $\mathfrak{X}$ and $\mathfrak{Y}$ have the same rank $n-r$. That is, A and A^* have the same rank and nullity. Further, A determines a one-one correspondence between $\mathfrak{V}_n \ominus \mathfrak{X}$ and $\mathfrak{R}$; A^* determines a one-one correspondence between $\mathfrak{V}_n \ominus \mathfrak{Y}$ and $\mathfrak{R}^*$.*

NOTE. We see from (6·31·1) that the equation $\mathfrak{X} = \mathfrak{V}_n \ominus \mathfrak{R}^*$ expresses the interpretation given in **5·2** of the system of homogeneous linear equations (5·2·3).

PROOF. For every η of $\mathfrak{Y}$ and every x of $\mathfrak{V}_n$ we obtain, by (6·3·1), $(Ax, \eta) = (x, A^*\eta) = 0$. Hence $Ax \in \mathfrak{V}_n \ominus \mathfrak{Y}$, and $\mathfrak{R} \subseteq \mathfrak{V}_n \ominus \mathfrak{Y}$.

For any y of $\mathfrak{V}_n \ominus \mathfrak{R}$ and every x of $\mathfrak{V}_n$, however, we have

$$(Ax, y) = 0 = (x, A^*y).$$

Hence $A^*y = 0$, $y \in \mathfrak{Y}$ and therefore $\mathfrak{V}_n \ominus \mathfrak{R} \subseteq \mathfrak{Y}$ and $\mathfrak{V}_n \ominus \mathfrak{Y} \subseteq \mathfrak{R}$. Thus, $\mathfrak{V}_n \ominus \mathfrak{Y} = \mathfrak{R}$. In the same way, since A is adjoint to A^*, we prove that $\mathfrak{V}_n \ominus \mathfrak{X} = \mathfrak{R}^*$.

If $\mathfrak{R}$ has rank r then, by Theorem **6·21**, $\mathfrak{X}$ has rank $n-r$ and, by **5·01**, $\mathfrak{R}^*$ has rank $n-(n-r)$, so that $\mathfrak{R}$ and $\mathfrak{R}^*$ have the same rank r. Again, by Theorem **6·21**, rank $\mathfrak{Y} = n -$ (rank $\mathfrak{R}^*$) $= n-r$, so that $\mathfrak{X}$ and $\mathfrak{Y}$ have the same rank $n-r$.

Since $\mathfrak{R}^*$ and $\mathfrak{X}$ are orthogonal complements, we deduce from the proof of Theorem **6·21** that $\mathfrak{R}$ is the image of $\mathfrak{R}^*$ with respect to A, and from Theorem **6·2** that A determines a one-one correspondence between $\mathfrak{R}^*$ and $\mathfrak{R}$. Similarly, $\mathfrak{R}^*$ is the image of $\mathfrak{R}$ with respect to A^*, and A^* determines a one-one correspondence between $\mathfrak{R}$ and $\mathfrak{R}^*$.

6·41. COROLLARY OF THEOREM **6·4**. *If, with the notation of Theorem **6·4**, we have $r = n$, then $\mathfrak{R} = \mathfrak{R}^* = \mathfrak{V}_n$ and $\mathfrak{X} = \mathfrak{Y} = \mathfrak{O}$. There corresponds to every vector x' of $\mathfrak{V}_n$ one and only one vector x such that $x' = Ax$ and one and only one vector y such that $x' = A^*y$.*

PROOF. The corollary follows at once from Theorem **6·4** when n is written for r.

6·42. By Theorem **6·4** and Corollary **2·42**, the four L.M.'s $\mathfrak{R}$, $\overline{\mathfrak{R}}$, $\mathfrak{R}^*$ and $\overline{\mathfrak{R}^*}$ have the same rank r. It follows from Theorem **5·3**, by (6·1·1) and (6·31·1), that each of the four systems of n homogeneous equations

$$\left.\begin{array}{ll}(x, a^\mu) = 0, & (x, \overline{a^\mu}) = 0, \\ (x, a^{*\mu}) = 0, & (x, \overline{a^{*\mu}}) = 0\end{array}\right\} \quad (\mu = 1, 2, \ldots, n),$$

and the equivalent forms obtained from (6·02·3), (6·3·4) and (6·3·6),

$$\left.\begin{array}{ll}\sum_{\nu=1}^{n} \overline{a_{\nu\mu}} x_\nu = 0, & \sum_{\nu=1}^{n} a_{\nu\mu} x_\nu = 0, \\ \sum_{\nu=1}^{n} a_{\mu\nu} x_\nu = 0, & \sum_{\nu=1}^{n} \overline{a_{\mu\nu}} x_\nu = 0\end{array}\right\} \quad (\mu = 1, 2, \ldots, n),$$

have solutions forming L.M.'s of rank $n-r$. Elements of the null manifold $\mathfrak{X}$ of A are obtained by writing $x'_\mu = 0$ in (6·02·4). This manifold is the set of solutions of the equations $(\xi, a^{*\mu}) = 0$ and, similarly, the null manifold $\mathfrak{Y}$ of A^* is the set of solutions of the equations $(\eta, a^\mu) = 0$.

6·5. The inverse transformation. When the L.T. $x' = Ax$ in $\mathfrak{B}_n$ has rank n, Corollary **6·41** suggests the consideration of the transformation

$$x = A^{-1}x', \tag{6·5·1}$$

by which x is correlated with x', since in this case we have a one-one correspondence between x and x'. The transformation (6·5·1) is linear, for αx and $\alpha x'$, $x+y$ and $x'+y'$ correspond to one another; it has rank n, for its range is the whole space $\mathfrak{B}_n$. The transformation $x = A^{-1}x'$ is said to be *inverse* to the transformation $x' = Ax$. In the same way, $x' = Ax$ is inverse to $x = A^{-1}x'$.

We justify the use of the notation A^{-1} in **7·42**.

6·51. Definition of a regular and of a singular L.T. We say that the L.T. A is *regular, or non-singular*, if the inverse transformation A^{-1} exists. Thus, *the L.T. A in $\mathfrak{B}_n$ is regular if its rank is n*. We say that *the L.T. A in $\mathfrak{B}_n$ is singular if its rank is less than n.*

6·6. If the L.T. A is real, that is, if all the elements $a_{\mu\nu}$ of the matrix A are real, then A^* is also real, by **6·3**, so that the ranges $\mathfrak{R}$ and $\mathfrak{R}^*$ are real, by **6·1**, and the mapping of $\mathfrak{R}^*$ on $\mathfrak{R}$, described in Theorem **6·4**, is such that every real element in $\mathfrak{R}$ corresponds by

A to a real element in $\mathfrak{R}^*$. For, if the real element x' of $\mathfrak{R}$ is the image of the element $x = a+ib$ of $\mathfrak{R}^*$, where a and b are real, we have $x' = Aa+iAb$, where Aa and Ab are both real. Hence, $Ab = 0$, so that $b \in \mathfrak{X}$. But $b \in \mathfrak{R}^*$, since $b = \frac{1}{2i}(x-\bar{x})$, $x \in \mathfrak{R}^*$ and $\mathfrak{R}^*$ is real. Therefore $b = 0$, since $\mathfrak{R}^* . \mathfrak{X} = \mathfrak{O}$. Thus x is real.

It follows by **6·41** and **6·5** that if the rank of A is n, so that the inverse transformation A^{-1} exists, then A^{-1} is real whenever A is real.

6·7. Systems of non-homogeneous linear equations. We obtain at once from **6·4**, **6·41** and **6·5** the following theorem for a set of n non-homogeneous equations in n variables:

THEOREM. *If the L.T. A in $\mathfrak{B}_n$ is regular, then the system of non-homogeneous linear equations*

$$Ax = x', \tag{6·7·1}$$

or

$$\sum_{\nu=1}^{n} a_{\mu\nu} x_\nu = x'_\mu \quad (\mu = 1, 2, \ldots, n),$$

has one and only one solution x corresponding to any given vector x' in $\mathfrak{B}_n$, and $x = A^{-1}x'$.

If the rank of the L.T. A is r, where $r < n$, then the equations (6·7·1) *have a solution if, and only if, $(x', \eta) = 0$ for every vector η of the null manifold $\mathfrak{Y}$ of A^*. If this condition is satisfied, the most general solution x can be represented in the form $x = q+\xi$, where ξ is any vector of the null manifold $\mathfrak{X}$ of A and where q is a vector of $\mathfrak{B}_n \ominus \mathfrak{X}$ uniquely determined by x'. Further,*

$$\| x \|^2 = \| q \|^2 + \| \xi \|^2 \geqslant \| q \|^2. \tag{6·7·2}$$

6·71. To solve a system of m non-homogeneous linear equations in n variables

$$\sum_{\nu=1}^{n} a_{\mu\nu} x_\nu = x'_\mu \quad (\mu = 1, 2, \ldots, m), \tag{6·71·1}$$

where $m \neq n$, we consider the elements

$$a^\nu = \sum_{\mu=1}^{m} a_{\mu\nu} u^\mu, \quad x' = \sum_{\mu=1}^{m} x'_\mu u^\mu \tag{6·71·2}$$

of the space $\mathfrak{B}_m$, and write the equations (6·71·1) in the form

$$\sum_{\nu=1}^{n} x_\nu a^\nu = x'. \tag{6·71·3}$$

If, further, we write $\mathfrak{R} = [a^1, a^2, \ldots, a^n]$, where $\mathfrak{R} \subseteq \mathfrak{B}_m$, we see at once that (6·71·3) has a solution if, and only if, $x' \in \mathfrak{R}$. By forming the L.M. $\mathfrak{R}_1 = [a^1, a^2, \ldots, a^n, x']$ we can write this condition as $\mathfrak{R} = \mathfrak{R}_1$. In every case we have $\mathfrak{R} \subseteq \mathfrak{R}_1$ and we deduce from Theorem **2·6** that $\mathfrak{R} = \mathfrak{R}_1$ if, and only if, $\mathfrak{R}$ and $\mathfrak{R}_1$ have the same rank. We therefore obtain the following theorem:

THEOREM. *The system* (6·71·1) *of m non-homogeneous linear equations in n variables has a solution if, and only if, the two L.M.'s in $\mathfrak{V}_m$,*

$$\mathfrak{R} = [a^1, a^2, \ldots, a^n], \quad \mathfrak{R}_1 = [a^1, a^2, \ldots, a^n, x'],$$

have the same rank, where the vectors x' and a^ν are given by (6·71·2).

6·72. To find the general solution of the equations (6·71·1) when the condition of Theorem **6·71** is satisfied, we write the equations in the form $(x, a^{*\mu}) = x'_\mu$, where the vectors $a^{*\mu} = \sum_{\nu=1}^{n} \overline{a_{\mu\nu}}\, u^\nu$ are vectors of $\mathfrak{V}_n$, and we consider the L.M. $\mathfrak{X}$ in $\mathfrak{V}_n$ of all vectors ξ such that $(\xi, a^{*\mu}) = 0$ for $\mu = 1, 2, \ldots, m$. Every vector x of $\mathfrak{V}_n$ can be written in the form $x = q + \xi$, where $\xi \in \mathfrak{X}$ and $q \in \mathfrak{V}_n \ominus \mathfrak{X}$; further, since $(x, a^{*\mu}) = (q, a^{*\mu})$, we see that, under the conditions of Theorem **6·71**, there is one and only one solution of the equations (6·71·1) contained in $\mathfrak{V}_n \ominus \mathfrak{X}$, namely, $x = q = \sum_{\nu=1}^{n} q_\nu u^\nu$. The general solution, as in Theorem **6·7**, is then given as $x = q + \xi$, where ξ is any element of $\mathfrak{X}$. The inequality (6·7·2) also holds in this general case.

6·73. If the coefficients $a_{\mu\nu}$ of the systems of equations (6·7·1) and (6·71·1) are all real, then the L.M.'s $\mathfrak{R}$, $\mathfrak{X}$ and $\mathfrak{V}_n \ominus \mathfrak{X}$ are all real, by Theorems **2·71**, **5·1** and **5·4**. If also x' is real, and if we write the coordinate q_ν of the solution q in the form $q_\nu = \alpha_\nu + i\beta_\nu$, we obtain the equations in the form

$$\sum_{\nu=1}^{n} a_{\mu\nu}(\alpha_\nu + i\beta_\nu) = x'_\mu,$$

where, since x'_μ is real,

$$\sum_{\nu=1}^{n} a_{\mu\nu}\alpha_\nu = x'_\mu, \quad \sum_{\nu=1}^{n} a_{\mu\nu}\beta_\nu = 0.$$

This means that the solution q must be of the form $\sum_{\nu=1}^{n} \alpha_\nu u^\nu$.

For, by (6·7·2), q is the solution of least absolute value. Hence since

$$\left\| \sum_{\nu=1}^{n} \alpha_\nu u^\nu \right\| \leqslant \left\| \sum_{\nu=1}^{n} (\alpha_\nu + i\beta_\nu)\, u^\nu \right\|,$$

$q = \sum_{\nu=1}^{n} \alpha_\nu u^\nu$, and is therefore real. Further, the vector ξ of $\mathfrak{X}$ can be represented by a real basis. Thus the real solutions $q+\xi$ of the equations (6·7·1) and (6·71·1) can be given in the form

$$x = q + \sum_\kappa \gamma_\kappa \xi^\kappa,$$

where the vectors ξ^κ form a real basis of $\mathfrak{X}$ and where the γ_κ are real constants.

§ 7. Sums and products of L.T.'s

7·0. Multiplication of a L.T. by a number. Let A be any L.T. in $\mathfrak{V}_n$ and λ any number. If $x' = Ax$ and $x'' = \lambda x'$, we write $x'' = \lambda Ax$ and say that x'' is correlated with x by the transformation λA.

It follows at once from **6·0** (i) that

$$\lambda Ax = A(\lambda x)$$

for every x of $\mathfrak{V}_n$, so that λA is a L.T. Further, the relation between the corresponding matrices A and λA is expressed by writing $A = (a_{\mu\nu})$ and

$$\lambda A = (\lambda a_{\mu\nu}). \tag{7·0·1}$$

In particular, we write $-A$ for λA when $\lambda = -1$.

7·01. From the relations between the bilinear forms

$$(\lambda Ax, y) = \lambda(Ax, y) = \lambda(x, A^*y) = (x, \bar{\lambda}A^*y),$$

we deduce that
$$(\lambda A)^* = \bar{\lambda}A^*.$$

7·1. Addition of L.T.'s. Let $x' = Ax$ and $x'' = Bx$ be any two L.T.'s in $\mathfrak{V}_n$. We define a new L.T. which we call their sum $A+B$ by writing

$$x''' = x' + x'' = Ax + Bx = (A+B)x,$$

where

$$x'_\mu = \sum_{\nu=1}^{n} a_{\mu\nu} x_\nu, \quad x''_\mu = \sum_{\nu=1}^{n} b_{\mu\nu} x_\nu, \quad x'''_\mu = \sum_{\nu=1}^{n} (a_{\mu\nu} + b_{\mu\nu}) x_\nu,$$

so that addition of the corresponding matrices is defined by

$$A + B = (a_{\mu\nu} + b_{\mu\nu}). \tag{7·1·1}$$

7·11. Laws of addition of L.T.'s. It is immediate that, for any L.T.'s A, B and C and for any number λ,

(i) $A+B = B+A$, (ii) $(A+B)+C = A+(B+C)$,

(iii) $A+O = A$, (iv) $\lambda(A+B) = \lambda A + \lambda B$, where O is the zero transformation defined in **6·01**. If $A+B=C$, we write $C-A=B$. It then appears that $C-A=C+(-A)$. In particular, we obtain from (iii) $A-A=A+(-A)=O$. We also have

$$\text{(v)}\quad (A+B)^* = A^*+B^*,$$

since

$$\begin{aligned}((A+B)x,y) &= (Ax,y)+(Bx,y)\\ &= (x,A^*y)+(x,B^*y)\\ &= (x,(A^*+B^*)y).\end{aligned}$$

7·2. The product of two L.T.'s. If we operate successively with the two L.T.'s in $\mathfrak{B}_n$, $x'=Ax$ and $x''=Bx'$, we obtain for every vector x of $\mathfrak{B}_n$ a corresponding vector x''. We have therefore defined a transformation $x''=Cx$ in $\mathfrak{B}_n$ and, clearly, C is a L.T. If we write the transformations in the analytical forms determined in (6·02·4),

$$x'_\nu = \sum_{\mu=1}^{n} a_{\nu\mu}x_\mu,\quad x''_\kappa = \sum_{\nu=1}^{n} b_{\kappa\nu}x'_\nu,\quad x''_\kappa = \sum_{\mu=1}^{n} c_{\kappa\mu}x_\mu,$$

we obtain

$$c_{\kappa\mu} = \sum_{\nu=1}^{n} b_{\kappa\nu}a_{\nu\mu}. \tag{7·2·1}$$

We write $C=BA$ and we say that the transformation C (and the matrix C) is the product of B with A. The elements of the matrix C are defined by (7·2·1).

We see that for any L.T. A and the identical transformation I, $AI=IA=A$, since, by the definition of I in **6·01**, $AIx=Ax$ and $IAx=Ax$ for every vector x.

7·3. It is immediate from (6·3·1) that, for any two vectors x and y,

$$(BAx,y) = (Ax,\ B^*y) = (x,A^*B^*y), \tag{7·3·1}$$

so that, if $C=BA$, then $C^*=A^*B^*$. This relation may be interpreted either as a property of L.T.'s or as an analytical relation between matrices.

7·4. Multiplication of L.T.'s is commutative only in exceptional cases. The most important of these cases are the three following.

7·41. If we have two diagonal L.T.'s with matrices

$$\Lambda = \begin{pmatrix}\lambda_1 & & & 0\\ & \lambda_2 & & \\ & & \ddots & \\ 0 & & & \lambda_n\end{pmatrix},\quad \mathrm{M} = \begin{pmatrix}\mu_1 & & & 0\\ & \mu_2 & & \\ & & \ddots & \\ 0 & & & \mu_n\end{pmatrix},$$

the notation meaning that the only non-zero elements of the matrices are in the leading diagonals, then

$$\Lambda \mathrm{M} = \mathrm{M}\Lambda = \begin{pmatrix} \lambda_1\mu_1 & & & 0 \\ & \lambda_2\mu_2 & & \\ & & \ddots & \\ 0 & & & \lambda_n\mu_n \end{pmatrix}.$$

7·42. If A is any L.T. of rank n then, by **6·5**, the inverse A^{-1} exists and A is the inverse of A^{-1}; hence

$$A^{-1}A = AA^{-1} = I,$$

where I is the identical transformation and the corresponding matrix I, with elements $\delta_{\mu\nu}$, is the unit matrix. This equation justifies the use of the notation A^{-1} for the inverse transformation.

If we write $A^{-1} = (b_{\mu\nu})$ we obtain from (7·2·1) the equations

$$\sum_{\nu=1}^{n} b_{\kappa\nu}a_{\nu\mu} = \sum_{\nu=1}^{n} a_{\kappa\nu}b_{\nu\mu} = \delta_{\kappa\mu}. \qquad (7\cdot 42\cdot 1)$$

7·43. If A is any L.T., I the identical transformation and λ any number, then

$$(\lambda I)A = A(\lambda I) = \lambda A,$$

so that λI is commutative with every L.T.A. Conversely, as we now show, any L.T. that is commutative with every L.T.A. of $\mathfrak{B}_n$ must be of the form λI.

THEOREM. *If the L.T.B. is such that $AB = BA$ for every L.T.A. of $\mathfrak{B}_n$, then $B = \lambda I$ for some number λ.*

PROOF. Write $B = (b_{\mu\nu})$ and first take $A = \Lambda$, where Λ is the diagonal L.T. of **7·41** with $\lambda_\mu \neq \lambda_\nu$ for $\mu \neq \nu$. The equation $\Lambda B = B\Lambda$ gives $\lambda_\mu b_{\mu\nu} = b_{\mu\nu}\lambda_\nu$ and so $b_{\mu\nu} = 0$ for $\mu \neq \nu$. Hence, B itself is a diagonal L.T. Λ. Now take $A = (a_{\mu\nu})$, where $a_{\mu\nu} \neq 0$ for $\mu \neq \nu$. The equation $A\Lambda = \Lambda A$ gives $a_{\mu\nu}\lambda_\nu = \lambda_\mu a_{\mu\nu}$ and $\lambda_\mu = \lambda_\nu = \lambda$, say Thus, $AB = BA$ for every L.T.A. of $\mathfrak{B}_n$ only if $B = \lambda I$.

7·5. The associative law of multiplication of L.T.'s. If A, B and C are any L.T.'s in $\mathfrak{B}_n$,

$$(AB)C = A(BC),$$

since the matrix corresponding to each side of the relation has elements

$$\sum_{\sigma,\tau=1}^{n} a_{\mu\sigma}b_{\sigma\tau}c_{\tau\nu}.$$

Thus it is possible to form positive integral powers A^m of any L.T. A, and the general index law $A^m A^k = A^{m+k}$ is satisfied for such powers. Further, if A is regular, the inverse A^{-1} exists and we can form negative integral powers. Then, by **7·42**, the index law is satisfied for any positive or negative integers m and k if we interpret A^0 as I.

7·6. The distributive law for L.T.'s. If we combine addition and multiplication of L.T.'s we obtain at once

$$C(A+B) = CA+CB, \quad (A+B)\,C = AC+BC.$$

7·7. THEOREM. *Let one of the L.T.'s B and A in $\mathfrak{B}_n$ have rank n and the other have rank r and let $C = BA$. Then the rank of C is r.*

PROOF. Consider first the case when A has rank n and B has rank r. By Definition **6·11**, A maps $\mathfrak{B}_n$ on itself and B maps $\mathfrak{B}_n$ on the range $\mathfrak{R}$ which is of rank r. Thus C maps $\mathfrak{B}_n$ on the L.M. $\mathfrak{R}$ of rank r and is therefore itself of rank r.

Now consider the case when A has rank r and B has rank n. By Definition **6·11**, A maps $\mathfrak{B}_n$ on $\mathfrak{R}$, where $\mathfrak{R}$ now denotes the range of A which is of rank r. Further, the null manifold of B is the L.M. $\mathfrak{O}$, so that, by Theorem **6·2**, B maps $\mathfrak{R}$ on a new L.M. $\mathfrak{M}$ which has the same rank r as $\mathfrak{R}$. Thus, C maps $\mathfrak{B}_n$ on the L.M. $\mathfrak{M}$ of rank r and is itself of rank r.

7·8. THEOREM. *Let the L.T.'s A and B in $\mathfrak{B}_n$ have rank r_1 and r_2 respectively; let $\mathfrak{Y}_1$ be the null manifold of A^* and $\mathfrak{X}_2$ the null manifold of B; let ρ be the rank of the L.M. $\mathfrak{X}_2 . (\mathfrak{B}_n \ominus \mathfrak{Y}_1)$ and let $BA = C$. Then the rank of C is $r_1 - \rho$ and*

$$max\,(0, r_1+r_2-n) \leqslant r_1-\rho \leqslant min\,(r_1, r_2).$$

Thus, if s_1, s_2 and s are the nullities of A, B and C respectively, then $s = n+\rho-r_1$ and

$$max\,(s_1, s_2) \leqslant s \leqslant min\,(n, s_1+s_2).$$

NOTE. The set of inequalities of Theorem **7·8** expresses *Sylvester's law of nullity.*

PROOF. By Theorem **6·4**, A maps $\mathfrak{B}_n$ on $\mathfrak{B}_n \ominus \mathfrak{Y}_1$. We write $\mathfrak{Z} = \mathfrak{X}_2 . (\mathfrak{B}_n \ominus \mathfrak{Y}_1)$ and

$$\mathfrak{M} = (\mathfrak{B}_n \ominus \mathfrak{Y}_1) \ominus \mathfrak{Z}, \quad \mathfrak{B}_n \ominus \mathfrak{Y}_1 = \mathfrak{M} \oplus \mathfrak{Z}. \tag{7·8·1}$$

Then $\mathfrak{M}$ has rank $r_1 - \rho$, since $\mathfrak{B}_n \ominus \mathfrak{Y}_1$ has rank r_1. Let B map

$\mathfrak{V}_n \ominus \mathfrak{Y}_1$ on the L.M. $\mathfrak{M}'$, so that C maps $\mathfrak{V}_n$ on $\mathfrak{M}'$ and the rank of C is the rank of $\mathfrak{M}'$, by Definition **6·11**. We complete the proof of the theorem by showing that $\mathfrak{M}$ and $\mathfrak{M}'$ have the same rank.

By (7·8·1), the vectors x of $\mathfrak{V}_n \ominus \mathfrak{Y}_1$ are the vectors $x = p + \zeta$, where p is any vector of $\mathfrak{M}$, ζ is any vector of $\mathfrak{Z}$ and is therefore a vector of $\mathfrak{X}_2$, and $(p, \zeta) = 0$. Thus $Bp = Bx$, and B maps $\mathfrak{M}$ on $\mathfrak{M}'$. Further, since by (7·8·1) $\mathfrak{M} . \mathfrak{X}_2 = \mathfrak{O}$, $\mathfrak{M}$ and $\mathfrak{M}'$ have the same rank, by Theorem **6·2**. Thus the rank of C is the rank of $\mathfrak{M}$ which is $r_1 - \rho$.

By Theorem **4·5** we have $\rho \geqslant \max(0, n - r_2 + r_1 - n)$, since $\mathfrak{X}_2$ is of rank $n - r_2$, and, further, we have $\rho \leqslant \min(r_1, n - r_2)$, since $\mathfrak{Z} \subseteq \mathfrak{X}_2$ and $\mathfrak{Z} \subseteq \mathfrak{V}_n \ominus \mathfrak{Y}_1$. Thus,

$$\max(0, r_1 + r_2 - n) \leqslant r_1 - \rho \leqslant \min(r_1, r_2).$$

Finally, since $s_1 = n - r_1$, $s_2 = n - r_2$ and $s = n - (r_1 - \rho)$, we deduce that $\max(s_1, s_2) \leqslant s \leqslant \min(n, s_1 + s_2)$.

7·81. Both bounds of ρ may be attained. The rank of C is r_1 if $\mathfrak{X}_2 . (\mathfrak{V}_n \ominus \mathfrak{Y}_1) = \mathfrak{O}$, which presupposes $r_1 \leqslant r_2$, by Theorem **4·5**; the rank of C is zero if $\mathfrak{V}_n \ominus \mathfrak{Y}_1 \subseteq \mathfrak{X}_2$, and it is $r_1 + r_2 - n$ if $\mathfrak{X}_2 \subseteq \mathfrak{V}_n \ominus \mathfrak{Y}_1$.

7·82. The example $B = A^*$. Consider Theorem **7·8** in the case when $B = A^*$. Then $\mathfrak{X}_2 = \mathfrak{Y}_1$, $\mathfrak{Z} = \mathfrak{Y}_1 . (\mathfrak{V}_n \ominus \mathfrak{Y}_1) = \mathfrak{O}$ and therefore $\rho = 0$. Thus

$$\operatorname{rank} A^*A = \operatorname{rank} A = \operatorname{rank} A^*$$

and hence

$$\operatorname{rank} AA^* = \operatorname{rank} A.$$

7·83. The example $B = A$. Consider Theorem **7·8** in the case when $B = A$. Let the rank of A be r, let its range be $\mathfrak{R}$ and let the null manifolds of A and A^* be $\mathfrak{X}$ and $\mathfrak{Y}$. We now have

$$\mathfrak{Z} = \mathfrak{X} . (\mathfrak{V}_n \ominus \mathfrak{Y}) = \mathfrak{X} . \mathfrak{R},$$

and, by Theorem **7·8**, rank $A^2 = r - \rho$, where $\rho = \operatorname{rank} \mathfrak{X} . \mathfrak{R}$, and $0 \leqslant \rho \leqslant \min(r, n - r)$. Again, both bounds of ρ can be attained. We have $\rho = 0$ by **7·82** if $A^* = A$, the condition characterizing the L.T.'s considered in §**8**. We have $\rho = \min(r, n-r)$ for the L.T. A obtained by writing in (6·02·1)

$$\left.\begin{aligned} Au^\nu &= a^\nu = 0 \qquad (\nu = r+1, r+2, \ldots, n), \\ Au^\nu &= a^\nu = u^{n-r+\nu} \quad (\nu = 1, 2, \ldots, r). \end{aligned}\right\} \qquad (7\cdot 83\cdot 1)$$

For here, $\mathfrak{X} = [u^{r+1}, u^{r+2}, \ldots, u^n]$, $\mathfrak{R} = [u^{n-r+1}, u^{n-r+2}, \ldots, u^n]$, and, if $n - r \leqslant r$, $\mathfrak{X} \subseteq \mathfrak{R}$ and $\rho = n - r$, while if $r \leqslant n - r$, $\mathfrak{R} \subseteq \mathfrak{X}$ and $\rho = r$.

When $r = n-1$ the L.T. A defined by the equations (7·83·1) has matrix representation

$$A = \begin{pmatrix} 0 & 0 & \dots & 0 & 0 \\ 1 & 0 & \dots & 0 & 0 \\ 0 & 1 & \dots & 0 & 0 \\ & & \ddots & & \\ 0 & 0 & \dots & 1 & 0 \end{pmatrix}. \qquad (7\cdot83\cdot2)$$

The investigation of the ranges and null manifolds of the positive powers A^κ of any L.T. A plays an important part in the argument of Chapter IV, while the matrix (7·83·2) provides the element with which the canonical form of any matrix is built up (see **21·1** and **22·1**).

7·84. If the L.T.'s A and B in $\mathfrak{B}_n$ are both of rank n, then BA is also of rank n, by Theorem **7·7**. Conversely, if BA is of rank n, then A and B are both of rank n, since otherwise, by Theorem **7·8**, the rank of BA would be less than n.

In the special case when $BA = I$, A and B are both of rank n and it is immediate from **6·5** that $B = A^{-1}$ and $A = B^{-1}$. Further, by (7·3·1), $I = I^* = A^*B^*$, so that

$$B^* = (A^{-1})^* = (A^*)^{-1}. \qquad (7\cdot84\cdot1)$$

Whenever BA has rank n, inverses A^{-1}, B^{-1} and $(BA)^{-1}$ exist and, since

$$I = BAA^{-1}B^{-1} = (BA)(BA)^{-1},$$

we have

$$(BA)^{-1} = A^{-1}B^{-1}. \qquad (7\cdot84\cdot2)$$

CHAPTER II

SPECIAL LINEAR TRANSFORMATIONS IN $\mathfrak{B}_n$

§ 8. Hermitian transformations; eigen-values, eigen-manifolds and reduction

8·0. The main part of this chapter is concerned with a particular class of linear transformations, the normal transformations. We begin with a discussion of the Hermitian transformations which form an important subclass of the class of normal transformations.

Definition of a Hermitian transformation. A L.T. $x' = Hx$ in $\mathfrak{B}_n$, with analytical representation $x'_\mu = \sum_{\nu=1}^{n} a_{\mu\nu} x_\nu$, is said to be a *Hermitian transformation (denoted by the abbreviation H.T.) if* $H^* = H$; that is, if $a_{\mu\nu} = \overline{a_{\nu\mu}}$.

If the H.T. H is a real transformation the constants $a_{\mu\nu}$ are real and $a_{\mu\nu} = a_{\nu\mu}$; we then call H a *symmetric transformation.*

The sum of two H.T.'s is a H.T., since

$$(H+K)^* = H^* + K^* = H+K$$

if $H^* = H$ and $K^* = K$. The inverse of a H.T. H of rank n is a H.T. since, by (7·84·1), $(H^{-1})^* = (H^*)^{-1} = H^{-1}$.

8·01. Definition of a skew H.T. A L.T. $x' = Sx$ in $\mathfrak{B}_n$, with analytical representation $x'_\mu = \sum_{\nu=1}^{n} a_{\mu\nu} x_\nu$, is said to be a *skew* H.T. if $S^* = -S$; that is, if $a_{\mu\nu} = -\overline{a_{\nu\mu}}$. The transformation $x' = iSx$ is then an ordinary H.T., since $(iS)^* = -iS^* = iS$.

If the skew H.T. S is a real transformation the constants $a_{\mu\nu}$ are real, $a_{\mu\nu} = -a_{\nu\mu}$, $a_{\mu\mu} = 0$, and then S is called a *skew symmetric transformation.*

8·1. Hermitian forms. Definition **8·0** implies, for the corresponding bilinear form defined in (6·04·1),

$$(Hx, y) = (x, Hy).$$

Writing $y = x$, we obtain the *Hermitian form*

$$(Hx, x) = (x, Hx) = \overline{(Hx, x)} = \sum_{\mu=1}^{n} \sum_{\nu=1}^{n} a_{\mu\nu} x_\nu \overline{x_\mu}$$

$$= \sum_{\mu=1}^{n} a_{\mu\mu} |x_\mu|^2 + \sum_{\mu=2}^{n} \sum_{\nu=1}^{\mu-1} (a_{\mu\nu} x_\nu \overline{x_\mu} + \overline{a_{\mu\nu}}\, \overline{x_\nu} x_\mu).$$

Since $(Hx, x) = \overline{(Hx, x)}$, we see that (Hx, x) is always a real number. The following theorem shows that the values taken by (Hx, x) in $\mathfrak{B}_n$ characterize the H.T. H.

8·11. THEOREM. *If H and K are two H.T.'s such that*

$$(Hx, x) = (Kx, x)$$

for every x of $\mathfrak{B}_n$, then $H = K$.

PROOF. The hypothesis $(Hx, x) = (Kx, x)$ implies that

$$(Hx - Kx, x) = ((H-K)x, x) = 0$$

for every x of $\mathfrak{B}_n$. Hence $H-K = O$, by Theorem **6·06**.

8·12. The bilinear form corresponding to the transformation KH, where H and K are H.T.'s, is

$$(KHx, y) = (Hx, Ky) = (x, HKy),$$

so that KH *is Hermitian if, and only if*, $KH = HK$.

8·2. Definition of definite, of semi-definite and of indefinite Hermitian forms. A Hermitian form (Hx, x) that takes *only positive values* when $x \neq 0$ is said to be a *positive definite form*. If it takes both *positive and zero values* when $x \neq 0$, but no negative values, it is said to be a *positive semi-definite form*. If the form $-(Hx, x)$ is positive definite or positive semi-definite, then (Hx, x) is said to be *negative definite*, or *negative semi-definite*. If the form (Hx, x) takes both *positive and negative values* it is said to be an *indefinite form*. The H.T. H is also called positive (negative) definite (semi-definite) according to the property of the corresponding Hermitian form (Hx, x).

8·21. THEOREM. *If the Hermitian form (Hx, x) takes no negative values in $\mathfrak{B}_n$ then the H.T. H is positive definite if it is regular, and positive semi-definite if it is singular. If H is semi-definite and if ξ is a non-zero vector for which $(H\xi, \xi) = 0$, then $H\xi = 0$.*

PROOF. (i) If the rank of H is less than n then, by Theorem **6·21**, there exists a non-zero vector ξ such that $H\xi = 0$. Thus $(H\xi, \xi) = 0$ and H is positive semi-definite since, by hypothesis, $(Hx, x) \geqslant 0$.

(ii) If H is positive semi-definite there exists a non-zero vector ξ such that $(H\xi, \xi) = 0$. If y is any vector of $\mathfrak{B}_n$ and ϵ any real number then, by hypothesis, $(H(\xi + \epsilon y), \xi + \epsilon y) \geqslant 0$. We have, however,

$$\begin{aligned}(H(\xi+\epsilon y), \xi+\epsilon y) &= (H\xi, \xi+\epsilon y) + \epsilon(Hy, \xi+\epsilon y)\\ &= \epsilon\{(H\xi, y) + (Hy, \xi)\} + \epsilon^2(Hy, y),\end{aligned}$$

and this expression is not negative for any real value of ϵ if, and only if, for every y,

$$(H\xi, y)+(Hy, \xi) = (H\xi, y)+(y, H\xi) = 0. \qquad (8\cdot21\cdot1)$$

If we take $y = H\xi$ we obtain from (8·21·1)

$$2(H\xi, H\xi) = 2\| H\xi \|^2 = 0. \qquad (8\cdot21\cdot2)$$

Hence $H\xi = 0$ and the rank of H is less than n by Theorem **6·21**; that is, H is singular.

(iii) If the rank of H is n then, by (ii), H cannot be semi-definite and must therefore be positive definite.

8·22. If we consider the two L.T.'s A^*A and AA^* corresponding to any L.T. A we obtain by **7·3** and (6·3·3)

$$(A^*A)^* = A^*A, \quad (AA^*)^* = AA^*,$$

and we see that both A^*A and AA^* are H.T.'s. Writing

$$H_1 = A^*A, \quad H_2 = AA^*,$$

we have

$$(H_1x, x) = (Ax, Ax) = \| Ax \|^2, \quad (H_2x, x) = (A^*x, A^*x) = \| A^*x \|^2,$$

and we verify directly that the two forms (H_1x, x) and (H_2x, x) are both positive definite or both positive semi-definite according as the rank of A is n or is less than n. We may also obtain this result from Theorem **8·21**, since, by **7·82**, A^*A and AA^* have the same rank as A.

8·3. If H is any H.T. and if $\mathfrak{X}$ and $\mathfrak{Y}$ are the null manifolds defined by $H\xi = 0$ and $H^*\eta = 0$, then $\mathfrak{X}$ and $\mathfrak{Y}$ coincide, since $H = H^*$, and Theorem **6·4** takes the following form:

THEOREM. *Let H be a H.T. in $\mathfrak{V}_n$ and let $\mathfrak{X}$ be the null manifold of H. Then the transformation $x' = Hx$ determines a one-one correspondence of the L.M. $\mathfrak{R} = \mathfrak{V}_n \ominus \mathfrak{X}$ with itself.*

8·4. Definition of the eigen-values, of the eigen-solutions and of the spectrum of any L.T. If, for any L.T. A and for any number λ (zero or not zero), there exists *a non-zero vector* ϕ such that

$$A\phi = \lambda\phi, \qquad (8\cdot4\cdot1)$$

then we say that λ is an *eigen-value* of A and that any *non-zero vector* ϕ that satisfies (8·4·1) is an *eigen-solution corresponding to* λ. If $A\phi = 0$ we say that ϕ is an *eigen-solution corresponding to zero.*

The equation (8·4·1) can be written as

$$(A-\lambda I)\phi = 0, \qquad (8\cdot4\cdot2)$$

where I is the identical transformation. In view of Theorem **6·21**, the eigen-values of A can be defined as those values of the parameter λ for which the L.T. $A - \lambda I$ becomes singular.

The set of all eigen-values of the L.T. A forms the spectrum of A.

8·41. We see, by **6·12**, that the set of eigen-solutions of any L.T. A corresponding to the eigen-value zero, with the addition of the zero vector, forms the null manifold $\mathfrak{X}$ of A, and we now deduce from (8·4·2) that the set of eigen-solutions corresponding to any other eigen-value λ, with the addition of the zero vector, also forms a L.M. This L.M. is called the *eigen-manifold corresponding to* λ.

If the transformation is Hermitian, and if the eigen-manifold is of rank k, we say that λ is an *eigen-value of multiplicity, or order, k.* If $k = 1$, that is, if the order of λ is 1, we call λ a *simple eigen-value.*

In § **17**, we define the multiplicity of an eigen-value of a general L.T. in a different way as the rank of a certain L.M. containing the eigen-manifold, since the eigen-manifolds of a general L.T. fail to have the property of complete reduction described in **8·7** and **8·82**.

It will appear in **13·21** that a H.T. in $\mathfrak{V}_n$ with a zero eigen-value may be regarded as a H.T. with no zero eigen-value in a subspace of $\mathfrak{V}_n$ of a smaller number of dimensions; that is, by **3·62**, in a L.M. of rank less than n.

We prove in **12·1** that every H.T. in $\mathfrak{V}_n$ has n linearly independent eigen-solutions. We give at once simple proofs of two other important properties of eigen-values and eigen-solutions of H.T.'s.

8·5. THEOREM. *Every eigen-value λ of a H.T. H is real.*

PROOF. By (8·4·1) we have $(H\phi, \phi) = \lambda(\phi, \phi)$, where the eigen-solution ϕ is a non-zero vector, so that (ϕ, ϕ) is real and not zero. But $(H\phi, \phi)$ is real, by **8·1**. It follows that λ is real.

8·6. THEOREM. *If ϕ^1 and ϕ^2 are eigen-solutions of a H.T. H corresponding respectively to distinct eigen-values λ_1 and λ_2, then $(\phi^1, \phi^2) = 0$.*

PROOF. We have $(H\phi^1, \phi^2) = \lambda_1(\phi^1, \phi^2).$

Also, $(H\phi^1, \phi^2) = (\phi^1, H\phi^2) = (\phi^1, \lambda_2 \phi^2) = \lambda_2(\phi^1, \phi^2),$

since, by Theorem **8·5**, λ_2 is real. Thus $\lambda_1(\phi^1, \phi^2) = \lambda_2(\phi^1, \phi^2)$ and therefore, since $\lambda_1 \neq \lambda_2$, $(\phi^1, \phi^2) = 0$.

The proof holds if one of the numbers λ_1, λ_2 is zero.

8·7. We are led by further discussion of the eigen-manifolds of a L.T. A to the idea of the reduction of A by any L.M. This conception is closely connected with the spectral analysis of A.

Definition of reduction and of complete reduction of a L.T. Let A be any L.T. and $\mathfrak{M}$ any L.M. in $\mathfrak{B}_n$. We say (i) that $\mathfrak{M}$ *reduces* A *if* $Ax \in \mathfrak{M}$ *whenever* $x \in \mathfrak{M}$ and (ii) that $\mathfrak{M}$ *reduces* A *completely if there exists a L.M.* $\mathfrak{N}$ *complementary to* $\mathfrak{M}$ *such that* $Ax \in \mathfrak{M}$, $Ay \in \mathfrak{N}$ *whenever* $x \in \mathfrak{M}$ *and* $y \in \mathfrak{N}$. In this second case we may also say that $\mathfrak{M}$ *and* $\mathfrak{N}$ *reduce* A *completely.*

8·71. If $\mathfrak{E}$ is any eigen-manifold of A, then $\mathfrak{E}$ reduces A, since, if λ is the eigen-value to which $\mathfrak{E}$ corresponds, and if $\phi \in \mathfrak{E}$, then $A\phi = \lambda\phi$ and $A\phi \in \mathfrak{E}$.

8·72. We prove in **8·82** that any eigen-manifold of a H.T. H reduces H completely, and in **17·51** we show that an eigen-manifold of a general L.T. A does not necessarily reduce A completely.

8·8. Theorem. *If* A *is any L.T. in* $\mathfrak{B}_n$ *and if* $\mathfrak{M}$ *is a L.M. that reduces* A, *then* $\mathfrak{B}_n \ominus \mathfrak{M}$ *reduces the adjoint* A^* *of* A.

Proof. Let x be any element of $\mathfrak{M}$ and y any element of $\mathfrak{B}_n \ominus \mathfrak{M}$. By (6·3·1),

$$(Ax, y) = (x, A^*y) = 0,$$

since $Ax \in \mathfrak{M}$. But this implies that $A^*y \in \mathfrak{B}_n \ominus \mathfrak{M}$ for every y of $\mathfrak{B}_n \ominus \mathfrak{M}$ and hence that $\mathfrak{B}_n \ominus \mathfrak{M}$ reduces A^*.

8·81. Corollary of Theorem **8·8.** *If a L.M.* $\mathfrak{M}$ *reduces a H.T.* H, *then* $\mathfrak{M}$ *and* $\mathfrak{B}_n \ominus \mathfrak{M}$ *reduce* H *completely.*

Proof. Write $\mathfrak{N} = \mathfrak{B}_n \ominus \mathfrak{M}$. By a remark at the end of **5·02**, the L.M. $\mathfrak{N}$ is complementary to $\mathfrak{M}$; by Theorem **8·8**, $\mathfrak{N}$ reduces H^*; but $H = H^*$ since H is Hermitian; and therefore, by Definition **8·7** (ii), $\mathfrak{M}$ and $\mathfrak{N}$ reduce H completely.

8·82. If $\mathfrak{E}$ is any eigen-manifold of a H.T. H, then, by **8·71**, $\mathfrak{E}$ reduces H and, by Corollary **8·81**, $\mathfrak{E}$ and $\mathfrak{B}_n \ominus \mathfrak{E}$ reduce H completely. This property is true, in particular, for the eigen-manifold $\mathfrak{X}$ corresponding to the eigen-value zero, and for $\mathfrak{B}_n \ominus \mathfrak{X}$ which is the range $\mathfrak{R}$.

§ 9. Normal transformations and unitary transformations

9·0. We have already seen that the coincidence of the null manifolds $\mathfrak{X}$ and $\mathfrak{Y}$ for any H.T. has interesting implications. For example, we have proved in Theorem **8·3** that any H.T. determines a one-one correspondence of its range $\mathfrak{R} = \mathfrak{V}_n \ominus \mathfrak{X}$ with itself. We now define another class of L.T.'s, the normal transformations, having the property that $\mathfrak{X} = \mathfrak{Y}$ and having most of the other properties of H.T.'s, with one important exception, namely, that the eigen-values of normal transformations are not necessarily real.

Definition of a normal transformation. A L.T. N in $\mathfrak{V}_n$ is said to be a *normal transformation if* $N^*N = NN^*$.

It is clear that N^* is normal if N is normal. The H.T.'s are obvious examples of normal transformations since, for any H.T. H, $H^*H = HH^* = H^2$. Other examples are given in **9·4** and in § **16.**

9·01. Theorem. *If the L.T. N is normal, then $N-\lambda I$ is also normal, for any value of the number λ, real or not real.*

Proof. We have, by **7·11** and **7·01,**

$$(N-\lambda I)^* = N^*-\bar{\lambda}I,$$

and, since $N^*N = NN^*$,

$$(N^*-\bar{\lambda}I)(N-\lambda I) = N^*N-\bar{\lambda}N-\lambda N^*+\bar{\lambda}\lambda I$$
$$= (N-\lambda I)(N^*-\bar{\lambda}I).$$

9·1. Theorem. *If N is a normal transformation and if the null manifolds of N and N^* are $\mathfrak{X}$ and $\mathfrak{Y}$, then $\mathfrak{X} = \mathfrak{Y}$, and hence*

$$\mathfrak{R} = \mathfrak{V}_n \ominus \mathfrak{X}.$$

Proof. If $\eta \in \mathfrak{Y}$, then $N^*N\eta = NN^*\eta = 0$ and hence $N\eta \in \mathfrak{Y}$. But $N\eta \in \mathfrak{R}$ so that $N\eta \in \mathfrak{R}.\mathfrak{Y}$, and since $\mathfrak{R} = \mathfrak{V}_n \ominus \mathfrak{Y}$ by Theorem **6·4,** we have $\mathfrak{R}.\mathfrak{Y} = \mathfrak{O}$ so that $N\eta = 0$. It follows that $\eta \in \mathfrak{X}$ and that $\mathfrak{Y} \subseteq \mathfrak{X}$. In a similar way, we show that $N^*\xi = 0$ for any ξ of $\mathfrak{X}$, that is, that $\mathfrak{X} \subseteq \mathfrak{Y}$. Hence, $\mathfrak{X} = \mathfrak{Y}$.

9·11. Theorem. *If λ is an eigen-value of the normal transformation N, then $\bar{\lambda}$ is an eigen-value of N^*, and if $\mathfrak{E}$ and $\mathfrak{E}^*$ are the eigen-manifolds of N and N^* corresponding to λ and $\bar{\lambda}$ respectively, then $\mathfrak{E} = \mathfrak{E}^*$.*

Proof. The eigen-manifold $\mathfrak{E}$ can be considered as the null manifold of $N-\lambda I$. By Theorem **9·01**, $N-\lambda I$ is also a normal transformation, and by Theorem **9·1** its adjoint $N* - \bar{\lambda}I$ has the same null manifold. Thus $\mathfrak{E}$ is the eigen-manifold of $N*$ corresponding to the eigen-value $\bar{\lambda}$.

9·2. THEOREM. *If ϕ^1 and ϕ^2 are eigen-solutions of a normal transformation N corresponding to distinct eigen-values λ_1 and λ_2, then $(\phi^1, \phi^2) = 0$.*

PROOF. By Theorem **9·11**, the equations $N\phi^1 = \lambda_1 \phi^1$, $N\phi^2 = \lambda_2 \phi^2$ imply that $N*\phi^1 = \bar{\lambda_1}\phi^1$, $N*\phi^2 = \bar{\lambda_2}\phi^2$. Hence

$$\lambda_1(\phi^1, \phi^2) = (N\phi^1, \phi^2) = (\phi^1, N*\phi^2)$$

$$= (\phi^1, \bar{\lambda_2}\phi^2) = \lambda_2(\phi^1, \phi^2),$$

and, since $\lambda_1 \neq \lambda_2$, we deduce that $(\phi^1, \phi^2) = 0$.

9·3. THEOREM. *If $\mathfrak{E}$ is the eigen-manifold of a normal transformation N corresponding to an eigen-value λ, then $\mathfrak{E}$ and $\mathfrak{V}_n \ominus \mathfrak{E}$ reduce both N and $N*$ completely.*

PROOF. By Theorem **9·11**, $\mathfrak{E}$ is an eigen-manifold of $N*$ corresponding to $\bar{\lambda}$ and therefore, by **8·71**, $\mathfrak{E}$ reduces both N and $N*$. Hence, by Theorem **8·8**, $\mathfrak{V}_n \ominus \mathfrak{E}$ reduces both $N*$ and N and so, by Definition **8·7** (ii), $\mathfrak{E}$ and $\mathfrak{V}_n \ominus \mathfrak{E}$ reduce N and $N*$ completely.

9·31. We have now seen that the eigen-manifolds of a normal transformation behave in the same way as those of a H.T., in that they reduce the transformation completely. We therefore go on to define the multiplicity of an eigen-value of a normal transformation as we defined, in **8·41**, the multiplicity of an eigen-value of a H.T.

Definition of the multiplicity of an eigen-value of a normal transformation. We define the *multiplicity*, or *order*, of any eigen-value of a normal transformation as *the rank of the corresponding eigen-manifold.*

9·4. Definition of a unitary transformation. A L.T. $x' = Ux$ in $\mathfrak{V}_n$ is said to be a *unitary transformation if it leaves unchanged the lengths of vectors* so that $(x', x') = (x, x)$. A unitary transformation that is *real* is called an *orthogonal transformation*.

It follows immediately from Theorem **6·21** that any unitary transformation U in $\mathfrak{V}_n$ has rank n, since $x' = Ux = 0$ if, and only if, $x = 0$, and therefore, by Corollary **6·41**, U determines a one-one correspondence of $\mathfrak{V}_n$ with itself. It also follows at once from Definition **9·4** that a unitary transformation maps the unit sphere

$(x, x) = 1$ on itself and, conversely, that any L.T. U that maps the unit sphere on itself is a unitary transformation, for we then have $(Ux, Ux) = (x, x)$ for every x.

9·41. It follows from Definition **9·4**, by (7·3·1), that, for any unitary transformation U,

$$(x, x) = (Ux, Ux) = (U^*Ux, x) = (x, U^*Ux), \qquad (9{\cdot}41{\cdot}1)$$

so that, by Theorem **6·06**, $U^*U = I$ and $U^* = U^{-1}$. Conversely, we see from (9·41·1) that the L.T. U is unitary if $U^*U = I$.

Let the analytical representation of the unitary transformation $x' = Ux$ be $x'_\mu = \sum_{\nu=1}^{n} u_{\mu\nu} x_\nu$. Then, since $U^*U = I$, we have by (7·42·1)

$$\sum_{\mu=1}^{n} \overline{u_{\mu\kappa}} u_{\mu\nu} = \delta_{\kappa\nu}.$$

We also have

$$(x', y') = (Ux, Uy) = (x, U^*Uy) = (x, y),$$

so that angles between vectors, defined by (1·42·2), as well as the lengths of vectors, are unchanged by U. Further, since

$$U^{-1}U = UU^{-1} = I,$$

we have
$$UU^* = I, \quad \sum_{\nu=1}^{n} u_{\mu\nu} \overline{u_{\kappa\nu}} = \delta_{\mu\kappa},$$

from which it follows that U^* is a unitary transformation. Finally, from the relation $U^*U = UU^* = I$, we see by Definition **9·0** that every unitary transformation is also a normal transformation.

By writing

$$g^\mu = \sum_{\nu=1}^{n} u_{\nu\mu} u^\nu, \quad g^{*\nu} = \sum_{\mu=1}^{n} \overline{u_{\nu\mu}} u^\mu, \qquad (9{\cdot}41{\cdot}2)$$

we see that the set of vectors g^μ and the set $g^{*\nu}$ each forms a complete orthonormal system. Conversely, we obtain two adjoint unitary transformations from any complete orthonormal system of vectors by taking the coordinates of the μth vector of the system as the μth column, or the conjugates of the coordinates as the μth row, of the corresponding matrix.

9·5. There is a twofold geometrical interpretation of any unitary transformation. First, we may interpret it as the replacement of every vector by another of equal length in such a way that angles between vectors are unchanged. This process we may describe as a mapping of the whole space on itself, conserving the metric magnitudes, or as a generalized rotation of $\mathfrak{B}_n$ about the origin.

Secondly, we may interpret it as the substitution for the coordinates of every vector referred to one system of coordinate vectors in terms of new coordinates referred to a new system. This process we may describe as a transformation of the coordinate system.

9·51. Taking the first interpretation and following the procedure described in **6·02**, we see that the unitary transformation $x' = Ux$ transforms the coordinate vectors into the orthonormal system of vectors g^{μ} of (9·41·2). This gives an illustration of the invariance of lengths and angles.

9·52. For the interpretation of a unitary transformation as a coordinate transformation it is more convenient to consider it as a substitution of the form

$$x = Ux', \quad x_{\mu} = \sum_{\nu=1}^{n} u_{\mu\nu} x'_{\nu}. \tag{9·52·1}$$

This implies, by **9·41**, that

$$x' = U^{-1}x = U^{*}x, \quad x'_{\nu} = \sum_{\mu=1}^{n} \overline{u_{\mu\nu}} x_{\mu}. \tag{9·52·2}$$

We now interpret the numbers x'_{ν} as the coordinates, in a new coordinate system $\{u'^{\nu}\}$, of the vector that has the coordinates x_{μ} in the initial coordinate system $\{u^{\mu}\}$. Thus

$$\sum_{\mu=1}^{n} x_{\mu} u^{\mu} = \sum_{\nu=1}^{n} x'_{\nu} u'^{\nu}.$$

Substituting for x_{μ} from (9·52·1) we obtain

$$\sum_{\mu=1}^{n} x_{\mu} u^{\mu} = \sum_{\mu,\nu=1}^{n} u_{\mu\nu} x'_{\nu} u^{\mu}.$$

Therefore, by (9·41·2),

$$u'^{\nu} = \sum_{\mu=1}^{n} u_{\mu\nu} u^{\mu} = g^{\nu}, \tag{9·52·3}$$

and these are the coordinate vectors of the new coordinate system. Their coordinates in the old system are given by the elements of the νth column of U.

9·6. If U_1 and U_2 are unitary transformations then the products $V = U_2 U_1$, $W = U_1 U_2$ are also unitary transformations since, by **7·3**, $V^{*} = U_1^{*} U_2^{*}$, $W^{*} = U_2^{*} U_1^{*}$ and therefore $V^{*}V = I$, $W^{*}W = I$.

§ 10. Projectors

10·0. We now interpret the formation of the projection of any vector x of $\mathfrak{B}_n$ on a L.M. $\mathfrak{M}$ of rank r, described in **3·31**, as a H.T. If the vectors $g^1, g^2, \ldots, g^r$ form an orthonormal basis of $\mathfrak{M}$ and if we write, as in (3·31·1),

$$P_{\mathfrak{M}} x = \sum_{\mu=1}^{r} (x, g^\mu) g^\mu, \tag{10·0·1}$$

we readily see that the transformation $x' = P_{\mathfrak{M}} x$ is a L.T. since, for any vectors x and y and any number α,

$$P_{\mathfrak{M}}(\alpha x) = \alpha P_{\mathfrak{M}} x, \quad P_{\mathfrak{M}}(x+y) = P_{\mathfrak{M}} x + P_{\mathfrak{M}} y.$$

Further, $$(P_{\mathfrak{M}} x, y) = \sum_{\mu=1}^{r} (x, g^\mu)(g^\mu, y) = (x, P_{\mathfrak{M}} y),$$

and therefore $P_{\mathfrak{M}}$ is a H.T. We call it the *projector of* $\mathfrak{B}_n$ *on* $\mathfrak{M}$ and, as before, we call $P_{\mathfrak{M}} x$ the *projection of* x *on* $\mathfrak{M}$.

If we write, by **5·01**,

$$x = \sum_{\mu=1}^{r} (x, g^\mu) g^\mu + \sum_{\mu=1}^{n-r} (x, h^\mu) h^\mu,$$

where the vectors h^μ form an orthonormal basis of the L.M. $\mathfrak{B}_n \ominus \mathfrak{M}$, then it is clear that the second sum,

$$(I - P_{\mathfrak{M}}) x = \sum_{\mu=1}^{n-r} (x, h^\mu) h^\mu,$$

gives the projection of x on $\mathfrak{B}_n \ominus \mathfrak{M}$. We have previously interpreted it as the perpendicular dropped from x on $\mathfrak{M}$.

10·01. We obtain at once from (10·0·1)

$$P_{\mathfrak{M}}^2 x = \sum_{\mu=1}^{r} (x, g^\mu) P_{\mathfrak{M}} g^\mu = \sum_{\mu=1}^{r} (x, g^\mu) g^\mu = P_{\mathfrak{M}} x,$$

since $P_{\mathfrak{M}} g^\mu = g^\mu$, and, further,

$$(P_{\mathfrak{M}} x, P_{\mathfrak{M}} y) = (P_{\mathfrak{M}}^2 x, y) = (P_{\mathfrak{M}} x, y). \tag{10·01·1}$$

Conversely, as we show in Theorem **10·2**, if P is a H.T. in $\mathfrak{B}_n$ such that $P^2 = P$, then P is a projector of the form (10·0·1).

10·1. Definition of general projection. We now introduce, in addition to the projection defined in **10·0**, a more general operation, called *general projection*, for which the projector is denoted by Q. The projector P will be called an *orthogonal projector* whenever the use of the term projector alone would lead to confusion.

Let $\mathfrak{M}$ and $\mathfrak{N}$ be two complementary L.M.'s of $\mathfrak{B}_n$, that is, such that $\mathfrak{M} . \mathfrak{N} = \mathfrak{O}$ and $\mathfrak{M} \oplus \mathfrak{N} = \mathfrak{B}_n$. Then every vector x of $\mathfrak{B}_n$ may be written in the form

$$x = a + b, \tag{10·1·1}$$

where $a \in \mathfrak{M}$ and $b \in \mathfrak{N}$. We call a the *projection of x on $\mathfrak{M}$ parallel to $\mathfrak{N}$* and b the *projection of x on $\mathfrak{N}$ parallel to $\mathfrak{M}$* and we write

$$a = Q_{\mathfrak{M}} x, \quad b = Q_{\mathfrak{N}} x = (I - Q_{\mathfrak{M}}) x = x - a. \tag{10·1·2}$$

If the L.M.'s $\mathfrak{M}$ and $\mathfrak{N}$ are given, then $Q_{\mathfrak{M}} x$ and $Q_{\mathfrak{N}} x$ are uniquely defined by (10·1·1) and (10·1·2) for any x of $\mathfrak{B}_n$, since a relation $x = a + b = a' + b'$ would imply that $a - a' = b' - b$, where $a - a' \in \mathfrak{M}$ and $b' - b \in \mathfrak{N}$, and so that $a - a' = b - b' = 0$, since $\mathfrak{M} . \mathfrak{N} = \mathfrak{O}$. It follows that the transformations $a = Q_{\mathfrak{M}} x$ and $b = Q_{\mathfrak{N}} x$ are linear, since we have, for vectors x and y and any number α,

$$\alpha x = \alpha Q_{\mathfrak{M}} x + \alpha Q_{\mathfrak{N}} x, \quad x + y = (Q_{\mathfrak{M}} x + Q_{\mathfrak{M}} y) + (Q_{\mathfrak{N}} x + Q_{\mathfrak{N}} y),$$

so that $Q_{\mathfrak{M}}(\alpha x) = \alpha Q_{\mathfrak{M}} x$ and $Q_{\mathfrak{M}}(x+y) = Q_{\mathfrak{M}} x + Q_{\mathfrak{M}} y$, with similar relations for $Q_{\mathfrak{N}}$. It is clear that $\mathfrak{M}$ is the range of $Q_{\mathfrak{M}}$ and that $\mathfrak{N}$ is its null manifold. We call the L.T.'s $Q_{\mathfrak{M}}$ and $Q_{\mathfrak{N}}$ the projectors of $\mathfrak{B}_n$ on $\mathfrak{M}$ parallel to $\mathfrak{N}$ and on $\mathfrak{N}$ parallel to $\mathfrak{M}$. The relations (10·1·2) show that, if $Q_{\mathfrak{M}}$ is the projector of $\mathfrak{B}_n$ on $\mathfrak{M}$ parallel to $\mathfrak{N}$, then $I - Q_{\mathfrak{M}}$ is the projector of $\mathfrak{B}_n$ on $\mathfrak{N}$ parallel to $\mathfrak{M}$.

Reference to Definition **3·2** shows that general projection reduces to orthogonal projection when the L.M.'s $\mathfrak{M}$ and $\mathfrak{N}$ are orthogonal complements; that is, when $\mathfrak{N} = \mathfrak{B}_n \ominus \mathfrak{M}$.

10·11. The L.T. $a = Q_{\mathfrak{M}} x$ defined in **10·1** is such that

$$Q_{\mathfrak{M}} a = a \quad \text{if} \quad a \in \mathfrak{M}, \qquad Q_{\mathfrak{M}} b = 0 \quad \text{if} \quad b \in \mathfrak{N},$$

and hence

$$Q_{\mathfrak{M}}^2 x = Q_{\mathfrak{M}} a = a = Q_{\mathfrak{M}} x, \text{ that is, } Q_{\mathfrak{M}}^2 = Q_{\mathfrak{M}}.$$

10·2. THEOREM. *If T is a L.T. in $\mathfrak{B}_n$ such that $T^2 = T$, then T is a general projector, and if, in addition, T is Hermitian, then T is an orthogonal projector.*

PROOF. (i) Let the rank of T be r, let its range be $\mathfrak{R}$ and its null manifold be $\mathfrak{X}$, as in Theorem **6·4**. Then, by Theorem **6·4**, the ranks of $\mathfrak{R}$ and $\mathfrak{X}$ are r and $n - r$ respectively. Moreover, $\mathfrak{R} . \mathfrak{X} = \mathfrak{O}$; for, since $T^2 = T$, we have $T(Tx) = Tx = a$ for any vector x and $Ta = a$ for any a of $\mathfrak{R}$, and therefore, within $\mathfrak{R}$, $Ta = 0$ only if $a = 0$. Thus, $\mathfrak{R} \oplus \mathfrak{X} = \mathfrak{B}_n$, by Theorem **4·21** and Corollary **2·61**, and we can write any x of $\mathfrak{B}_n$ in the form $x = a+\xi$, where $a \in \mathfrak{R}$ and $\xi \in \mathfrak{X}$. Hence, $Tx = Ta+T\xi = a$ and T is $Q_{\mathfrak{R}}$, the projector of $\mathfrak{B}_n$ on $\mathfrak{R}$ parallel to $\mathfrak{X}$.

(ii) If, in addition, T is Hermitian, then, by Theorem **8·3**, $\mathfrak{X} = \mathfrak{B}_n \ominus \mathfrak{R}$ and therefore, by the remark at the end of **10·1**, T is the orthogonal projector $P_{\mathfrak{R}}$ of $\mathfrak{B}_n$ on $\mathfrak{R}$.

Note. Reference to Theorem **9·1** shows that the condition in Theorem **10·2** that T is Hermitian may be replaced by the weaker condition that T is normal.

10·3. Theorem. *If $Q_{\mathfrak{M}}$ is the projector of $\mathfrak{B}_n$ on $\mathfrak{M}$ parallel to $\mathfrak{N}$, then $Q^*_{\mathfrak{M}}$ is the projector of $\mathfrak{B}_n$ on $\mathfrak{B}_n \ominus \mathfrak{N}$ parallel to $\mathfrak{B}_n \ominus \mathfrak{M}$.*

Proof. The transformation $Q^*_{\mathfrak{M}}$ is a projector, by Theorem **10·2**, since the relation $Q^2_{\mathfrak{M}} = Q_{\mathfrak{M}}$ implies $(Q^*_{\mathfrak{M}})^2 = Q^*_{\mathfrak{M}}$. By Theorem **6·4**, the range of $Q^*_{\mathfrak{M}}$ is $\mathfrak{B}_n \ominus \mathfrak{N}$, since $\mathfrak{N}$ is the null manifold of $Q_{\mathfrak{M}}$, and the null manifold of $Q^*_{\mathfrak{M}}$ is $\mathfrak{B}_n \ominus \mathfrak{M}$, since $\mathfrak{M}$ is the range of $Q_{\mathfrak{M}}$. Therefore, by Theorem **10·2**, $Q^*_{\mathfrak{M}}$ is the projector of $\mathfrak{B}_n$ on $\mathfrak{B}_n \ominus \mathfrak{N}$ parallel to $\mathfrak{B}_n \ominus \mathfrak{M}$.

10·4. Theorem. *Let Q_1 and Q_2 be general projectors. Then Q_1+Q_2 is a projector if, and only if, $Q_1 Q_2 = Q_2 Q_1 = O$. If Q_1 and Q_2 are both orthogonal projectors and if $Q_1 Q_2 = O$, then $Q_2 Q_1 = O$ and Q_1+Q_2 is an orthogonal projector.*

Proof. Write $Q = Q_1+Q_2$. We have

$$Q^2 = Q_1+Q_1 Q_2+Q_2 Q_1+Q_2, \tag{10·4·1}$$

since $Q_1^2 = Q_1$ and $Q_2^2 = Q_2$ by **10·11**.

(i) If then $Q_1 Q_2 = Q_2 Q_1 = O$, we have $Q^2 = Q_1+Q_2 = Q$ and Q is a projector by Theorem **10·2**.

(ii) If Q_1 and Q_2 are both orthogonal projectors, then Q_1, Q_2 and Q are all H.T.'s. If $Q_1 Q_2 = O$, then $(Q_1 Q_2)^* = O$. But since $(Q_1 Q_2)^* = Q_2^* Q_1^* = Q_2 Q_1$, this means that $Q_2 Q_1 = O$ and therefore that Q is a projector, by (i). Moreover, by Theorem **10·2**, Q is an orthogonal projector since Q is a H.T.

(iii) Conversely, if Q is a projector, we deduce from (10·4·1) that

$$Q_1 Q_2+Q_2 Q_1 = O, \tag{10·4·2}$$

since $Q^2 = Q = Q_1+Q_2$. By multiplying (10·4·2) by Q_1, first from the left and then from the right, and using the relation $Q_1^2 = Q_1$, we obtain

$$Q_1 Q_2 + Q_1 Q_2 Q_1 = O, \quad Q_1 Q_2 Q_1 + Q_2 Q_1 = O,$$

and then, by subtracting these equations,

$$Q_1 Q_2 - Q_2 Q_1 = O.$$

In virtue of (10·4·2) we obtain $Q_1 Q_2 = Q_2 Q_1 = O$.

10·41. Theorem. *If Q_1, Q_2 and $Q_1 + Q_2$ are general projectors with ranges $\mathfrak{M}_1$, $\mathfrak{M}_2$ and $\mathfrak{M}$ and null manifolds $\mathfrak{N}_1$, $\mathfrak{N}_2$ and $\mathfrak{N}$ respectively, then*

$$\mathfrak{M}_1 . \mathfrak{M}_2 = \mathfrak{O}, \quad \mathfrak{M}_1 \oplus \mathfrak{M}_2 = \mathfrak{M} \quad \text{and} \quad \mathfrak{N}_1 . \mathfrak{N}_2 = \mathfrak{N}.$$

Proof. Write $Q = Q_1 + Q_2$. By hypothesis, Q is a projector and therefore, by Theorem **10·4**, $Q_1 Q_2 = Q_2 Q_1 = O$. But the equation $Q_1 Q_2 = O$ implies that $\mathfrak{M}_2 \subseteq \mathfrak{N}_1$, so that, since $\mathfrak{M}_1 . \mathfrak{N}_1 = \mathfrak{O}$, we have $\mathfrak{M}_1 . \mathfrak{M}_2 = \mathfrak{O}$. The two L.M.'s $\mathfrak{M}_1$ and $\mathfrak{M}_2$ are therefore linearly independent and $Q_1 x + Q_2 x = 0$ if, and only if, $x \in \mathfrak{N}_1$ and $x \in \mathfrak{N}_2$, that is, if $x \in \mathfrak{N}_1 . \mathfrak{N}_2$. Hence, $\mathfrak{N} = \mathfrak{N}_1 . \mathfrak{N}_2$. Further, if $x = a^1 + a^2$, where $a^1 \in \mathfrak{M}_1$ and $a^2 \in \mathfrak{M}_2$, we have

$$Q_1 x = a^1, \quad Q_2 x = a^2, \quad Qx = a^1 + a^2 = x \quad \text{and} \quad \mathfrak{M}_1 \oplus \mathfrak{M}_2 \subseteq \mathfrak{M}.$$

Also, $\mathfrak{M} \subseteq \mathfrak{M}_1 \oplus \mathfrak{M}_2$ since, for any x of $\mathfrak{B}_n$, $Qx = Q_1 x + Q_2 x$, where $Q_1 x \in \mathfrak{M}_1$ and $Q_2 x \in \mathfrak{M}_2$. Hence, $\mathfrak{M} = \mathfrak{M}_1 \oplus \mathfrak{M}_2$.

10·42. Theorem. *Let Q_μ, for $\mu = 1, 2, \ldots, m$, be general projectors with ranges $\mathfrak{M}_\mu$ and null manifolds $\mathfrak{N}_\mu$. Write $Q = \sum_{\mu=1}^{m} Q_\mu$ and let the range and null manifold of Q be $\mathfrak{M}$ and $\mathfrak{N}$ respectively. Then Q is a projector if $Q_\mu Q_\nu = \delta_{\mu\nu} Q_\mu$ for $1 \leqslant \mu, \nu \leqslant m$; the L.M.'s $\mathfrak{M}_\mu$ are moreover linearly independent, $\mathfrak{M}_\mu . \mathfrak{M}_\nu = \delta_{\mu\nu} \mathfrak{M}_\mu$, and*

$$\mathfrak{M} = \sum_{\mu=1}^{m} \mathfrak{M}_\mu \oplus, \quad \mathfrak{N} = \mathfrak{N}_1 . \mathfrak{N}_2 . \ldots . \mathfrak{N}_m.$$

If the projectors Q_μ are orthogonal projectors then Q is an orthogonal projector if, and only if, $Q_\mu Q_\nu = \delta_{\mu\nu} Q_\mu$ for $1 \leqslant \mu \leqslant \nu \leqslant m$.

Note. In **10·82** we show that the condition $Q_\mu Q_\nu = \delta_{\mu\nu} Q_\mu$ is necessarily satisfied for general projectors Q_μ when Q is a projector.

Proof. The first part of the theorem follows almost at once on repeated applications of Theorems **10·4** and **10·41**. It remains to prove the second part about orthogonal projectors.

It follows by Theorem **10·4** that Q is an orthogonal projector if $Q_\mu Q_\nu = \delta_{\mu\nu} Q_\mu$ for $1 \leqslant \mu \leqslant \nu \leqslant m$ and if each Q_μ is an orthogonal projector. Conversely, suppose that Q and all the Q_μ are orthogonal projectors, with ranges $\mathfrak{M}, \mathfrak{M}_\mu$ and null manifolds $\mathfrak{N}, \mathfrak{N}_\mu$, and let a be any vector of $\mathfrak{M}_\nu$. Then, by (3·22·1), and since Q and Q_μ are H.T.'s,

$$(a, a) \geqslant (Qa, Qa) = (Qa, a) = \sum_{\mu=1}^{m} (Q_\mu a, a) = \sum_{\mu=1}^{m} (Q_\mu a, Q_\mu a)$$
$$\geqslant (Q_\nu a, Q_\nu a) = (a, a).$$

The equality sign must hold throughout in the relations above and therefore $Q_\mu a = 0$ for $\mu \neq \nu$ whenever $a \in \mathfrak{M}_\nu$. It follows that $Q_\mu Q_\nu x = 0$ for $\mu \neq \nu$ and for any vector x of $\mathfrak{B}_n$. Finally, since Q_μ is a projector, $Q_\mu^2 x = Q_\mu x$. This completes the proof of the theorem.

10·5. THEOREM. *Let Q_1 and Q_2 be general projectors with ranges $\mathfrak{M}_1$ and $\mathfrak{M}_2$ and null manifolds $\mathfrak{N}_1$ and $\mathfrak{N}_2$. Then $Q_1 Q_2 = Q_2$ if, and only if, $\mathfrak{M}_2 \subseteq \mathfrak{M}_1$, and $Q_2 Q_1 = Q_2$ if, and only if, $\mathfrak{N}_1 \subseteq \mathfrak{N}_2$.*

NOTE. The theorem implies that $Q_1 Q_2 = Q_2 Q_1 = Q_2$ if, and only if, both $\mathfrak{M}_2 \subseteq \mathfrak{M}_1$ and $\mathfrak{N}_1 \subseteq \mathfrak{N}_2$.

PROOF. (i) If $\mathfrak{M}_2 \subseteq \mathfrak{M}_1$, then, since $Q_2 x \in \mathfrak{M}_2$ and so $Q_2 x \in \mathfrak{M}_1$, we have $Q_1 Q_2 x = Q_2 x$ for any vector x, and therefore $Q_1 Q_2 = Q_2$.

(ii) Conversely, if $Q_1 Q_2 = Q_2$, then $Q_1 Q_2$ is a projector with range $\mathfrak{M}_2$. But the range of $Q_1 Q_2$ is contained in $\mathfrak{M}_1$, and therefore $\mathfrak{M}_2 \subseteq \mathfrak{M}_1$.

(iii) The ranges of the projectors $I - Q_1$ and $I - Q_2$ are $\mathfrak{N}_1$ and $\mathfrak{N}_2$ respectively. Hence we deduce from (i) and (ii) above that the condition $\mathfrak{N}_1 \subseteq \mathfrak{N}_2$ is the necessary and sufficient condition for the equality

$$(I - Q_2)(I - Q_1) = I - Q_1.$$

But this is equivalent to the equality

$$I - Q_2 - Q_1 + Q_2 Q_1 = I - Q_1,$$

or $Q_2 Q_1 = Q_2$. Thus, $Q_2 Q_1 = Q_2$ if, and only if, $\mathfrak{N}_1 \subseteq \mathfrak{N}_2$.

10·51. COROLLARY OF THEOREM **10·5**. *Let P_1 and P_2 be orthogonal projectors with ranges $\mathfrak{M}_1$ and $\mathfrak{M}_2$. If $P_1 P_2 = P_2$, then $P_2 P_1 = P_2$, $\mathfrak{M}_2 \subseteq \mathfrak{M}_1$ and*

$$\mathfrak{N}_1 = \mathfrak{B}_n \ominus \mathfrak{M}_1 \subseteq \mathfrak{N}_2 = \mathfrak{B}_n \ominus \mathfrak{M}_2.$$

Conversely, if $\mathfrak{M}_2 \subseteq \mathfrak{M}_1$, then $P_1 P_2 = P_2 P_1 = P_2$.

PROOF. Since the orthogonal projectors P_1 and P_2 are H.T.'s, the equality $P_1 P_2 = P_2$ implies $P_2 = P_2^* = P_2^* P_1^* = P_2 P_1$. The remaining assertions of the corollary now follow at once from the theorem and note of **10·5**.

10·6. We now give a matrix representation for any projector. We consider first the orthogonal projection $P_{\mathfrak{M}}$ of $\mathfrak{B}_n$ on the L.M. $\mathfrak{M}$ of rank r. Let $g^1, g^2, \ldots, g^r$ be an orthonormal basis of $\mathfrak{M}$, let x be any vector of $\mathfrak{B}_n$ and write

$$g^\kappa = \sum_{\nu=1}^{n} p_{\nu\kappa} u^\nu, \quad x = \sum_{\nu=1}^{n} x_\nu u^\nu.$$

Then, by (10·0·1),

$$P_{\mathfrak{M}} x = \sum_{\kappa=1}^{r} (x, g^\kappa) g^\kappa = \sum_{\kappa=1}^{r} \sum_{\nu=1}^{n} \sum_{\mu=1}^{n} (x_\nu \overline{p_{\nu\kappa}}) p_{\mu\kappa} u^\mu$$

$$= \sum_{\mu=1}^{n} \sum_{\nu=1}^{n} x_\nu \left(\sum_{\kappa=1}^{r} p_{\mu\kappa} \overline{p_{\nu\kappa}} \right) u^\mu = \sum_{\mu=1}^{n} x'_\mu u^\mu,$$

where

$$x'_\mu = \sum_{\nu=1}^{n} \left(\sum_{\kappa=1}^{r} p_{\mu\kappa} \overline{p_{\nu\kappa}} \right) x_\nu. \tag{10·6·1}$$

Thus the matrix representation for $P_{\mathfrak{M}}$ is given by

$$P_{\mathfrak{M}} = \left(\sum_{\kappa=1}^{r} p_{\mu\kappa} \overline{p_{\nu\kappa}} \right).$$

The rectangular matrix $(p_{\nu\kappa})$ of n rows and r columns consists of the coordinates of vectors forming an orthonormal basis of $\mathfrak{M}$. Since $(g^\iota, g^\kappa) = \delta_{\iota\kappa}$, we have

$$\sum_{\nu=1}^{n} (p_{\nu\iota} \overline{p_{\nu\kappa}}) = \delta_{\iota\kappa} \quad (\iota, \kappa = 1, 2, \ldots, r),$$

which means that the vectors defined by the columns of the matrix $(p_{\nu\kappa})$ are orthogonal to one another. Thus, this matrix may be interpreted as an incomplete unitary matrix which could be completed by the addition of $n-r$ columns consisting of the coordinates of vectors forming an orthonormal basis of $\mathfrak{B}_n \ominus \mathfrak{M}$.

10·7. We now consider a general projector $Q_{\mathfrak{M}}$. Let $\mathfrak{M}$ and $\mathfrak{N}$ be L.M.'s, as in **10·1**, with bases $a^1, a^2, \ldots, a^r$ and $b^1, b^2, \ldots, b^{n-r}$ respectively, such that $Q_{\mathfrak{M}}$ is the projector of $\mathfrak{B}_n$ on $\mathfrak{M}$ parallel to $\mathfrak{N}$. Let T be the L.T. defined according to (6·02·1) by the relations

$$Tu^\mu = a^\mu \ (\mu = 1, 2, \ldots, r), \quad Tu^{\mu+r} = b^\mu \ (\mu = 1, 2, \ldots, n-r). \tag{10·7·1}$$

By **6·11**, T is of rank n, the n vectors $a^1, a^2, \ldots, a^r, b^1, b^2, \ldots, b^{n-r}$

being linearly independent since $\mathfrak{M} \cdot \mathfrak{N} = \mathfrak{O}$. Thus the inverse T^{-1} exists. Further, if we write $T = (t_{\mu\nu})$, we obtain from (6·02·3),

$$\left.\begin{aligned} a^\nu &= \sum_{\mu=1}^{n} t_{\mu\nu} u^\mu \qquad (\nu = 1, 2, \ldots, r), \\ b^\nu &= \sum_{\mu=1}^{n} t_{\mu, r+\nu} u^\mu \quad (\nu = 1, 2, \ldots, n-r). \end{aligned}\right\} \tag{10·7·2}$$

Writing $x = \sum_{\mu=1}^{n} x_\mu u^\mu$, we deduce from (10·1·1) and (10·7·2)

$$\begin{aligned} x = \sum_{\mu=1}^{n} x_\mu u^\mu &= \sum_{\nu=1}^{r} \alpha_\nu a^\nu + \sum_{\nu=1}^{n-r} \beta_\nu b^\nu \\ &= \sum_{\mu=1}^{n} \left(\sum_{\nu=1}^{r} \alpha_\nu t_{\mu\nu} u^\mu + \sum_{\nu=1}^{n-r} \beta_\nu t_{\mu, r+\nu} u^\mu \right), \end{aligned}$$

so that
$$x_\mu = \sum_{\nu=1}^{r} t_{\mu\nu} \alpha_\nu + \sum_{\nu=1}^{n-r} t_{\mu, r+\nu} \beta_\nu.$$

If now we write $T^{-1} = (s_{\mu\nu})$ we obtain by (7·42·1)

$$\alpha_\nu = \sum_{\mu=1}^{n} s_{\nu\mu} x_\mu \quad (\nu = 1, 2, \ldots, r). \tag{10·7·3}$$

Finally, from (10·1·2), (10·7·2) and (10·7·3),

$$Q_{\mathfrak{M}} x = a = \sum_{\kappa=1}^{r} \alpha_\kappa a^\kappa = \sum_{\kappa=1}^{r} \sum_{\mu=1}^{n} \sum_{\nu=1}^{n} t_{\mu\kappa} s_{\kappa\nu} x_\nu u^\mu,$$

and this gives the matrix representation of $Q_{\mathfrak{M}}$

$$Q_{\mathfrak{M}} = \left(\sum_{\kappa=1}^{r} t_{\mu\kappa} s_{\kappa\nu} \right), \quad x'_\mu = \sum_{\nu=1}^{n} \left(\sum_{\kappa=1} t_{\mu\kappa} s_{\kappa\nu} \right) x_\nu, \tag{10·7·4}$$

comparable in form with (10·6·1).

10·8. We deduce from the matrix representation (10·7·4) of a general projector $Q_{\mathfrak{M}}$ a property of the trace of the matrix.

Definition of the trace of a matrix. We define the *trace* τ_A of an nth order matrix $A = (a_{\mu\nu})$ as the *sum of the diagonal elements of the matrix,*

$$\tau_A = \sum_{\mu=1}^{n} (Au^\mu, u^\mu) = \sum_{\mu=1}^{n} a_{\mu\mu}. \tag{10·8·1}$$

The trace and its invariant properties are discussed more fully in **13·42**, **13·43** and **22·43**.

10·81. THEOREM. *The trace τ_Q of the matrix representing a general projector Q equals the rank r of Q.*

Proof. We represent Q by the matrix, $Q = (q_{\mu\nu})$, and we deduce from (10·8·1) and (10·7·4) that

$$\tau_Q = \sum_{\mu=1}^{n} q_{\mu\mu} = \sum_{\mu=1}^{n}\left(\sum_{\kappa=1}^{r} t_{\mu\kappa}s_{\kappa\mu}\right) = \sum_{\kappa=1}^{r}\left(\sum_{\mu=1}^{n} s_{\kappa\mu}t_{\mu\kappa}\right) = \sum_{\kappa=1}^{r}\delta_{\kappa\kappa} = r.$$

10·82. The preceding theorem enables us to prove the converse of Theorem **10·42** to which we referred in Note **10·42**.

Theorem. *Let Q_μ, for $\mu = 1, 2, \ldots, m$, be a general projector with rank r_μ and range $\mathfrak{M}_\mu$. If the sum $Q = \sum_{\mu=1}^{m} Q_\mu$ is also a projector, with rank r and range $\mathfrak{M}$, then the m L.M.'s $\mathfrak{M}_\mu$ are linearly independent, $\mathfrak{M} = \sum_{\mu=1}^{m} \mathfrak{M}_\mu \oplus$ and $Q_\mu Q_\nu = \delta_{\mu\nu} Q_\mu$ for $1 \leqslant \mu, \nu \leqslant m$.*

Proof. (i) We first show that the set of m L.M.'s $\mathfrak{M}_\mu$ is linearly independent and that $\mathfrak{M} = \sum_{\mu=1}^{m} \mathfrak{M}_\mu \oplus$. We obtain from Definition **10·8** and Theorem **10·81** that

$$\tau_Q = \sum_{\mu=1}^{m} \tau_{Q_\mu} = \sum_{\mu=1}^{m} r_\mu = r,$$

and this gives the rank r of $\mathfrak{M}$. We deduce, however, from the equality $Qx = \sum_{\mu=1}^{m} Q_\mu x$ for every vector x that

$$\mathfrak{M} \subseteq [a^{11}, a^{12}, \ldots, a^{1r_1}, \ldots, a^{\mu 1}, a^{\mu 2}, \ldots, a^{\mu r_\mu}, \ldots, a^{m1}, a^{m2}, \ldots, a^{mr_m}], \tag{10·82·1}$$

where $a^{\mu 1}, a^{\mu 2}, \ldots, a^{\mu r_\mu}$ denotes a basis of $\mathfrak{M}_\mu$. But the number of elements in the square bracket above is $\sum_{\mu=1}^{m} r_\mu$, which is the rank r of $\mathfrak{M}$, and hence this set of r elements is linearly independent, since otherwise the L.M. defined by the square bracket (10·82·1) would have rank less than the rank of $\mathfrak{M}$. It follows by Definition **4·4** that the m L.M.'s $\mathfrak{M}_\mu$ are linearly independent and that (10·82·1) may be written in the form

$$\mathfrak{M} \subseteq \sum_{\mu=1}^{m} \mathfrak{M}_\mu \oplus;$$

the equality follows by Theorem **2·6**.

(ii) We show that $Q_\nu x^\mu = 0$ when x^μ is any element of $\mathfrak{M}_\mu$ and $\mu \neq \nu$; it then follows that $Q_\mu Q_\nu = O$ for $\mu \neq \nu$. Since $\mathfrak{M}_\mu \subseteq \mathfrak{M}$ we have

$Qx^{\mu} = Q_{\mu}x^{\mu} = x^{\mu}$ and hence $\sum_{\nu \neq \mu} Q_{\nu}x^{\mu} = 0$. But this implies that $Q_{\nu}x^{\mu} = 0$ for $\nu \neq \mu$, since $Q_{\nu}x^{\mu} \in \mathfrak{M}_{\nu}$ and since the L.M.'s $\mathfrak{M}_{\nu}$ are linearly independent.

10·9. We add a theorem concerning the application of projection to the reduction of a L.T. A.

THEOREM. *Two complementary L.M.'s $\mathfrak{M}$ and $\mathfrak{N}$ of $\mathfrak{B}_n$ reduce the L.T. A completely if, and only if, the projector Q of $\mathfrak{B}_n$ on $\mathfrak{M}$ parallel to $\mathfrak{N}$ satisfies the condition $AQ = QA$.*

PROOF. (i) If $\mathfrak{M}$ and $\mathfrak{N}$ reduce A completely, then $Aa \in \mathfrak{M}$ and $Ab \in \mathfrak{N}$ when $a \in \mathfrak{M}$ and $b \in \mathfrak{N}$. Now, since $\mathfrak{M} \oplus \mathfrak{N} = \mathfrak{B}_n$, every x of $\mathfrak{B}_n$ can be written as $x = a+b$, where $a \in \mathfrak{M}$ and $b \in \mathfrak{N}$. Hence, $AQx = Aa$,

$$QAx = QAa + QAb = QAa = Aa = AQx.$$

(ii) If $AQ = QA$, then, for every a of $\mathfrak{M}$,

$$Aa = AQa = QAa \in \mathfrak{M},$$

and, for every b of $\mathfrak{N}$, $QAb = AQb = 0$. But if $QAb = 0$, then $Ab \in \mathfrak{N}$. Hence $\mathfrak{M}$ and $\mathfrak{N}$ reduce A completely.

10·91. We may apply the preceding theorem to the eigen-manifold $\mathfrak{E}$ of a normal transformation N corresponding to an eigen-value λ. Let P be the orthogonal projector of $\mathfrak{B}_n$ on $\mathfrak{E}$ and let x be any vector of $\mathfrak{B}_n$. Then $Px \in \mathfrak{E}$, so that Px is an eigen-solution of N corresponding to λ and therefore $NPx = \lambda Px$. By Theorem **9·3**, however, $\mathfrak{E}$ and $\mathfrak{B}_n \ominus \mathfrak{E}$ reduce N completely. Whence, by Theorem **10·9**, we obtain

$$NPx = \lambda Px = PNx. \tag{10·91·1}$$

CHAPTER III

SPECTRAL REPRESENTATION OF HERMITIAN TRANSFORMATIONS IN $\mathfrak{B}_n$

§ 11. Continuous functions in $\mathfrak{B}_n$

11·0. In this chapter we give a representation of any H.T. in $\mathfrak{B}_n$ in terms of its eigen-values and eigen-solutions. One possible method of finding such a representation would begin with an algebraic discussion of the properties of a general L.T. in $\mathfrak{B}_n$ and would then go on to deal with a H.T. as a special case; we use this method in Chapter IV. The properties of a H.T., however, are considerably simpler than those of a general L.T., and it is therefore worth while to look for a direct approach to the problem without reference to the more elaborate theory of the general L.T. Thus, in the present chapter we find the eigen-values of a H.T. H as the maxima of the function (Hx, x), continuous in $\mathfrak{B}_n$, in certain bounded closed subsets of $\mathfrak{B}_n$. The powerful possibilities of this method are revealed when it is applied, as Hilbert first applied it, to the problem of the spectral representation of an important class of Hermitian forms in an infinite number of variables, the completely continuous forms. In the simpler case of a finite number of variables the method may seem foreign to the algebraic nature of the problem, but it provides a short cut to the main result and it also gives certain inequalities for the eigen-values, here obtained in § **14**, that have proved of value in recent computational work.

The theorem that a real (numerical) function in $\mathfrak{B}_n$, continuous in a bounded closed set, is bounded above and attains its least upper bound in the set leads directly to the proof of the existence of the eigen-values of a H.T. in $\mathfrak{B}_n$. The theorem is the familiar Weierstrass Theorem concerning a real continuous function of m real variables; further extension to Hilbert space of a denumerable infinity of dimensions is only possible for the class of completely continuous functions. The Weierstrass Theorem may itself be regarded as a consequence of the Bolzano-Weierstrass Theorem on the existence of a limit point in a bounded infinite set in real space of m dimensions. The latter theorem, which is true in $\mathfrak{B}_n$, is true only in a modified form in Hilbert space, and consideration of the necessity for the modification throws a revealing light on the structure of the space.

We give below a brief survey of the relation between the Bolzano-Weierstrass Theorem and the theorem that a real continuous function in $\mathfrak{V}_n$ attains its maximum in a bounded closed set. The structure of this argument, and that of the arguments in the rest of the chapter which depend upon it, remain substantially the same for the consideration of the spectral properties of completely continuous H.T.'s in Hilbert space.

11·1. Definition of a bounded set and of a compact set in $\mathfrak{V}_n$. A set $\mathfrak{S}$ of points x of $\mathfrak{V}_n$ is said to be *bounded* if there exists a *number M such that $\| x \| \leqslant M$ for every x of $\mathfrak{S}$.*

The set $\mathfrak{S}$ is said to be *compact if every infinite sequence of its elements contains a convergent infinite subsequence.* If the limit element of the subsequence always belongs to $\mathfrak{S}$, then $\mathfrak{S}$ is both compact and closed; in this case we say that $\mathfrak{S}$ *is compact in itself.*

11·2. We may readily prove that a compact set $\mathfrak{S}$ in $\mathfrak{V}_n$ is bounded. For, if $\mathfrak{S}$ were not bounded there would exist an infinite sequence $\{x^n\}$ of elements of $\mathfrak{S}$ such that $\| x^n \| > 2 \| x^{n-1} \| > 2^n$, and, since $\mathfrak{S}$ is compact, this sequence would contain a convergent subsequence. But the distance between two elements of the subsequence would exceed 2, contrary to the defining property of a convergent sequence. Therefore $\mathfrak{S}$ is bounded.

11·21. The Bolzano-Weierstrass Theorem states that every infinite bounded set in $\mathfrak{V}_n$ is compact, and this clearly implies that every infinite bounded closed set in $\mathfrak{V}_n$ is compact in itself. It follows that the space $\mathfrak{V}_n$ is locally compact, in that every point $\mathring{x}$ is the centre of a neighbourhood, $\| x - \mathring{x} \| < \delta$, which is compact, but $\mathfrak{V}_n$ itself is not compact since it is not bounded. It can be shewn that Hilbert space is neither compact nor locally compact in the ordinary sense.

11·3. We define continuity of a numerical function in $\mathfrak{V}_n$ in the usual way.

Definition of continuity of a numerical function in $\mathfrak{V}_n$. Let $f(x)$ be a numerical function defined in a set $\mathfrak{S}$ of $\mathfrak{V}_n$ and therefore mapping $\mathfrak{S}$ on a set $\mathfrak{S}_1$ of $\mathfrak{V}_1$. We say that $f(x)$ *is continuous in $\mathfrak{S}$ if it maps every sequence $\{x^n\}$ of points of $\mathfrak{S}$ that converges to a point $\mathring{x}$ of $\mathfrak{S}$ on a sequence $\{f(x^n)\}$ of points of $\mathfrak{S}_1$ that converges to $f(\mathring{x})$ of $\mathfrak{S}_1$.*

11·31. In what follows we are concerned with the function (Hx, x), where H is a H.T. in $\mathfrak{B}_n$. Since (Hx, x) takes only real values it can be considered as a real function of the $2n$ real variables ξ_ν, η_ν, where

$$(x, u^\nu) = x_\nu = \xi_\nu + i\eta_\nu.$$

Now (Hx, x) is continuous in $\mathfrak{B}_n$ since for any two points x^1 and x^2 we have

$$(Hx^1, x^1) - (Hx^2, x^2) = (Hx^1, x^1 - x^2) + (x^1 - x^2, Hx^2),$$

and hence, by (6·05·2),

$$|(Hx^1, x^1) - (Hx^2, x^2)| \leqslant M(\| x^1 \| + \| x^2 \|) \| x^1 - x^2 \|,$$

where the constant M is independent of x^1 and x^2. Thus (Hx, x) is a real continuous function of the $2n$ variables ξ_ν, η_ν.

11·4. THEOREM. *A function $f(x)$ continuous in $\mathfrak{B}_n$ maps any bounded closed set $\mathfrak{S}$ in $\mathfrak{B}_n$ on a bounded closed set $\mathfrak{S}_1$ in $\mathfrak{B}_1$.*

PROOF. We need only consider an infinite set $\mathfrak{S}_1$. Any infinite sequence in $\mathfrak{S}_1$ may be considered as the image $\{f(x^m)\}$ of an infinite sequence $\{x^m\}$ in $\mathfrak{S}$. But the compactness of $\mathfrak{S}$, asserted in **11·21**, implies the existence of an infinite subsequence $\{x'^m\}$ of the sequence $\{x^m\}$ converging to a point $\mathring{x}$ of $\mathfrak{S}$. By the continuity of $f(x)$, the corresponding subsequence $\{f(x'^m)\}$ in $\mathfrak{S}_1$ is convergent to a point $f(\mathring{x})$ of $\mathfrak{S}_1$. Thus, $\mathfrak{S}_1$ is compact in itself, which means that it is bounded and closed.

11·5. We now recall the familiar Weierstrass Theorem.

THEOREM. *If the real function $f(x)$ is continuous in the bounded closed set $\mathfrak{S}$ of $\mathfrak{B}_n$, then $f(x)$ is bounded above in $\mathfrak{S}$ and attains its least upper bound in $\mathfrak{S}$ at a point $\mathring{x}$ of $\mathfrak{S}$.*

PROOF. By Theorem **11·4**, the set of values taken by $f(x)$ in $\mathfrak{S}$ is a bounded closed set of real numbers; it therefore contains its least upper bound.

§ 12. ORTHONORMAL SYSTEMS OF EIGEN-SOLUTIONS OF A H.T. THE SPECTRAL REPRESENTATIONS

12·0. THEOREM. *Let the Hermitian form (Hx, x) considered on the unit sphere $\| x \| = 1$ in $\mathfrak{B}_n$ attain its maximum value λ_1 at a point ϕ^1. Then λ_1 is an eigen-value of the H.T. H and ϕ^1 an eigen-solution corresponding to λ_1.*

PROOF. The set $\|x\| = 1$ is a bounded closed set. By Theorem **11·5**, the real continuous function (Hx, x) has a maximum value in the set which it attains at at least one point ϕ^1. We write

$$\max(Hx, x) = \lambda_1 \quad \text{for} \quad \|x\| = 1,$$
$$(H\phi^1, \phi^1) = \lambda_1. \tag{12·0·1}$$

Now $\|x\|^{-1}x$ lies on the unit sphere for any non-zero vector x of $\mathfrak{B}_n$ and therefore

$$\|x\|^{-2}(Hx, x) \leqslant \lambda_1, \quad \lambda_1\|x\|^2 - (Hx, x) \geqslant 0. \tag{12·0·2}$$

Writing (12·0·2) and (12·0·1) as

$$((\lambda_1 I - H)x, x) \geqslant 0, \quad ((\lambda_1 I - H)\phi^1, \phi^1) = 0,$$

we see that the Hermitian form $((\lambda_1 I - H)x, x)$ is positive semi-definite and vanishes for $x = \phi^1$. We may therefore apply Theorem **8·21** (ii) to deduce that $(\lambda_1 I - H)\phi^1 = 0$. Thus, λ_1 is an eigen-value of H and ϕ^1 a corresponding eigen-solution.

12·1. The preceding theorem enables us to find all the eigen-values of any H.T. H in $\mathfrak{B}_n$ with their corresponding eigen-manifolds, and to deduce the spectral representation of H. We establish the result by an induction process.

We first determine the null manifold $\mathfrak{X}$ of H. If $\mathfrak{X} \neq \mathfrak{O}$, it is the eigen-manifold corresponding to the eigen-value zero; if $\mathfrak{X} = \mathfrak{B}_n$, every vector is an eigen-solution corresponding to zero, H vanishes identically, and there is nothing further to discuss. We therefore take $\mathfrak{X} \neq \mathfrak{B}_n$, we suppose that $\mathfrak{X}$ has rank k_0, where $0 \leqslant k_0 < n$, and we write $r_1 = n - k_0$. By **8·82**, $\mathfrak{X}$ and $\mathfrak{B}_n \ominus \mathfrak{X}$ reduce H completely and, by Theorem **10·9**,

$$HP_0 = P_0 H = O,$$

where P_0 is the orthogonal projector of $\mathfrak{B}_n$ on $\mathfrak{X}$. We now write

$$P_1' = I - P_0,$$

so that P_1' is the orthogonal projector of $\mathfrak{B}_n$ on the L.M.

$$\mathfrak{B}_{r_1} = \mathfrak{B}_n \ominus \mathfrak{X}$$

of rank r_1 which can be interpreted, according to **3·62**, as a subspace of $\mathfrak{B}_n$ with the same value for its scalar product. We define

$$H_1 = HP_1' = P_1'H,$$

so that $H_1 = H$ in $\mathfrak{B}_{r_1}$, $H_1 = O$ in $\mathfrak{X}$, and H_1 is Hermitian in the subspace $\mathfrak{B}_{r_1}$ which reduces H. By Theorem **12·0**, the maximum value λ_1 of the Hermitian form $(H_1 x', x')$ on the unit sphere $\|x'\| = 1$ in $\mathfrak{B}_{r_1}$ is an eigen-value of H_1. We see that $\lambda_1 \neq 0$, since $H_1 x' \neq 0$ for every unit vector x' in $\mathfrak{B}_{r_1}$. The set of eigen-solutions of

H_1 corresponding to λ_1 forms an eigen-manifold $\mathfrak{E}_1$ contained in $\mathfrak{V}_{r_1}$ and, clearly, $\mathfrak{E}_1$ is also an eigen-manifold of H corresponding to λ_1, since the eigen-manifolds of H for all eigen-values other than zero are by Theorem **8·6** contained in $\mathfrak{V}_{r_1} = \mathfrak{V}_n \ominus \mathfrak{X}$. Thus, we have $0 < k_1 \leqslant r_1$, where k_1 is the rank of $\mathfrak{E}_1$. We denote by P_1 the orthogonal projector of $\mathfrak{V}_n$ on $\mathfrak{E}_1$, and we recall that $\mathfrak{E}_1$ and $\mathfrak{X}$ are orthogonal to one another, so that

$$P_0 P_1 = P_1 P_0 = O.$$

We also have

$$HP_1 = \lambda_1 P_1 = P_1 H,$$

by Theorem **10·9**, since $\mathfrak{E}_1$ reduces H completely. Moreover, $P_0 + P_1$ and $I - P_0 - P_1$ are orthogonal projectors, by Theorem **10·4** and by **10·0**. We write

$$P_2' = I - P_0 - P_1, \quad r_2 = n - k_0 - k_1, \quad \mathfrak{V}_{r_2} = \mathfrak{V}_n \ominus (\mathfrak{X} \oplus \mathfrak{E}_1),$$

where $\mathfrak{V}_{r_2}$, the range of P_2', has rank r_2. Then, if $r_2 = 0$, we have $P_2' = O$,

$$I = P_0 + P_1, \quad H = HP_0 + HP_1 = HP_1 = \lambda_1 P_1, \quad n = k_0 + k_1,$$
$$\mathfrak{V}_n = \mathfrak{E}_1 \oplus \mathfrak{X},$$

and the process comes to an end. If, however, $r_2 > 0$, we go on to consider the subspace $\mathfrak{V}_{r_2}$.

We now assume that we have established the existence of μ non-zero eigen-values λ_κ of H with corresponding eigen-manifolds $\mathfrak{E}_\kappa$ of rank k_κ, for $1 \leqslant \kappa \leqslant \mu$. Then, by Theorem **8·6**, the L.M.'s $\mathfrak{E}_\kappa$ are orthogonal to one another and to $\mathfrak{X}$ and, by **8·82**, they each reduce H completely. Hence, if P_κ denotes the orthogonal projector of $\mathfrak{V}_n$ on $\mathfrak{E}_\kappa$, we have $P_\nu P_\kappa = \delta_{\nu\kappa} P_\kappa$ for $0 \leqslant \nu \leqslant \mu$ and, by Theorem **10·9**,

$$HP_\kappa = P_\kappa H = \lambda_\kappa P_\kappa.$$

We write

$$P'_{\mu+1} = I - \sum_{\kappa=0}^{\mu} P_\kappa.$$

Then, by **10·0** and by Theorem **10·42**, $P'_{\mu+1}$ is the orthogonal projector of $\mathfrak{V}_n$ on the L.M.

$$\mathfrak{V}_n \ominus \left(\mathfrak{X} \oplus \sum_{\kappa=1}^{\mu} \mathfrak{E}_\kappa \oplus \right) = \mathfrak{V}_{r_{\mu+1}}$$

of rank $r_{\mu+1}$, where

$$r_{\mu+1} = n - \sum_{\kappa=0}^{\mu} k_\kappa.$$

If $r_{\mu+1} = 0$, then $P'_{\mu+1} = O$,

$$I = \sum_{\kappa=0}^{\mu} P_\kappa, \quad H = \sum_{\kappa=0}^{\mu} HP_\kappa = \sum_{\kappa=1}^{\mu} \lambda_\kappa P_\kappa,$$

since $HP_0 = O$,

$$n = \sum_{\kappa=0}^{\mu} k_\kappa, \quad \mathfrak{B}_n = \mathfrak{X} \oplus \sum_{\kappa=1}^{\mu} \mathfrak{E}_\kappa \oplus,$$

and the process comes to an end. If, however, $r_{\mu+1} > 0$, we write

$$H_{\mu+1} = HP'_{\mu+1} = P'_{\mu+1} H.$$

Then $H_{\mu+1} = H$ in $\mathfrak{B}_{r\mu+1}$, $H_{\mu+1} = O$ in $\mathfrak{B}_n \ominus \mathfrak{B}_{r\mu+1}$, and $H_{\mu+1}$ is Hermitian in the subspace $\mathfrak{B}_{r\mu+1}$ which reduces H completely. Moreover, the eigen-values of H other than $0, \lambda_1, \ldots, \lambda_\mu$ coincide with the eigen-values of $H_{\mu+1}$ and the corresponding eigen-manifolds also coincide, since by Theorem **8·6** they are contained in $\mathfrak{B}_{r\mu+1}$. By Theorem **12·0**, the maximum value $\lambda_{\mu+1}$ of the Hermitian form $(H_{\mu+1}x', x')$ on the unit sphere $\| x' \| = 1$ in $\mathfrak{B}_{r\mu+1}$ is an eigen-value of $H_{\mu+1}$. It is therefore an eigen-value of H different from $0, \lambda_1, \ldots, \lambda_\mu$, and the corresponding eigen-manifold $\mathfrak{E}_{\mu+1}$, of rank $k_{\mu+1}$, is contained in $\mathfrak{B}_{r\mu+1}$. We denote by $P_{\mu+1}$ the orthogonal projector of $\mathfrak{B}_n$ on $\mathfrak{E}_{\mu+1}$ and we obtain, as before,

$$P_\kappa P_{\mu+1} = P_{\mu+1} P_\kappa = O \quad (0 \leqslant \kappa \leqslant \mu).$$

We also have
$$HP_{\mu+1} = \lambda_{\mu+1} P_{\mu+1} = P_{\mu+1} H,$$

by Theorem **10·9**, since $\mathfrak{E}_{\mu+1}$ reduces H completely.

In this way we obtain a succession of non-zero eigen-values λ_κ as the maximum values of (Hx, x) on the unit spheres in the subspaces $\mathfrak{B}_{r\kappa}$. Since $\mathfrak{B}_{r\kappa} \subset \mathfrak{B}_{r\kappa-1}$ and $\lambda_\kappa \neq \lambda_{\kappa-1}$, we have $\lambda_\kappa < \lambda_{\kappa-1}$. Further, since $r_\kappa < r_{\kappa-1}$ the process ends after we have obtained m non-zero eigen-values, where $r_m > r_{m+1} = 0$. Clearly, $0 \leqslant m \leqslant r_1 \leqslant n$. We have therefore

$$I = \sum_{\kappa=0}^{m} P_\kappa, \quad H = \sum_{\kappa=0}^{m} HP_\kappa = \sum_{\kappa=1}^{m} \lambda_\kappa P_\kappa, \quad HP_0 = O, \qquad (12·1·1)$$

$$n = \sum_{\kappa=0}^{m} k_\kappa, \quad \mathfrak{B}_n = \mathfrak{X} \oplus \sum_{\kappa=1}^{m} \mathfrak{E}_\kappa \oplus. \qquad (12·1·2)$$

If now we take an orthonormal basis in each eigen-manifold $\mathfrak{E}_\kappa$, for $\kappa = 1, 2, \ldots, m$, and in $\mathfrak{X}$, we obtain by (12·1·2) (and by Theorem **8·6**) a complete orthonormal system of vectors $\phi^1, \phi^2, \ldots, \phi^n$, so that $[\phi^1, \phi^2, \ldots, \phi^n] = \mathfrak{B}_n$. Here

$$\left.\begin{array}{ll} \phi^1, \phi^2, \ldots, \phi^{k_1} & \in \mathfrak{E}_1 \\ \phi^{k_1+1}, \phi^{k_1+2}, \ldots, \phi^{k_1+k_2} & \in \mathfrak{E}_2 \\ \ldots & \ldots \\ \phi^{n-k_0+1}, \phi^{n-k_0+2}, \ldots, \phi^n & \in \mathfrak{X}. \end{array}\right\} \qquad (12·1·3)$$

We see that there can exist no eigen-solution χ of H belonging to a non-zero eigen-value ω different from the λ_κ obtained above. For such a vector would not belong either to $\mathfrak{X}$ or to any of the $\mathfrak{E}_\kappa$, since by Theorem **8·6** it would be orthogonal to all vectors of these manifolds and therefore, by (12·1·2), it could only be the zero vector and no eigen-solution. Thus the eigen-values found above form a complete set of eigen-values for H.

12·2. We may summarize the results just obtained in the following theorem.

THEOREM. *Every H.T. in $\mathfrak{B}_n$, not identically zero, has a finite set of non-zero eigen-values $\lambda_1, \lambda_2, \ldots, \lambda_m$, where $1 \leqslant m \leqslant n$. If $\mathfrak{X}$ is the eigen-manifold of H corresponding to zero (the null manifold of H) of rank k_0, and if $\mathfrak{E}_\kappa$, of rank k_κ, is the eigen-manifold corresponding to λ_κ ($\kappa = 1, 2, \ldots, m$), we have*

$$\mathfrak{B}_n = \mathfrak{X} \oplus \sum_{\kappa=1}^{m} \mathfrak{E}_\kappa \oplus, \quad n = \sum_{\kappa=0}^{m} k_\kappa,$$

where the number k_κ is also the order of the eigen-value λ_κ. If P_0 and P_κ are the orthogonal projectors of $\mathfrak{B}_n$ on $\mathfrak{X}$ and $\mathfrak{E}_\kappa$ ($1 \leqslant \kappa \leqslant m$) respectively, we have

$$P_\iota P_\kappa = \delta_{\iota\kappa} P_\kappa, \quad \sum_{\kappa=0}^{m} P_\kappa = I, \tag{12·2·1}$$

$$HP_\kappa = \lambda_\kappa P_\kappa = P_\kappa H \quad (0 \leqslant \iota, \kappa \leqslant m). \tag{12·2·2}$$

If we take orthonormal bases in the $\mathfrak{E}_\kappa$ and in $\mathfrak{X}$, we obtain a complete orthonormal system of vectors $\phi^1, \phi^2, \ldots, \phi^n$.

When H is identically zero, $\lambda = 0$ is the only eigen-value and $\mathfrak{X} = \mathfrak{B}_n$.

12·21. The orthogonal projector $P_{\mathfrak{M}}$ defined in **10·0** furnishes a simple example of a H.T. for which we can give at once the complete set of eigen-values and eigen-solutions. Let $\mathfrak{M}$ be of rank r, let $\phi^1, \phi^2, \ldots, \phi^r$ form an orthonormal basis of $\mathfrak{M}$, and let $\phi^{r+1}, \phi^{r+2}, \ldots, \phi^n$ form an orthonormal basis of $\mathfrak{B}_n \ominus \mathfrak{M}$. Then

$$\begin{aligned} P_{\mathfrak{M}} \phi^\nu &= \phi^\nu \quad (\nu = 1, 2, \ldots, r) \\ &= 0 \quad (\nu = r+1, r+2, \ldots, n). \end{aligned}$$

Hence, 1 and 0 are the only eigen-values of $P_{\mathfrak{M}}$, $\lambda = 1$ is of order r, $\lambda = 0$ is of order $n-r$, and the vectors ϕ^ν ($\nu = 1, 2, \ldots, n$) form a complete orthonormal set of eigen-solutions.

12·22. If H has only a single eigen-value λ_1 of order n, then every vector of $\mathfrak{B}_n$ is an eigen-solution and we have $Hx = \lambda_1 x$ for every x of $\mathfrak{B}_n$. This implies $H = \lambda_1 I$. If, further, $\lambda_1 = 0$, then $H = O$.

12·3. Theorem. *There is a complete orthonormal system of real eigen-solutions for any real symmetric transformation H.*

Proof. If H is real, then all the L.M.'s $\mathfrak{X}, \mathfrak{E}_1, \mathfrak{E}_2, \ldots, \mathfrak{E}_m$ of Theorem **12·2** are real, by Theorem **5·4**, since they are defined by the equations $H\xi = 0$ and $(H-\lambda_\kappa I)\phi^\kappa = 0$ ($\kappa = 1, 2, \ldots, m$). Therefore, by Theorem **3·5**, each of these L.M.'s has a real orthonormal basis, and thus the set of bases forms a complete orthonormal system of real eigen-solutions.

12·4. Theorem **12·2** enables us to give a remarkable representation of any H.T. H. We write any vector x of $\mathfrak{V}_n$ in the form

$$x = \sum_{\nu=1}^{n} (x, \phi^\nu)\phi^\nu,$$

where, as before, the ϕ^ν form a complete orthonormal set of eigen-solutions of H, but where the corresponding eigen-values λ_ν are arranged in descending order of magnitude, $\lambda_1 \geqslant \lambda_2 \geqslant \ldots \geqslant \lambda_n$. We then obtain

$$Hx = \sum_{\nu=1}^{n} (x, \phi^\nu) H\phi^\nu = \sum_{\nu=1}^{n} \lambda_\nu (x, \phi^\nu)\phi^\nu. \qquad (12\cdot4\cdot1)$$

In this notation, different from that used in **12·1** and **12·2**, the λ_ν are not necessarily all distinct or different from zero, but each distinct eigen-value occurs as many times as its order indicates.

12·41. If H is a real symmetric transformation and if

$$\lambda_\nu \geqslant 0, \quad (\nu = 1, 2, \ldots, n),$$

the representation (12·4·1) admits a simple geometrical interpretation. We consider the n components $(x, \phi^\nu)\phi^\nu$ of the vector x in the n orthogonal directions determined by the real eigen-solutions ϕ^ν of H and suppose each of these components submitted to a magnification equal to the eigen-value λ_ν, the sum of the resulting vectors giving Hx. In this way, Hx may be considered as determining a certain dilation of the vector space, which may be interpreted as a physical strain.

12·42. It will readily be seen that there was no need to deal separately with the eigen-value zero in **12·1**, but that we could have obtained all the eigen-values, zero included, by considering the maxima of (Hx, x) on a set of unit spheres. We have given a separate discussion of the eigen-value zero and its eigen-manifold $\mathfrak{X}$ so that the argument can be taken over, with as little change as possible, for the case of a completely continuous H.T. in Hilbert space, in which case the point $\lambda = 0$ plays a distinct role in the spectrum and needs a separate discussion.

12·43. From now on, when we refer to the set of distinct eigen-values of a H.T. H we shall denote them by $\lambda_1, \lambda_2, \ldots, \lambda_m$, and this set of eigen-values will include zero if zero is an eigen-value. We shall denote the corresponding eigen-manifolds by $\mathfrak{E}_1, \mathfrak{E}_2, \ldots, \mathfrak{E}_m$, their ranks by $k_1, k_2, \ldots, k_m$, and the orthogonal projectors of $\mathfrak{V}_n$ on the eigen-manifolds by $P_1, P_2, \ldots, P_m$. Instead of (12·1·2), we shall have

$$n = \sum_{\mu=1}^{m} k_\mu, \quad \mathfrak{V}_n = \sum_{\mu=1}^{m} \mathfrak{E}_\mu \oplus. \tag{12·43·1}$$

We shall then obtain from (12·2·1) and (12·2·2), for any x of $\mathfrak{V}_n$, the representations

$$x = \sum_{\mu=1}^{m} P_\mu x, \tag{12·43·2}$$

$$Hx = \sum_{\mu=1}^{m} HP_\mu x = \sum_{\mu=1}^{m} \lambda_\mu P_\mu x, \tag{12·43·3}$$

and, finally, from (12·43·2) and (12·43·3),

$$(H - \lambda I)\, x = \sum_{\mu=1}^{m} (\lambda_\mu - \lambda)\, P_\mu x, \tag{12·43·4}$$

for any number λ.

The representations (12·4·1), (12·43·3) and (12·43·4) will be called the *spectral representations* of H and $H - \lambda I$.

In interpreting the representation (12·43·3) geometrically we consider the m components of x obtained by orthogonal projection on the m eigen-manifolds $\mathfrak{E}_\mu$ and suppose each of them submitted to an appropriate magnification, with an additional reflection with regard to the origin when λ_μ is negative, so that Hx is again interpreted as determining a dilation of $\mathfrak{V}_n$. The vector x, however, is here considered as the resultant of m components instead of n components as in **12·41**.

12·5. Definition of the resolvent, of the resolvent set and of the multiplicity of the spectrum. We write $H_\lambda = H - \lambda I$ for any H.T. H and any number λ. We consider the transformation H_λ for every value of λ, real or not, and we say that λ *belongs to the resolvent set of* H *if* H_λ^{-1} *exists*, that is, if $H - \lambda I$ is of rank n.

It is clear that λ belongs to the resolvent set if, and only if, λ is not an eigen-value of H, so that *the spectrum of H consists of all numbers λ that do not belong to the resolvent set.*

If all the eigen-values of H are simple (see the definition in **8·41**) we say that H has a *simple spectrum*. If $\lambda_1, \lambda_2, \ldots, \lambda_m$, with orders $k_1, k_2, \ldots, k_m$, are all the distinct eigen-values of H, and if k is equal to the greatest of the numbers k_μ, we say that H has a *spectrum of multiplicity k*.

The transformation H_λ^{-1}, depending on the parameter λ, is called the *resolvent of H* and is denoted by R_λ.

As we show later, R_λ depends analytically on λ.

§ 13. Unitary transformations of a Hermitian form to principal axes

13·0. The spectral representation of a H.T. leads to a representation and a transformation of the corresponding Hermitian form. We consider the bilinear form $((H-\lambda I)x, y)$ associated with a Hermitian form (Hx, x) and obtain at once, from (12·43·4) and (10·01·1), the spectral form

$$((H-\lambda I)x, y) = \sum_{\mu=1}^{m} (\lambda_\mu - \lambda)(P_\mu x, y)$$

$$= \sum_{\mu=1}^{m} (\lambda_\mu - \lambda)(P_\mu x, P_\mu y) \qquad (13·0·1)$$

which includes the expression of the Hermitian form itself as

$$(Hx, x) = \sum_{\mu=1}^{m} \lambda_\mu \| P_\mu x \|^2. \qquad (13·0·2)$$

Every vector contained in one of the L.M.'s $\mathfrak{E}_\mu$ ($\mu = 1, 2, \ldots, m$) is called a principal direction of the Hermitian form, and every orthonormal system of n eigen-solutions is called a system of principal axes. The existence of at least one system of principal axes $\{\phi^\nu\}$ ($\nu = 1, 2, \ldots, n$) has already been established in (12·1·3), and it is plain that the ϕ^ν are uniquely determined, except for a factor $e^{i\theta_\nu}$, where θ_ν is real, if, and only if, all the eigen-values λ_μ of H are simple, that is, if $m = n$.

If we substitute in (Hx, y)

$$x = \sum_{\nu=1}^{n} x'_\nu \phi^\nu, \quad y = \sum_{\nu=1}^{n} y'_\nu \phi^\nu, \qquad (13·0·3)$$

$$x'_\nu = (x, \phi^\nu), \quad y'_\nu = (y, \phi^\nu),$$

we obtain its normal form, that is, the form referred to a coordinate system $\{\phi^\nu\}$ of principal axes,

$$(Hx,y) = \sum_{\nu=1}^{n}\sum_{\mu=1}^{n} x'_\nu \overline{y'_\mu}(H\phi^\nu,\phi^\mu) = \sum_{\nu=1}^{n}\sum_{\mu=1}^{n} \lambda_\nu \delta_{\nu\mu} x'_\nu \overline{y'_\mu}$$
$$= \sum_{\nu=1}^{n} \lambda_\nu x'_\nu \overline{y'_\nu}. \qquad (13\cdot0\cdot4)$$

13·1. In the course of this paragraph we show how the normal form can be obtained by a coordinate transformation of the kind defined in **9·52**. The result may also be represented by a matrix relation. We first, however, give some immediate theorems concerning the operation of a coordinate transformation on a Hermitian bilinear form and on the associated matrix.

13·11. If we subject any bilinear form (Hx,y) to a coordinate transformation, that is, to a unitary transformation $x = Ux'$, $y = Uy'$, we obtain, by (7·3·1),

$$(Hx,y) = (HUx',Uy') = (U^*HUx',y') = (x',U^*H^*Uy')$$
$$= (Kx',y') \qquad = (x',K^*y'), \quad (13\cdot11\cdot1)$$

with the matrix relations

$$K = U^*HU, \quad H = UKU^*.$$

We see that the transformation K is Hermitian if H is Hermitian.

13·12. Theorem. *Any eigen-value λ_μ of order k_μ of the H.T. H is also an eigen-value of order k_μ of the H.T. U^*HU, where U is any unitary transformation.*

Proof. Since λ_μ is an eigen-value of order k_μ of H, $H-\lambda_\mu I$ has rank $n-k_\mu$. Now

$$U^*(H-\lambda_\mu I)\,U = U^*HU-\lambda_\mu I = K-\lambda_\mu I,$$

say, so that, if ϕ is any vector satisfying the equation

$$(H-\lambda_\mu I)\,\phi = 0,$$

the vector $\phi' = U^*\phi$ will satisfy the equation $(K-\lambda_\mu I)\phi' = 0$. Further, since U and U^* are both of rank n, $K-\lambda_\mu I$ has the same rank, $n-k_\mu$, as $H-\lambda_\mu I$, by Theorem **7·7**. Thus λ_μ is an eigen-value of K of order k_μ.

13·2. To obtain the coordinate transformation that takes the bilinear form (Hx,y) into its normal form (13·0·4) we consider a system $\{\phi^\nu\}$ of principal axes and write

$$\phi^\nu = \sum_{\mu=1}^{n} u_{\mu\nu}u^\mu, \quad x = \sum_{\mu=1}^{n} x_\mu u^\mu, \quad y = \sum_{\mu=1}^{n} y_\mu u^\mu. \quad (13\cdot2\cdot1)$$

We substitute for ϕ^ν from (13·2·1) in (13·0·3) and obtain

$$x = \sum_{\mu=1}^{n} x_\mu u^\mu = \sum_{\nu=1}^{n} \sum_{\mu=1}^{n} x'_\nu u_{\mu\nu} u^\mu.$$

Hence, as in (9·52·1),

$$x_\mu = \sum_{\nu=1}^{n} u_{\mu\nu} x'_\nu, \tag{13·2·2}$$

or $x = Ux'$, $x' = U^*x$ where, by (13·2·1), the elements of the νth column of the matrix U are the coordinates of ϕ^ν. The substitution $x = Ux'$, $y = Uy'$ in (Hx, y) leads by (13·0·4) to

$$(Hx, y) = (HUx', Uy') = (U^*HUx', y') = (\Lambda x', y') \tag{13·2·3}$$

$$= \sum_{\nu=1}^{n} \lambda_\nu x'_\nu \overline{y'_\nu},$$

whence

$$U^*HU = \Lambda = \begin{pmatrix} \lambda_1 & & & 0 \\ & \lambda_2 & & \\ & & \ddots & \\ 0 & & & \lambda_n \end{pmatrix}, \tag{13·2·4}$$

where, as in (12·4·1), λ_ν is the eigen-value corresponding to the eigen-solution ϕ^ν and the λ_ν are not necessarily distinct.

The transformation of (Hx, y) to the normal form appears in (13·2·3) as a coordinate transformation defined by (13·2·2), where, by (9·52·3), the coordinate vectors of the new coordinate system are a system of principal axes of H as defined in **13·0**. Hence, the transformation to the normal form is also called the transformation of the Hermitian bilinear form to principal axes.

The transformation problem may also be interpreted by (13·2·4) as the problem of finding a unitary matrix U such that the matrix U^*HU is a diagonal matrix Λ.

13·21. If H has a zero eigen-value of order $n-r$ so that, say, $\lambda_{r+1} = \lambda_{r+2} = \ldots = \lambda_n = 0$, then we may write (13·2·3) as

$$(Hx, x) = \sum_{\nu=1}^{r} \lambda_\nu |x'_\nu|^2 = (Hz, z),$$

where z is the projection of x on the L.M. $\mathfrak{R} = [\phi^1, \phi^2, \ldots, \phi^r]$. By Theorem **8·3**, H maps $\mathfrak{R}$ on itself and, by **8·82**, $\mathfrak{R}$ reduces H completely. We see therefore that H may be considered in $\mathfrak{R}$, which is a subspace of r dimensions, as a H.T. in $\mathfrak{V}_r$ with no zero eigen-value.

13·22. We obtain from (13·0·2) an immediate test as to whether a H.T. is definite, semi-definite or indefinite. Thus, we see that

(Hx, x) is positive (or negative) definite if all the eigen-values of H are positive (or negative). It is positive (or negative) semi-definite if at least one of the eigen-values is zero while the non-zero eigen-values are all positive (or negative). It is indefinite if H has both positive and negative eigen-values.

13·3. If the H.T. H is real, there is a real unitary (that is, orthogonal) transformation U which transforms (Hx, x) to principal axes. A corresponding real unitary matrix U is obtained from a complete system of real orthonormal eigen-solutions determined as in Theorem **12·3**.

13·4. Definition of equivalence of H.T.'s. *Two H.T.'s H and K are said to be equivalent to one another if there is a unitary transformation U such that $K = U^*HU$.*

According to **13·11**, two equivalent H.T.'s can be interpreted as representing the same H.T. referred to different coordinate systems.

13·41. Theorem. *The H.T.'s H and K are equivalent to one another if, and only if, they have the same spectrum; that is, if H and K have all their eigen-values in common and each eigen-value is of the same order with regard to both transformations.*

Proof. (i) If $K = U^*HU$, then it follows at once from Theorem **13·12** that H and K have the same spectrum.

(ii) If H and K have the same spectrum, then there are two unitary transformations U_1 and U_2 that transform H and K into the same diagonal transformation Λ, so that

$$H = U_1 \Lambda U_1^*, \quad K = U_2 \Lambda U_2^*.$$

Hence,

$$K = U_2 U_1^* H U_1 U_2^* = U^*HU,$$

where $U = U_1 U_2^*$, $U^* = U_2 U_1^*$, and the theorem follows.

13·42. The trace of the matrix representation (see Definition **10·8**) is invariant throughout a set of equivalent H.T.'s.

Theorem. *Let H and K be equivalent H.T.'s. Then the matrix representations have the same trace, which is equal to the sum of the eigen-values* $\sum_{\nu=1}^{n} \lambda_\nu$.

Proof. By definition **13·4** we may write $K = U^*HU$. We write the corresponding matrices as $H = (a_{\mu\nu})$, $K = (b_{\mu\nu})$ and $U = (u_{\mu\nu})$, and we establish the equality of the traces τ_K and τ_H by the equations

$$\tau_K = \sum_{\mu=1}^{n} b_{\mu\mu} = \sum_{\mu=1}^{n}\sum_{\nu=1}^{n}\sum_{\kappa=1}^{n} \overline{u_{\nu\mu}} a_{\nu\kappa} u_{\kappa\mu} = \sum_{\nu=1}^{n}\sum_{\kappa=1}^{n} a_{\nu\kappa} \sum_{\mu=1}^{n} \overline{u_{\nu\mu}} u_{\kappa\mu}$$

$$= \sum_{\nu=1}^{n}\sum_{\kappa=1}^{n} a_{\nu\kappa}\delta_{\nu\kappa} = \sum_{\nu=1}^{n} a_{\nu\nu} = \tau_H.$$

The equation (13·2·4), however, shows that the matrix H is equivalent to the diagonal matrix Λ in which the elements λ_ν of the diagonal are the eigen-values of H. Hence

$$\tau_K = \tau_H = \tau_\Lambda = \sum_{\nu=1}^{n} \lambda_\nu, \tag{13·42·1}$$

where the eigen-values λ_ν are arranged as in **12·4**; that is, the eigen-values are not necessarily all distinct, but each distinct eigen-value occurs in the sum (13·42·1) as many times as its order indicates.

13·43. Note. Definition **10·8**, by which the trace is associated with the matrix A, does not reveal whether or not the trace corresponding to a L.T. represented by different matrices in different coordinate systems depends on the choice of the coordinate system. It follows from Theorem **13·42** that the trace of a H.T. can be defined as the sum of its eigen-values, independently of any matrix representation, so that τ_H may be associated with the H.T. itself and not only with the matrix representation.

A discussion of the trace τ_A of a general L.T. is given in **22·43** of Chapter IV.

13·5. Illustration from the theory of infinitesimal displacements. Consider a real vector space of n dimensions and let $x = (x_1, x_2, \dots, x_n)$ be a point $\mathscr{P}$ of this space. Submit $\mathscr{P}$ to an infinitesimal displacement w that takes it to $\mathscr{P}'$, where $\mathscr{P}'$ is the point $x+w = (x_1+w_1, x_2+w_2, \dots, x_n+w_n)$ and where the w_ν are infinitesimal functions $w_\nu = w_\nu(x_1, x_2, \dots, x_n)$ of the coordinates of $\mathscr{P}$. For example, if we assume a finite displacement dependent on the time t and represented by a vector $z = z(x_1, x_2, \dots, x_n; t)$, differentiable with regard to t, we can interpret the infinitesimal vector w as $\left(\frac{\partial z}{\partial t} dt\right)_{t=0}$.

Suppose now that the w_ν have differentiable partial derivatives of the first order with regard to the x_μ and consider the displacement of a point $\mathscr{Q}$ in the neighbourhood of $\mathscr{P}$ and represented by $x+dx$. Then $\mathscr{Q}$ is displaced to $\mathscr{Q}'$ which is represented by $x+dx+w+dw$, where $dx = (dx_1, dx_2, \dots, dx_n)$,

$$dw = \sum_{\nu=1}^{n} \frac{\partial w}{\partial x_\nu} dx_\nu, \quad \frac{\partial w}{\partial x_\nu} = \left(\frac{\partial w_1}{\partial x_\nu}, \frac{\partial w_2}{\partial x_\nu}, \dots, \frac{\partial w_n}{\partial x_\nu}\right). \tag{13·5·1}$$

Write
$$w_{\mu\nu} = \frac{\partial w_\mu}{\partial x_\nu}, \quad W = (w_{\mu\nu}),$$

and assume each element of the matrix W to be infinitesimal. Then, dw_μ is small in comparison with dx_ν and, by (6·05·1),

$$\| Wx \| \leqslant \delta \| x \|, \quad \| W^* x \| \leqslant \delta \| x \|, \tag{13·5·2}$$

where δ is a positive infinitesimal number. Further, from (13·5·1),

$$dw = W dx, \quad \overrightarrow{\mathscr{P}\mathscr{Q}} = dx, \quad \overrightarrow{\mathscr{P}'\mathscr{Q}'} = dx + dw = (I+W)\,dx. \tag{13·5·3}$$

We can therefore say that in the neighbourhood of $\mathscr{P}$ the relative displacement is determined by the L.T. $I+W$. Write now

$$H = \tfrac{1}{2}(W+W^*), \quad S = \tfrac{1}{2}(W-W^*),$$

so that $H+S = W$. Then H is symmetric (real Hermitian) and S is skew symmetric, since $H^* = H$, $S^* = -S$ (see Definition **8·01**). We notice further that H and S, as well as W, are both infinitesimal transformations and that, by (13·5·2),

$$\| Hx \| \leqslant \delta \| x \|. \tag{13·5·4}$$

Neglecting infinitesimal terms of second and higher orders, that is, products of matrices such as HS and S^2, we obtain the relations

$$(I+H)(I+S) = (I+S)(I+H) = I+H+S = I+W,$$
$$(I+S)(I+S^*) = I+S+S^* = I+S-S = I,$$

so that we can interpret $I+S$ as an orthogonal transformation and $I+W$ as the product of an orthogonal and a symmetric transformation. Hence, by (13·5·3),

$$\overrightarrow{\mathscr{P}'\mathscr{Q}'} = (I+S)(I+H)\,dx$$

and $\overrightarrow{\mathscr{P}'\mathscr{Q}'}$ is obtained from $\overrightarrow{\mathscr{P}\mathscr{Q}} = dx$ by submitting dx to an orthogonal transformation represented by $I+S$ (an infinitesimal rotation) and a symmetric transformation $I+H$ which we now investigate in more detail.

We obtain from (12·4·1)

$$(I+H)\,x = \sum_{\nu=1}^{n} \lambda_\nu (x, \phi^\nu)\,\phi^\nu,$$

where the λ_ν and ϕ^ν are the (real) eigen-values and eigen-solutions of $I+H$. If we write $\lambda_\nu = 1+\delta_\nu$ we obtain $H\phi^\nu = \delta_\nu \phi^\nu$ and, by (13·5·4),

$$\| H\phi^\nu \| = |\delta_\nu| \leqslant \delta,$$

so that the δ_ν are also infinitesimal numbers. Hence the numbers $\lambda_\nu = 1+\delta_\nu$ are all positive, and, by reference to **12·41**, we can interpret the transformation

$$(I+H)\,dx = \sum_{\nu=1}^{n} (1+\delta_\nu)(dx, \phi^\nu)\,\phi^\nu$$

as a dilation such as is caused by a homogeneous strain of an elastic medium. A set of eigen-solutions ϕ^ν defines a set of principal axes of strain at $\mathscr{P}$ which are mutually orthogonal in the original state as well as after the displacement $I+W$, since $I+H$ takes the axes determined by the ϕ^ν into themselves and $I+S$ defines a rotation of the principal axes which conserves the angles.

13·51. In the case of a pure strain, that is, a dilation without rotation, S must vanish. Then W is symmetric and $\dfrac{\partial w_\mu}{\partial x_\nu} = \dfrac{\partial w_\nu}{\partial x_\mu}$. This is the necessary and sufficient condition for the existence of a (numerical) function

$$v(x_1, x_2, \ldots, x_n)$$

such that $w_\mu = \dfrac{\partial v}{\partial x_\mu}$; we then obtain

$$W = (w_{\mu\nu}) = \left(\frac{\partial^2 v}{\partial x_\mu \partial x_\nu}\right).$$

13·52. The surfaces

$$\| \mathscr{P}' \mathscr{Q}' \|^2 = ((I+W)\,dx,\,(I+W)\,dx) = ((I+H)\,dx,(I+H)\,dx) = \text{constant}$$

form a family of similar ellipsoids with $\mathscr{P}$ as centre which displace into a family of concentric spheres with $\mathscr{P}'$ as centre. We obtain, as in **13·21**,

$$\begin{aligned}((I+H)\,dx,(I+H)\,dx) &= \left(\sum_{\nu=1}^{n} \lambda_\nu(dx,\phi^\nu)\phi^\nu,(I+H)\,dx\right)\\ &= \left(\sum_{\nu=1}^{n} \lambda_\nu(dx,\phi^\nu)(I+H)\phi^\nu,dx\right)\\ &= \sum_{\nu=1}^{n} (1+\delta_\nu)^2\,|(dx,\phi^\nu)|^2\\ &= \sum_{\nu=1}^{n} (1+2\delta_\nu)\,|(dx,\phi^\nu)|^2\\ &= \text{constant}, \qquad (13\cdot52\cdot1)\end{aligned}$$

by neglecting the infinitesimals δ_ν^2 of second order. We notice that the principal axes of the ellipsoid defined by (13·52·1) coincide with a set of principal axes of strain as described in **13·5**. The ellipsoid (13·52·1) is called the inverse, or reciprocal, strain ellipsoid.

§ 14. Further maximal properties of the eigen-values. Inequalities

14·0. We now enumerate the eigen-values of the H.T. H in descending order of magnitude, as in **12·4**, writing

$$\lambda_1 \geqslant \lambda_2 \geqslant \ldots \geqslant \lambda_n.$$

The n numbers λ_ν are not necessarily distinct, but each distinct eigen-value occurs as many times as its order indicates and, if zero is an eigen-value, there will be an appropriate number of zeros among the λ's.

We write the spectral representation of H in the form (12·4·1), and immediately obtain the following theorem.

Theorem. *Let λ_1 and λ_n respectively be the greatest and least of the eigen-values of the H.T. H in $\mathfrak{B}_n$. Then λ_1 and λ_n respectively are the maximum and minimum values of (Hx, x) on the unit sphere $\| x \| = 1$ in $\mathfrak{B}_n$.*

PROOF. By (12·4·1),

$$\lambda_1 \| x \|^2 = \lambda_1 \sum_{\nu=1}^{n} (x, \phi^\nu)(\phi^\nu, x) \geqslant \sum_{\nu=1}^{n} \lambda_\nu (x, \phi^\nu)(\phi^\nu, x) = (Hx, x)$$
$$\geqslant \lambda_n \| x \|^2.$$

Hence, for $\| x \| = 1$, $\lambda_1 \geqslant (Hx, x) \geqslant \lambda_n$. Moreover, $(H\phi, \phi) = \lambda_1$ and $(H\psi, \psi) = \lambda_n$, where ϕ and ψ are eigen-solutions corresponding to λ_1 and λ_n respectively and such that $\| \phi \| = \| \psi \| = 1$.

14·01. THEOREM. *Let M be the greatest of the absolute values of the eigen-values of the H.T. H in $\mathfrak{V}_n$. Then, for any vector x,*

$$\| Hx \| \leqslant M \| x \|.$$

PROOF. With the notation of **12·43** and using (12·43·3), we have

$$\| Hx \|^2 = (Hx, Hx) = \sum_{\mu=1}^{m} \lambda_\mu (P_\mu x, Hx)$$
$$= \sum_{\mu=1}^{m} \lambda_\mu (P_\mu x, P_\mu Hx) = \sum_{\mu=1}^{m} \lambda_\mu^2 \| P_\mu x \|^2, \quad (14·01·1)$$

since, by (12·2·2), $P_\mu Hx = \lambda_\mu P_\mu x$. But $\lambda_\mu^2 \leqslant M^2$, so that, using (12·43·2), we have

$$\| Hx \|^2 \leqslant M^2 \sum_{\mu=1}^{m} \| P_\mu x \|^2 = M^2 \| x \|^2.$$

14·1. We again write the eigen-values of the H.T. H in the same order as in **12·4** and **14·0**; that is $\lambda_1 \geqslant \lambda_2 \geqslant \ldots \geqslant \lambda_n$, where the λ_ν are not necessarily distinct. In **12·1**, any non-zero eigen-value of H appears as the maximum of the function (Hx, x) for $\| x \| = 1$ within a L.M. of which the construction depends on the eigen-solutions corresponding to the eigen-values greater than the one under consideration. Using a device given by E. Fischer and R. Courant, we again define the eigen-value λ_{r+1} by a maximal property, but independently of the larger eigen-values.

THEOREM. *Let H be a H.T. in $\mathfrak{V}_n$, $\phi^1, \phi^2, \ldots, \phi^n$ an orthonormal set of eigen-solutions corresponding to the eigen-values $\lambda_1 \geqslant \lambda_2 \geqslant \ldots \geqslant \lambda_n$; let $a^1, a^2, \ldots, a^r$ be r linearly independent vectors of $\mathfrak{V}_n$, write*

$$\mathfrak{N} = [a^1, a^2, \ldots, a^r]$$

and $\mathfrak{M} = \mathfrak{V}_n \ominus \mathfrak{N}$, and consider the Hermitian form (Hx, x) in the L.M. $\mathfrak{M}$. Then the maximum for $\| x \| = 1$ is not less than λ_{r+1}, while for $a^1 = \phi^1, a^2 = \phi^2, \ldots, a^r = \phi^r$ the maximum equals λ_{r+1}. Thus, λ_{r+1} is the minimum of all the maxima attained by (Hx, x) for $\| x \| = 1$ in the L.M.'s $\mathfrak{M}$ of rank $n-r$.

Proof. We consider the L.M. $\mathfrak{N}' = [a^1, a^2, \ldots, a^r, \phi^{r+2}, \phi^{r+3}, \ldots, \phi^n]$ of which the rank does not exceed $n-1$. By Theorem **5·3**, there exists at least one vector y, with $\| y \| = 1$, that is orthogonal to every vector of $\mathfrak{N}'$; this vector y is an element of $\mathfrak{M}$. Moreover, we can write y in the form $y = \sum_{\nu=1}^{r+1} \eta_\nu \phi^\nu$, where $\sum_{\nu=1}^{r+1} |\eta_\nu|^2 = 1$, and obtain

$$(Hy, y) = \sum_{\mu,\nu=1}^{r+1} (H\phi^\nu, \phi^\mu)\,\eta_\nu \overline{\eta_\mu} = \sum_{\nu=1}^{r+1} \lambda_\nu |\eta_\nu|^2,$$

$$(Hy, y) \geqslant \lambda_{r+1} \sum_{\nu=1}^{r+1} |\eta_\nu|^2 = \lambda_{r+1}.$$

Since the maximum of (Hx, x) for $\| x \| = 1$ in $\mathfrak{M}$ is not less than (Hy, y) it is not less than λ_{r+1}.

Further, if $a^\nu = \phi^\nu$ for $\nu = 1, 2, \ldots, r$, we have

$$\mathfrak{M} = [\phi^{r+1}, \phi^{r+2}, \ldots, \phi^n]$$

and if any element x of $\mathfrak{M}$ is written as $x = \sum_{\nu=r+1}^{n} \xi_\nu \phi^\nu$, we have in $\mathfrak{M}$

$$(Hx, x) = \sum_{\mu,\nu=r+1}^{n} (H\phi^\nu, \phi^\mu)\,\xi_\nu \overline{\xi_\mu} = \sum_{\nu=r+1}^{n} \lambda_\nu |\xi_\nu|^2,$$

$$(Hx, x) \leqslant \lambda_{r+1} \| x \|^2.$$

Finally, $(Hx, x) = \lambda_{r+1}$ for $x = \phi^{r+1}$, and thus λ_{r+1} is the maximum of (Hx, x) for $\| x \| = 1$ in $\mathfrak{M}$.

14·2. Certain inequalities for the eigen-values follow at once from the preceding theorem.

Theorem. (**Cauchy's Inequalities.**) *Let H, $\mathfrak{M}$ and $\mathfrak{N}$ have the same meanings as in Theorem* **14·1**; *let $P_{\mathfrak{M}}$ be the orthogonal projector of $\mathfrak{B}_n$ on $\mathfrak{M}$, write $H_1 = P_{\mathfrak{M}} H P_{\mathfrak{M}}$ and consider the Hermitian form $(H_1 x, x)$ in $\mathfrak{M}$. If the eigen-values of H in $\mathfrak{B}_n$ are $\lambda_1 \geqslant \lambda_2 \geqslant \ldots \geqslant \lambda_n$* (as in **14·1**), *and if the eigen-values of H_1 in $\mathfrak{M}$ are $\lambda'_1 \geqslant \lambda'_2 \geqslant \ldots \geqslant \lambda'_{n-r}$, then $\lambda_{s+r} \leqslant \lambda'_s \leqslant \lambda_s$ for $s = 1, 2, \ldots, n-r$.*

Proof. Let $\phi'^1, \phi'^2, \ldots, \phi'^{s-1}$ be eigen-solutions of H_1 in $\mathfrak{M}$ corresponding to the first $s-1$ eigen-values $\lambda'_1, \lambda'_2, \ldots, \lambda'_{s-1}$ of H_1. Write

$$\mathfrak{F}_{s-1} = [\phi'^1, \phi'^2, \ldots, \phi'^{s-1}],$$

$$\mathfrak{M}' = \mathfrak{M} \ominus \mathfrak{F}_{s-1} = (\mathfrak{B}_n \ominus \mathfrak{N}) \ominus \mathfrak{F}_{s-1} = \mathfrak{B}_n \ominus (\mathfrak{N} \oplus \mathfrak{F}_{s-1}),$$

and apply Theorem **14·1** to the L.M. $\mathfrak{M}'$ which has rank $n-r-s+1$.

We find that $\lambda_{s+r} \leqslant \max(Hy, y)$ on the unit sphere in $\mathfrak{M}'$. But $\mathfrak{M}' \subset \mathfrak{M}$, so that $P_{\mathfrak{M}} y = y$ for every y of $\mathfrak{M}'$, and therefore

$$(Hy, y) = (HP_{\mathfrak{M}} y, P_{\mathfrak{M}} y) = (H_1 y, y)$$

for every y of $\mathfrak{M}'$. Further, by **12·0** and **12·1**, $\lambda'_s = \max(H_1 y, y)$ on the unit sphere in $\mathfrak{M}'$. Hence, $\lambda_{s+r} \leqslant \lambda'_s$.

We obtain the remaining inequality $\lambda'_s \leqslant \lambda_s$ by considering the Hermitian form $(-Hx, x)$. Its eigen-values $\omega_1 \geqslant \omega_2 \geqslant \ldots \geqslant \omega_n$ are given by the equations $\omega_\mu = -\lambda_{n+1-\mu}$ and the eigen-values

$$\omega'_1 \geqslant \omega'_2 \geqslant \ldots \geqslant \omega'_{n-r}$$

of $-H_1$ in $\mathfrak{M}$ are given by $\omega'_\mu = -\lambda'_{n+1-r-\mu}$. Hence the inequality $\omega_{s+r} \leqslant \omega'_s$ implies $-\lambda_{n+1-s-r} \leqslant -\lambda'_{n+1-r-s}$, and this gives the result required if we substitute s for $n+1-r-s$.

14·21. We see the value of the previous result for the consideration of a particular H.T. if we define the H.T. by a matrix $H = (a_{\mu\nu})$ and take $\mathfrak{M} = [u^1, u^2, \ldots, u^{n-r}] = \mathfrak{B}_{n-r}$. Then

$$(Hx, x) = \sum_{\mu, \nu=1}^{n} a_{\mu\nu} x_\nu \overline{x_\mu}, \quad (H_1 y, y) = \sum_{\mu, \nu=1}^{n-r} a_{\mu\nu} y_\nu \overline{y_\mu}.$$

The form $(H_1 y, y)$ is called the reduced form of (Hx, x), and λ'_s is its sth eigen-value. Theorem **14·2** gives bounds for the eigen-values of a Hermitian form in terms of the eigen-values of its reduced form which are, clearly, easier to calculate.

14·3. When the H.T. H is positive definite we can deduce from Theorem **14·1** a more precise set of inequalities than those of Theorem **14·2**. The new inequalities are due to Aronszajn. We need a preliminary lemma.

LEMMA. *Let α and γ be positive numbers and β a complex number such that*

$$f(\zeta) = \alpha\zeta\bar{\zeta} + \beta\zeta + \bar{\beta}\bar{\zeta} + \gamma \geqslant 0$$

for every complex number ζ. Then

$$\alpha\gamma \geqslant \beta\bar{\beta}, \tag{14·3·1}$$

and

$$f(\zeta) \leqslant (1 + \zeta\bar{\zeta})(\alpha + \gamma), \tag{14·3·2}$$

with equality in (14·3·1) *if, and only if, $f(\zeta) = 0$ for some value of ζ.*

PROOF. Write $\zeta = re^{i\theta}$, $\beta = \rho e^{i\theta_0}$, where r and ρ are positive or zero and θ and θ_0 are real. Then

$$f(\zeta) = \alpha r^2 + 2\rho r \cos(\theta + \theta_0) + \gamma \geqslant 0, \tag{14·3·3}$$

$$f(\zeta) \geqslant \alpha r^2 - 2\rho r + \gamma \qquad \geqslant 0,$$

for all values of r and θ, with equality in the inequality on the left only for $\cos(\theta+\theta_0) = -1$. Hence, $\alpha\gamma \geqslant \rho^2$, with equality if, and only if, for some value ζ_0,

$$f(\zeta_0) = \alpha r_0^2 - 2\rho r_0 + \gamma = 0,$$

where $|\zeta_0| = r_0$. Thus, (14·3·1) is verified. It follows that

$$\rho r \leqslant r\sqrt{(\alpha\gamma)} \leqslant \tfrac{1}{2}(\alpha + \gamma r^2). \tag{14·3·4}$$

We now deduce from (14·3·3) and (14·3·4) that

$$f(\zeta) \leqslant \alpha r^2 + 2\rho r + \gamma \leqslant (1+r^2)(\alpha+\gamma),$$

and (14·3·2) is verified.

14·4. THEOREM. **(Aronszajn's Inequalities.)** *Let H be a positive definite H.T. in $\mathfrak{B}_n$, let $\mathfrak{M}$ and $\mathfrak{N}$ have the same meanings as in Theorem* **14·1**, *and let $P_{\mathfrak{M}}$ and $P_{\mathfrak{N}}$ be the orthogonal projectors of $\mathfrak{B}_n$ on $\mathfrak{M}$ and $\mathfrak{N}$ respectively. Write*

$$H_1 = P_{\mathfrak{M}} H P_{\mathfrak{M}}, \quad H_2 = P_{\mathfrak{N}} H P_{\mathfrak{N}},$$

and consider the Hermitian forms $(H_1 x, x)$ and $(H_2 x, x)$ in $\mathfrak{M}$ and $\mathfrak{N}$ respectively. Let the eigen-values of H in $\mathfrak{B}_n$ be

$$\lambda_1 \geqslant \lambda_2 \geqslant \ldots \geqslant \lambda_n > 0$$

(as in **14·1**), *those of H_1 in $\mathfrak{M}$ be $\lambda'_1 \geqslant \lambda'_2 \geqslant \ldots \geqslant \lambda'_{n-r}$* (as in **14·2**) *and those of H_2 in $\mathfrak{N}$ be $\lambda''_1 \geqslant \lambda''_2 \geqslant \ldots \geqslant \lambda''_r$. Then*

$$\lambda_{s+t+1} \leqslant \lambda'_{s+1} + \lambda''_{t+1} \quad (0 \leqslant s \leqslant n-r-1,\ 0 \leqslant t \leqslant r-1).$$

PROOF. Let $\phi'^1, \phi'^2, \ldots, \phi'^s$ be eigen-solutions of H_1 in $\mathfrak{M}$ corresponding to the first s eigen-values $\lambda'_1, \lambda'_2, \ldots, \lambda'_s$ of H_1, and let $\phi''^1, \phi''^2, \ldots, \phi''^t$ be eigen-solutions of H_2 in $\mathfrak{N}$ corresponding to the first t eigen-values $\lambda''_1, \lambda''_2, \ldots, \lambda''_t$ of H_2. Write

$$\mathfrak{F}'_s = [\phi'^1, \phi'^2, \ldots, \phi'^s], \quad \mathfrak{F}''_t = [\phi''^1, \phi''^2, \ldots, \phi''^t],$$
$$\mathfrak{M}' = \mathfrak{M} \ominus \mathfrak{F}'_s, \qquad \mathfrak{N}' = \mathfrak{N} \ominus \mathfrak{F}''_t,$$

remarking that $\mathfrak{F}'_s \subset \mathfrak{M}$, $\mathfrak{F}''_t \subset \mathfrak{N}$, $\mathfrak{M}' . \mathfrak{N}' = \mathfrak{O}$, and $\mathfrak{F}'_s . \mathfrak{F}''_t = \mathfrak{O}$. The application of Theorem **14·1** to the L.M.

$$\mathfrak{M}' \oplus \mathfrak{N}' = \mathfrak{B}_n \ominus (\mathfrak{F}'_s \oplus \mathfrak{F}''_t) = (\mathfrak{B}_n \ominus \mathfrak{F}'_s) \ominus \mathfrak{F}''_t,$$

which has rank $n-s-t$, shows that $\lambda_{s+t+1} \leqslant \max(Hy, y)$ for $\|y\| = 1$ when $y \in \mathfrak{M}' \oplus \mathfrak{N}'$. We can, however, write $y = \sigma p + \tau q$, where σ and τ are complex numbers, $p \in \mathfrak{M}'$, $q \in \mathfrak{N}'$,

$$\|p\| = \|q\| = 1, \quad (p, q) = 0,$$

and $|\sigma|^2+|\tau|^2=1$. Hence

$$(Hy,y) = |\sigma|^2(Hp,p)+\sigma\bar{\tau}(Hp,q)+\bar{\sigma}\tau(Hq,p)+|\tau|^2(Hq,q).$$

We may assume, without loss of generality, that $\tau \neq 0$. We now apply Lemma **14·3**, writing

$$\zeta = \frac{\sigma}{\tau}, \quad \alpha = (Hp,p), \quad \gamma = (Hq,q), \quad \beta = (Hp,q),$$

and obtain

$$0<(Hy,y) = |\tau|^2 f(\zeta) \leqslant |\tau|^2\left(1+\left|\frac{\sigma}{\tau}\right|^2\right)(\alpha+\gamma)$$

$$= (|\sigma|^2+|\tau|^2)((Hp,p)+(Hq,q)) = (Hp,p)+(Hq,q). \quad (14·4·1)$$

Since $\mathfrak{M}'\subset\mathfrak{M}$ and $\mathfrak{N}'\subset\mathfrak{N}$, however, we have $P_{\mathfrak{M}}p = p$ for every p of $\mathfrak{M}'$ and $P_{\mathfrak{N}}q = q$ for every q of $\mathfrak{N}'$. Hence

$$(Hp,p) = (HP_{\mathfrak{M}}p, P_{\mathfrak{M}}p) = (H_1p,p), \quad (Hq,q) = (H_2q,q).$$

Further, by **12·0** and **12·1**, $\lambda'_{s+1} = \max(H_1p,p)$ for p on the unit sphere in $\mathfrak{M}\ominus\mathfrak{F}'_s$, and $\lambda''_{t+1} = \max(H_2q,q)$ for q on the unit sphere in $\mathfrak{N}\ominus\mathfrak{F}''_t$. Therefore, since (14·4·1) gives

$$\max(Hy,y) \leqslant \max(H_1p,p)+\max(H_2q,q),$$

where y is on the unit sphere in $\mathfrak{M}'\oplus\mathfrak{N}'$, p is on the unit sphere in $\mathfrak{M}'$, and q is on the unit sphere in $\mathfrak{N}'$ we obtain the required inequality

$$\lambda_{s+t+1} \leqslant \lambda'_{s+1}+\lambda''_{t+1}.$$

14·41. As in **14·21**, we may take $\mathfrak{M} = [u^1, u^2, \ldots, u^{n-r}]$ and $\mathfrak{N} = [u^{n-r+1}, u^{n-r+2}, \ldots, u^n]$. We then have

$$(Hx,x) = \sum_{\mu,\nu=1}^{n} a_{\mu\nu}x_\nu\bar{x}_\mu, \quad (H_1p,p) = \sum_{\mu,\nu=1}^{n-r} a_{\mu\nu}p_\nu\bar{p}_\mu,$$

$$(H_2q,q) = \sum_{\mu,\nu=n-r+1}^{n} a_{\mu\nu}q_\nu\bar{q}_\mu.$$

§ 15. Functional calculus of H.T.'s. The resolvent and its properties

15·0. We consider the set of distinct eigen-values of the H.T. H in $\mathfrak{B}_n$ and use the notation of **12·43**. By (12·43·3) and (12·2·2),

$$H^2x = \sum_{\mu=1}^{m} \lambda_\mu P_\mu Hx = \sum_{\mu=1}^{m} \lambda_\mu^2 P_\mu x,$$

and, similarly, for any positive integer κ,

$$H^{\kappa}x = \sum_{\mu=1}^{m} \lambda_{\mu}^{\kappa} P_{\mu} x,$$

since $H^{\kappa-1}H = H^{\kappa}$. We also write

$$H^{0}x = Ix = \sum_{\mu=1}^{m} P_{\mu} x.$$

We now consider a scalar polynomial $p(t)$ of degree k, where

$$p(t) = \sum_{\kappa=0}^{k} \alpha_{\kappa} t^{\kappa},$$

and write, for any x of $\mathfrak{V}_n$,

$$p(H)x = \sum_{\kappa=0}^{k} \alpha_{\kappa} H^{\kappa} x,$$

$$p(H)x = \sum_{\kappa=0}^{k} \alpha_{\kappa} \sum_{\mu=1}^{m} \lambda_{\mu}^{\kappa} P_{\mu} x = \sum_{\mu=1}^{m} p(\lambda_{\mu}) P_{\mu} x. \qquad (15{\cdot}0{\cdot}1)$$

This relation shows that the L.T. $p(H)$ is a H.T. if, and only if, all the values $p(\lambda_{\mu})$ are real.

15·01. If we write

$$q(t) = (t-\lambda_1)^{k_1}(t-\lambda_2)^{k_2}\dots(t-\lambda_m)^{k_m},$$

where $k_1+k_2+\dots+k_m = n$, we obtain from (15·0·1)

$$q(H)x = \sum_{\mu=1}^{m} q(\lambda_{\mu}) P_{\mu} x = 0.$$

This is the *Cayley-Hamilton Theorem* for a H.T.

If we write $\quad q_1(t) = (t-\lambda_1)(t-\lambda_2)\dots(t-\lambda_m)$,

we obtain $q_1(H) = O$. Plainly, (15·0·1) implies that $q_1(H)$ is the polynomial in H of lowest degree that vanishes identically.

15·02. It may be noted that the function $q(t)$ of **15·01** is the determinant of the matrix $tI-\Lambda$, where Λ is given by (13·2·4).

15·1. Before we define $f(H)$ for a continuous function $f(t)$ of the real variable t we need certain results about sequences of L.T.'s.

Convergence of a sequence of L.T.'s. We say that *an infinite sequence of L.T.'s A_{κ} in $\mathfrak{V}_n$ is convergent if the sequence of vectors $\{A_{\kappa}x\}$ converges for each x of $\mathfrak{V}_n$.* We then write $x' = \lim_{\kappa\to\infty} A_{\kappa}x = Ax$, thereby defining a transformation $x' = Ax$ that is readily seen to be a L.T. We say that the sequence $\{A_{\kappa}\}$ converges to A and we write $A = \lim_{\kappa\to\infty} A_{\kappa}$.

By **1·53** *it is a necessary and sufficient condition for the convergence of a sequence* $\{A_\kappa\}$ that for each x of $\mathfrak{B}_n$ and for any positive number ϵ there should exist an integer $\kappa_0(\epsilon, x)$ such that

$$\| A_{\kappa_1} x - A_{\kappa_2} x \| < \epsilon \quad (\kappa_1, \kappa_2 \geqslant \kappa_0). \tag{15·1·1}$$

If $B_\kappa = \sum_{\nu=1}^{\kappa} A_\nu$, and if the sequence $\{B_\kappa\}$ converges to B, we write $B = \sum_{\nu=1}^{\infty} A_\nu$.

15·11. Uniform convergence. *If the sequence* $\{A_\kappa x\}$ *converges uniformly on the unit sphere* $\| x \| = 1$ *in* $\mathfrak{B}_n$, that is to say, if there exists an integer $\kappa_0(\epsilon)$, independent of x, such that

$$\| A_{\kappa_1} x - A_{\kappa_2} x \| < \epsilon \quad (\| x \| = 1;\ \kappa_1, \kappa_2 \geqslant \kappa_0),$$

we have
$$\| A_{\kappa_1} x - A_{\kappa_2} x \| \leqslant \epsilon \| x \|$$

for all x of $\mathfrak{B}_n$ and for all $\kappa_1, \kappa_2 \geqslant \kappa_0(\epsilon)$. We then say that *the sequence* $\{A_\kappa\}$ *converges uniformly to A in* $\mathfrak{B}_n$.

15·12. Theorem. *Every convergent sequence* $\{A_\kappa\}$ *of L.T.'s in* $\mathfrak{B}_n$ *is uniformly convergent.*

Proof. If we write $A_\kappa u^\nu = a^{\kappa\nu}$, we deduce from the application of (15·1·1) to the n coordinate vectors that

$$\sum_{\nu=1}^{n} \| a^{\kappa_1 \nu} - a^{\kappa_2 \nu} \| < \epsilon \quad (\kappa_1, \kappa_2 \geqslant \kappa_0(\epsilon)),$$

and hence, by (6·05·1), for any x of $\mathfrak{B}_n$,

$$\begin{aligned} \| A_{\kappa_1} x - A_{\kappa_2} x \| &= \| (A_{\kappa_1} - A_{\kappa_2}) x \| \\ &\leqslant \| x \| \sum_{\nu=1}^{n} \| a^{\kappa_1 \nu} - a^{\kappa_2 \nu} \| \\ &\leqslant \epsilon \| x \| \quad (\kappa_1, \kappa_2 \geqslant \kappa_0(\epsilon)). \end{aligned}$$

15·13. There is no theorem for Hilbert space corresponding to Theorem **15·12** and, indeed, the distinction between uniform and non-uniform convergence of infinite sequences plays an important part in the development of the theory of L.T.'s in Hilbert space.

15·14. Corollary of Theorem **15·12**. *Let*

$$\mathscr{P}(\zeta) = \sum_{\nu=0}^{\infty} \alpha_\nu \zeta^\nu \quad (|\zeta| < r)$$

be a power series with radius of convergence r, and let A be a L.T. in $\mathfrak{B}_n$

such that $\| Ax \| \leqslant M \| x \|$ *for every element* x *of* $\mathfrak{B}_n$, *where* $0 < M < r$. *Then the power series*

$$\mathscr{P}(A) = \sum_{\nu=0}^{\infty} \alpha_\nu A^\nu = \lim_{\kappa \to \infty} \sum_{\nu=0}^{\kappa} \alpha_\nu A^\nu$$

is uniformly convergent in $\mathfrak{B}_n$.

Proof. Since $0 < M < r$, there exists for any prescribed positive number ϵ a positive integer $\kappa_0(\epsilon)$ such that

$$\sum_{\nu=\kappa_1+1}^{\kappa_2} |\alpha_\nu| M^\nu < \epsilon \quad (\kappa_1, \kappa_2 \geqslant \kappa_0).$$

Thus, for any x of $\mathfrak{B}_n$,

$$\left\| \sum_{\nu=\kappa_1+1}^{\kappa_2} \alpha_\nu A^\nu x \right\| \leqslant \sum_{\nu=\kappa_1+1}^{\kappa_2} |\alpha_\nu| M^\nu \| x \|$$
$$< \epsilon \| x \| \quad (\kappa_1, \kappa_2 \geqslant \kappa_0),$$

and it follows that the sequence of partial sums $\sum_{\nu=0}^{\kappa} \alpha_\nu A^\nu$ is uniformly convergent in $\mathfrak{B}_n$.

15·2. Let H be a H.T. in $\mathfrak{B}_n$, let λ_μ and P_μ have the same meanings as in **15·0** and, as in **14·01**, take $M = \max\{|\lambda_\mu|\}$. (We write $\max\{\alpha_\mu\}$ for the greatest of m real numbers α_μ.) Let $f(t)$ be a (complex) function of the real variable t continuous in the range $|t| \leqslant M$. Then, by a theorem of Weierstrass, there exists a sequence of polynomials $p_\kappa(t)$ such that, for any positive ϵ,

$$|f(t) - p_\kappa(t)| < \epsilon \quad (|t| \leqslant M)$$

if κ exceeds a suitably chosen $\kappa_0(\epsilon)$. We use this approximating sequence of polynomials to justify a definition of the function $f(H)$ developed from the expression (15·0·1) for the polynomial $p(H)$.

Definition of a continuous function of a H.T. *We define the L.T.* $f(H)$ *by writing*

$$f(H)x = \sum_{\mu=1}^{m} f(\lambda_\mu) P_\mu x \qquad (15·2·1)$$

for any x *of* $\mathfrak{B}_n$, where $f(t)$ is continuous for $|t| \leqslant M$.

We first remark that (15·2·1) coincides with (15·0·1) whenever $f(t)$ is a polynomial $p(t)$; we then show that

$$f(H) = \lim_{\kappa \to \infty} p_\kappa(H) \qquad (15·2·2)$$

uniformly in $\mathfrak{B}_n$. By (15·0·1) and (15·2·1),

$$(f(H) - p_\kappa(H))x = \sum_{\mu=1}^{m} (f(\lambda_\mu) - p_\kappa(\lambda_\mu)) P_\mu x.$$

and further,

$$\| (f(H)-p_\kappa(H))\,x \|^2 = \sum_{\mu=1}^{m} |f(\lambda_\mu)-p_\kappa(\lambda_\mu)|^2 \| P_\mu x \|^2$$

$$\leqslant \epsilon^2 \sum_{\mu=1}^{m} \| P_\mu x \|^2 = \epsilon^2 \| x \|^2 \quad (\kappa \geqslant \kappa_0(\epsilon)),$$

so that (15·2·2) is satisfied.

15·21. Note. The expression (15·2·1) defines $f(H)$ not only for a function $f(t)$ continuous in the interval $|t| \leqslant M$, but also for any function $f(t)$ continuous in some neighbourhood of each point $t = \lambda_\mu$. We can readily extend Weierstrass's Theorem to this case by determining a function $g(t)$ continuous in the interval $|t| \leqslant M$ that coincides with $f(t)$ in the neighbourhoods of the λ_μ. We then obtain

$$f(H) = g(H) = \lim_{\kappa \to \infty} p_\kappa(H).$$

The representation (15·2·1) for $f(H)$, moreover, shows that we can always determine a polynomial $p(t)$, of degree not greater than $m-1$, such that $f(H) = p(H)$. We have only to construct the Lagrange polynomial satisfying the conditions $p(\lambda_\mu) = f(\lambda_\mu)$ for $\mu = 1, 2, \ldots, m$.

15·22. We deduce at once from (15·2·1) and (12·2·1) the commutativity property

$$f(H)\,P_\nu = \sum_{\mu=1}^{m} f(\lambda_\mu)\,P_\mu P_\nu = f(\lambda_\nu)\,P_\nu = P_\nu f(H).$$

This relation also implies that the values $f(\lambda_\mu)$ are eigen-values of $f(H)$ and that the eigen-manifolds $\mathfrak{E}_\mu$ of H are contained in the corresponding eigen-manifolds of $f(H)$. We may go further and show that there are no other eigen-values. In virtue of (12·43·1), any representation of a vector x of $\mathfrak{V}_n$ in the form $x = \sum_{\mu=1}^{m} p^\mu$, where $p^\mu \in \mathfrak{E}_\mu$, is unique. If, however, we consider an eigen-solution ψ of $f(H)$ corresponding to any eigen-value ω we have

$$\psi = \sum_{\mu=1}^{m} P_\mu \psi, \quad f(H)\,\psi = \sum_{\mu=1}^{m} f(\lambda_\mu)\,P_\mu \psi = \omega \sum_{\mu=1}^{m} P_\mu \psi,$$

where $P_\mu \psi \in \mathfrak{E}_\mu$, and it follows that, for each μ, either $\omega = f(\lambda_\mu)$ or $P_\mu \psi = 0$, and therefore that ω coincides with at least one of the values $f(\lambda_\mu)$. If it coincides with precisely ν values, say

$$\omega = f(\lambda_1) = f(\lambda_2) = \ldots = f(\lambda_\nu),$$

we deduce that the corresponding eigen-manifold is

$$\mathfrak{E}_1 \oplus \mathfrak{E}_2 \oplus \ldots \oplus \mathfrak{E}_\nu,$$

which, by Theorem **10·42**, is the range of the projector

$$P_1 + P_2 + \ldots + P_\nu.$$

15·23. We also deduce from (15·2·1) that

$$(f(H))^* x = \sum_{\mu=1}^{m} \overline{f(\lambda_\mu)}\, P_\mu x = \bar{f}(H)\, x,$$

and we see that $f(H)$ is a H.T. if, and only if, all the values $f(\lambda_\mu)$ are real.

15·3. If the functions $f(t)$ and $g(t)$ are continuous in the neighbourhoods of the points λ_μ, and if we write

$$F(t) = f(t) + g(t), \quad G(t) = f(t)\, g(t),$$

we have, for any x of $\mathfrak{B}_n$,

$$F(H)\, x = \sum_{\mu=1}^{m} (f(\lambda_\mu) + g(\lambda_\mu))\, P_\mu x, \quad G(H)\, x = \sum_{\mu=1}^{m} f(\lambda_\mu)\, g(\lambda_\mu)\, P_\mu x.$$

However,

$$f(H)\,(g(H)\, x) = \sum_{\mu=1}^{m} f(\lambda_\mu)\, P_\mu \left(\sum_{\nu=1}^{m} g(\lambda_\nu)\, P_\nu x \right)$$

$$= \sum_{\mu=1}^{m} f(\lambda_\mu)\, g(\lambda_\mu)\, P_\mu x,$$

since $P_\mu P_\nu x = \delta_{\mu\nu} P_\mu x$. Hence

$$F(H) = f(H) + g(H), \quad G(H) = f(H)\, g(H) = g(H) f(H). \quad (15·3·1)$$

15·31. Let $\{f_\kappa(t)\}$ be an infinite sequence of functions continuous in the neighbourhoods of the points $t = \lambda_\mu$ and convergent to a function $f(t)$ at these points. An argument similar to that of **15·2** shows that if we again define $f(H)\, x$ by (15·2·1), as

$$f(H)\, x = \sum_{\mu=1}^{m} f(\lambda_\mu)\, P_\mu x$$

for every x of $\mathfrak{B}_n$, we obtain the relation corresponding to (15·2·2), namely,

$$\lim_{\kappa \to \infty} f_\kappa(H) = f(H),$$

uniformly in $\mathfrak{B}_n$.

15·4. The resolvent. Let λ belong to the resolvent set of H, so that $\lambda \neq \lambda_1, \lambda_2, \ldots, \lambda_m$. Write

$$f(t) = \frac{1}{t-\lambda}, \quad f(H) = R_\lambda = \sum_{\mu=1}^{m} \frac{1}{\lambda_\mu - \lambda} P_\mu, \tag{15·4·1}$$

$$g(t) = t-\lambda, \quad g(H) = H - \lambda I = H_\lambda = \sum_{\mu=1}^{m} (\lambda_\mu - \lambda) P_\mu,$$

by (15·2·1). Now, by (15·3·1), the relation $f(t)\,g(t) = g(t)f(t) = 1$ implies that $R_\lambda H_\lambda = H_\lambda R_\lambda = I$. Hence, R_λ is the resolvent of H defined in **12·5**.

15·41. If we now write, for any two distinct numbers λ, μ of the resolvent set of H,

$$f(t) = \frac{1}{t-\lambda}, \quad g(t) = \frac{1}{t-\mu},$$

we have

$$\frac{1}{t-\lambda} - \frac{1}{t-\mu} = \frac{\lambda-\mu}{(t-\lambda)(t-\mu)}, \quad f(t) - g(t) = (\lambda-\mu) f(t)\,g(t),$$

and therefore, by **15·3**,

$$f(H) - g(H) = (\lambda-\mu) f(H)\,g(H) = (\lambda-\mu)\,g(H) f(H),$$

$$R_\lambda - R_\mu = (\lambda-\mu)\,R_\lambda R_\mu = (\lambda-\mu)\,R_\mu R_\lambda.$$

This is the fundamental functional equation for the resolvent.

15·42. Since the power series

$$\frac{1}{t-\lambda} = -\sum_{\kappa=0}^{\infty} \frac{1}{\lambda^{\kappa+1}} t^\kappa \quad (|t| < |\lambda|)$$

is uniformly convergent for $|t| \leqslant M = \max |\lambda_\mu|$ if

$$|\lambda| \geqslant M + \delta > M,$$

it follows by **15·31** that

$$R_\lambda = -\sum_{\kappa=0}^{\infty} \frac{1}{\lambda^{\kappa+1}} H^\kappa \quad (|\lambda| > M), \tag{15·42·1}$$

where, in accordance with **15·14**, the power series on the right-hand side is to be interpreted as

$$\lim_{\kappa \to \infty} \sum_{\nu=0}^{\kappa} \frac{1}{\lambda^{\nu+1}} H^\nu.$$

Now let l be any number, real or not, different from all the m numbers λ_μ, and let d be the least of the m numbers $|l - \lambda_\mu|$. We may write, for $|t| \leqslant M$,

$$\frac{1}{t-\lambda} = \sum_{\kappa=0}^{\infty} (\lambda - l)^\kappa \frac{1}{(t-l)^{\kappa+1}} \quad (|\lambda - l| < |t - l|),$$

and the series is convergent for $t = \lambda_1, \lambda_2, \ldots, \lambda_m$ if

$$|\lambda - l| \leqslant d - \delta < d.$$

It follows by **15·31** that

$$R_\lambda = \sum_{\kappa=0}^{\infty} (\lambda - l)^\kappa R_l^{\kappa+1} \quad (|\lambda - l| < d). \tag{15·42·2}$$

15·43. Finally, we can represent R_λ by a series of ascending powers of $\lambda - \lambda_\nu$. We write (15·4·1) in the form

$$R_\lambda = -\frac{1}{\lambda - \lambda_\nu} P_\nu - \sum_{\mu \neq \nu} \frac{1}{\lambda - \lambda_\mu} P_\mu = -\frac{1}{\lambda - \lambda_\nu} P_\nu - \Sigma(\lambda);$$

then we readily obtain for $\Sigma(\lambda)$ the power series representation

$$-\Sigma(\lambda) = \sum_{\kappa=0}^{\infty} \left(\sum_{\mu \neq \nu} \frac{1}{(\lambda_\mu - \lambda_\nu)^{\kappa+1}} P_\mu \right) (\lambda - \lambda_\nu)^\kappa$$

with radius of convergence equal to the smallest distance of λ_ν from the $m-1$ other eigen-values. Writing

$$S = \sum_{\mu \neq \nu} \frac{1}{\lambda_\mu - \lambda_\nu} P_\mu, \tag{15·43·1}$$

we easily verify that

$$\sum_{\mu \neq \nu} \frac{1}{(\lambda_\mu - \lambda_\nu)^{\kappa+1}} P_\mu = S^{\kappa+1},$$

and hence that

$$R_\lambda = -\frac{1}{\lambda - \lambda_\nu} P_\nu + \sum_{\kappa=0}^{\infty} (\lambda - \lambda_\nu)^\kappa S^{\kappa+1}. \tag{15·43·2}$$

This is the desired representation of R_λ.

Further, we deduce from (15·43·1) and (12·43·4) that

$$SH_{\lambda_\nu} = H_{\lambda_\nu} S = \left(\sum_{\mu \neq \nu} \frac{1}{\lambda_\mu - \lambda_\nu} P_\mu \right) \left(\sum_{\mu=1}^{m} (\lambda_\mu - \lambda_\nu) P_\mu \right)$$

$$= \sum_{\mu \neq \nu} P_\mu = I - P_\nu. \tag{15·43·3}$$

Thus, by (15·43·3) and (15·43·1),

$$SH_{\lambda_\nu} x = H_{\lambda_\nu} S x = x \quad \text{for} \quad x \in \mathfrak{B}_n \ominus \mathfrak{E}_\nu,$$
$$Sx = 0 \qquad\qquad \text{for} \quad x \in \mathfrak{E}_\nu.$$

These equations determine S as an inverse of H_{λ_ν} in the subspace $\mathfrak{B}_n \ominus \mathfrak{E}_\nu$.

15·5. We obtain another interesting example of a function of H by considering $f(t) = (t-i)(t+i)^{-1}$; then

$$f(H) = H_i (H_{-i})^{-1} = (H_{-i})^{-1} (H_i).$$

This L.T. is called the *Cayley transform* of H. It can be written, by (15·2·1), as

$$f(H) = (H_{-i})^{-1} H_i = \sum_{\mu=1}^{m} \frac{\lambda_\mu - i}{\lambda_\mu + i} P_\mu. \tag{15·5·1}$$

Since $\bar{f}(t) = (t+i)(t-i)^{-1}$ and $f(t)\bar{f}(t) = 1$, we have $f(H)(f(H)^* = I$, by **15·23**, so that the Cayley transform of a H.T. is a unitary transformation. The eigen-values of the Cayley transform are $(\lambda_\mu - i)(\lambda_\mu + i)^{-1}$, and they all lie on the unit circle in the complex plane. We shall show in § **16** that every unitary transformation U can be considered as the Cayley transform of a H.T. provided that U has no eigen-value equal to 1.

15·51. If we take $f(t) = \exp(it)$, then $f(t)\bar{f}(t) = 1$ and $f(H)$ is again a unitary transformation. It will be shown in § **16** that every unitary transformation can be written in the form $U = \exp(iH)$, where H is a suitable H.T.

§ 16. Transformations commutative with H.T.'s. Normal transformations

16·0. Theorem. *Let the spectral representation of a H.T. H in $\mathfrak{B}_n$ be*

$$Hx = \sum_{\mu=1}^{m} \lambda_\mu P_\mu x.$$

Then the L.T. A in $\mathfrak{B}_n$ is commutative with H, that is, $AH = HA$, if, and only if, $AP_\mu = P_\mu A$ for $\mu = 1, 2, \ldots, m$.

Note. According to Theorem **10·9** the above condition for A is equivalent to the demand that the L.M. on which A maps every $\mathfrak{E}_\mu$ for $\mu = 1, 2, \ldots, m$ should be either contained in, or equal to, $\mathfrak{E}_\mu$.

Proof. We deduce at once from the spectral representation that $AH = HA$ if $AP_\mu = P_\mu A$ for $\mu = 1, 2, \ldots, m$.

Conversely, if $AH = HA$, then $\lambda_\mu AP_\mu x = AHP_\mu x = HAP_\mu x$, since $HP_\mu x = \lambda_\mu P_\mu x$ for $\mu = 1, 2, \ldots, m$.

Hence, $AP_\mu x \in \mathfrak{E}_\mu$ and therefore $P_\nu AP_\mu x = \delta_{\mu\nu} AP_\mu x$. Thus

$$P_\nu Ax = P_\nu A\left(\sum_{\mu=1}^{m} P_\mu x\right) = P_\nu AP_\nu x$$
$$= AP_\nu x.$$

16·1. Theorem. *Two H.T.'s H and K in $\mathfrak{B}_n$ are commutative, that is, $HK = KH$, if, and only if, they have a complete orthonormal system of eigen-solutions in common.*

PROOF. (i) Let $\{\phi^\kappa\}$ be a common orthonormal system of eigen-solutions and let the corresponding eigen-values of H and K be λ_κ, μ_κ respectively, so that, by (12·4·1),

$$Hx = \sum_{\kappa=1}^{n} \lambda_\kappa(x, \phi^\kappa)\phi^\kappa, \quad Kx = \sum_{\kappa=1}^{n} \mu_\kappa(x, \phi^\kappa)\phi^\kappa. \tag{16·1·1}$$

Here, as in **12·4**, the sets of eigen-values λ_κ and μ_κ are not necessarily distinct, but in each set each distinct eigen-value occurs as many times as its order indicates. We at once obtain from (16·1·1) that

$$\begin{aligned} HKx &= \sum_{\kappa=1}^{n} \mu_\kappa(x, \phi^\kappa) H\phi^\kappa \\ &= \sum_{\kappa=1}^{n} \lambda_\kappa\mu_\kappa(x, \phi^\kappa)\phi^\kappa \\ &= KHx. \end{aligned} \tag{16·1·2}$$

(ii) Let $HK = KH$, let λ_1 be an eigen-value of H of order k_1, $\mathfrak{E}_1$ the L.M. of rank k_1 formed by the corresponding eigen-solutions of H, and P_1 the orthogonal projector of $\mathfrak{V}_n$ on $\mathfrak{E}_1$. Then, by Theorem **16·0**, $P_1Kx = KP_1x$. Hence, if we interpret $\mathfrak{E}_1$ as a space $\mathfrak{V}_{k_1}$, K determines a H.T. in $\mathfrak{V}_{k_1}$ mapping $\mathfrak{V}_{k_1}$ on itself and having an orthonormal system of k_1 eigen-solutions $\phi^1, \phi^2, \ldots, \phi^{k_1}$ in $\mathfrak{V}_{k_1}$. These vectors ϕ^κ, as elements of $\mathfrak{E}_1$, are also eigen-solutions of H. We treat all the eigen-values of H in this way and obtain a system of eigen-solutions common to H and K. Their number is the sum of the orders of the eigen-values of H, which is n. The sets of eigen-solutions corresponding to the different eigen-values of H are orthogonal to one another, by Theorem **8·6**. Thus we obtain a complete orthonormal system of eigen-solutions common to H and K.

16·2. The preceding theorem often appears in a different form, as follows.

THEOREM. *Two H.T.'s H and K in $\mathfrak{V}_n$ are commutative if, and only if, there exists a H.T. J, with a simple spectrum, such that*

$$H = f(J), \quad K = g(J), \tag{16·2·1}$$

where $f(t)$ and $g(t)$ are real continuous functions.

If H has a simple spectrum we can take $J = H$ and then $K = g(H)$.

PROOF. The sufficiency of the condition follows at once from **15·3**. To prove the necessity, we remark that, if $HK = KH$ then, by Theorem **16·1**, H and K have a common orthonormal system of

n eigen-solutions $\{\phi^\kappa\}$. Let λ_κ and μ_κ, for $\kappa = 1, 2, \ldots, n$, be the eigen-values corresponding to ϕ^κ of H and K respectively, and let ω_κ, for $\kappa = 1, 2, \ldots, n$, be n distinct real numbers. For instance, if the λ_κ are all distinct we may write $\omega_\kappa = \lambda_\kappa$. We can determine two real continuous functions $f(t)$ and $g(t)$ (for example, two real polynomials of degree $n-1$ at most) such that

$$\lambda_\kappa = f(\omega_\kappa), \quad \mu_\kappa = g(\omega_\kappa) \quad (\kappa = 1, 2, \ldots, n).$$

If we write, for every x of $\mathfrak{B}_n$,

$$Jx = \sum_{\kappa=1}^{n} \omega_\kappa (x, \phi^\kappa)\, \phi^\kappa,$$

then, by (15·2·1) and (16·1·1),

$$f(J)\, x = \sum_{\kappa=1}^{n} f(\omega_\kappa)(x, \phi^\kappa)\, \phi^\kappa = \sum_{\kappa=1}^{n} \lambda_\kappa (x, \phi^\kappa)\, \phi^\kappa = Hx,$$

$$g(J)\, x = \sum_{\kappa=1}^{n} g(\omega_\kappa)(x, \phi^\kappa)\, \phi^\kappa = Kx.$$

16·3. Referring to **15·23**, we see that $f(H)$ is not necessarily Hermitian if $f(t)$ is not a real function. We notice at once, however, that the transformation $N = f(H)$ is a normal transformation, since, by **15·23**, $N^* = \bar{f}(H)$ and, by (15·3·1),

$$NN^* = N^*N = f(H)\bar{f}(H).$$

Thus we are led to the normal transformations by consideration of the L.T.'s generated by the Hermitian transformations. We show in **16·5** that every normal transformation N can be written in the form $N = f(H)$, where H is a suitable H.T. We first, however, prove the following theorem.

THEOREM. *Let N be a L.T. and $\{\phi^\kappa\}$ $(\kappa = 1, 2, \ldots, n)$ a complete orthonormal system in $\mathfrak{B}_n$ such that the ϕ^κ are eigen-solutions of N corresponding to eigen-values l_κ; that is, $N\phi^\kappa = l_\kappa \phi^\kappa$. Then N is a normal transformation and the l_κ are all its eigen-values.*

NOTE. The numbers l_κ are complex, not necessarily distinct, and some of them may be zero.

PROOF. Since the ϕ^κ form a complete orthonormal system we can write any x of $\mathfrak{B}_n$ as $x = \sum_{\kappa=1}^{n} (x, \phi^\kappa)\, \phi^\kappa$, and since $N\phi^\kappa = l_\kappa \phi^\kappa$ we have

$$Nx = \sum_{\kappa=1}^{n} l_\kappa (x, \phi^\kappa)\, \phi^\kappa, \quad (Nx, y) = \sum_{\kappa=1}^{n} l_\kappa (x, \phi^\kappa)(\phi^\kappa, y) = (x, N^* y),$$

so that
$$N^*y = \sum_{\kappa=1}^{n} \overline{l_\kappa}(y, \phi^\kappa)\phi^\kappa. \qquad (16\cdot3\cdot1)$$

Hence, as in (16·1·2),
$$NN^*x = \sum_{\kappa=1}^{n} l_\kappa \overline{l_\kappa}(x, \phi^\kappa)\phi^\kappa = N^*Nx, \qquad (16\cdot3\cdot2)$$

and N is a normal transformation. Finally, if ψ is an eigen-solution corresponding to any eigen-value ω of N, we have
$$\psi = \sum_{\kappa=1}^{n} (\psi, \phi^\kappa)\phi^\kappa, \quad N\psi = \sum_{\kappa=1}^{n} l_\kappa(\psi, \phi^\kappa)\phi^\kappa = \omega \sum_{\kappa=1}^{n} (\psi, \phi^\kappa)\phi^\kappa,$$

so that, for each κ, either $\omega = l_\kappa$ or $(\psi, \phi^\kappa) = 0$. Thus ω coincides with at least one of the numbers l_κ. If $\omega = l_1 = l_2 = \ldots = l_\nu$, say, we see that the corresponding eigen-manifold is $[\phi^1, \phi^2, \ldots, \phi^\nu]$.

16·4. The converse of Theorem **16·3** is also true and gives the spectral representation for any normal transformation.

THEOREM. *Corresponding to any normal transformation N in $\mathfrak{B}_n$ there exists a complete orthonormal system $\{\phi^\kappa\}$ and a set of n complex numbers $\{l_\kappa\}$ such that*
$$Nx = \sum_{\kappa=1}^{n} l_\kappa(x, \phi^\kappa)\phi^\kappa. \qquad (16\cdot4\cdot1)$$

NOTE. By this theorem, the normal transformation appears as a natural generalization of a H.T. By Theorem **16·3**, the numbers l_κ form the complete set of eigen-values of N and, by (16·3·1), the H.T.'s are those normal transformations of which the eigen-values l_κ are all real.

PROOF. We write
$$H = \tfrac{1}{2}(N + N^*), \quad K = \frac{1}{2i}(N - N^*).$$

Then, plainly, H and K are both H.T.'s. Further,
$$HK = \frac{1}{4i}(N^2 + N^*N - NN^* - N^{*2}) = \frac{1}{4i}(N^2 - N^{*2}) = KH.$$

Hence, by Theorem **16·1**, H and K have a common orthonormal system of eigen-solutions $\{\phi^\kappa\}$ $(\kappa = 1, 2, \ldots, n)$, and, by (16·1·1), they can be written in the forms
$$Hx = \sum_{\kappa=1}^{n} \lambda_\kappa(x, \phi^\kappa)\phi^\kappa, \quad Kx = \sum_{\kappa=1}^{n} \mu_\kappa(x, \phi^\kappa)\phi^\kappa.$$

We now have

$$Nx = (H+iK)x = \sum_{\kappa=1}^{n} (\lambda_\kappa + i\mu_\kappa)(x, \phi^\kappa)\phi^\kappa,$$

and this gives the required form (16·4·1) for N if we write

$$l_\kappa = \lambda_\kappa + i\mu_\kappa.$$

16·5. We deduce at once from Theorem **16·4** the form of representation of a normal transformation in terms of a H.T. mentioned in **16·3**.

THEOREM. *Corresponding to any normal transformation N there exist a H.T. H with simple spectrum and a continuous function $g(t)$ such that $N = g(H)$.*

PROOF. Let N be a normal transformation with the spectral representation (16·4·1), let $\{\lambda_\kappa\}$ be a set of n distinct real numbers and $g(t)$ a continuous function of the real variable t (for example, a polynomial of degree not greater than $n-1$) such that $g(\lambda_\kappa) = l_\kappa$ for $\kappa = 1, 2, \ldots, n$, and write

$$Hx = \sum_{\kappa=1}^{n} \lambda_\kappa (x, \phi^\kappa)\phi^\kappa.$$

Then H is a H.T. with simple spectrum and

$$Nx = g(H)x = \sum_{\kappa=1}^{n} g(\lambda_\kappa)(x, \phi^\kappa)\phi^\kappa = \sum_{\kappa=1}^{n} l_\kappa (x, \phi^\kappa)\phi^\kappa.$$

16·6. We now consider, as special cases of normal transformations, the unitary transformations and their representations in terms of H.T.'s mentioned in **15·5** and **15·51**. We need a preliminary theorem, however, before we can obtain these representations.

THEOREM. *All the eigen-values l_κ of a unitary transformation U lie on the unit circle; that is, $|l_\kappa| = 1$.*

PROOF. Let l_κ be an eigen-value of U and ϕ a corresponding eigen-solution. Then

$$(\phi, \phi) = (U\phi, U\phi) = (l_\kappa \phi, l_\kappa \phi) = l_\kappa \bar{l}_\kappa (\phi, \phi).$$

Hence $l_\kappa \bar{l}_\kappa = 1$ and $|l_\kappa| = 1$.

16·61. The converse of the preceding theorem is also true.

THEOREM. *Every normal transformation N of which all the eigen-values lie on the unit circle is a unitary transformation.*

PROOF. If all the eigen-values l_κ of N satisfy the condition $l_\kappa \bar{l}_\kappa = 1$ we obtain from (16·3·2)

$$NN^*x = \sum_{\kappa=1}^{n} (x, \phi^\kappa) \phi^\kappa = x.$$

Hence, $NN^* = I$ and N is a unitary transformation.

16·62. If U is a unitary transformation then, as a normal transformation, it has a spectral representation of the form (16·4·1) and we may write

$$Ux = \sum_{\kappa=1}^{n} l_\kappa (x, \phi^\kappa) \phi^\kappa. \qquad (16{\cdot}62{\cdot}1)$$

We then deduce from Theorem **16·6** that $l_\kappa = \exp(i\lambda_\kappa)$, where λ_κ is real, and if we define the H.T. H by the representation

$$Hx = \sum_{\kappa=1}^{n} \lambda_\kappa (x, \phi^\kappa) \phi^\kappa,$$

we obtain the representation $U = \exp(iH)$.

16·63. Suppose now that none of the eigen-values l_κ in (16·62·1) is equal to 1, define the real numbers ω_κ and the function $g(t)$ by the equations

$$\omega_\kappa = -i\left(\frac{l_\kappa + 1}{l_\kappa - 1}\right), \quad l_\kappa = \frac{\omega_\kappa - i}{\omega_\kappa + i}, \quad g(t) = \frac{t-i}{t+i},$$

and write

$$Hx = \sum_{\kappa=1}^{n} \omega_\kappa (x, \phi^\kappa) \phi^\kappa.$$

Then H is a H.T. and $U = g(H)$. We have therefore proved the following theorem.

THEOREM. *Every unitary transformation that has no eigen-value equal to 1 can be written as the Cayley transform of a H.T.*

The inverse of the Cayley transform, by which every H.T. is written as a function of a unitary transformation, is considered in **16·73**.

16·7. Functional calculus for normal transformations. Let l_μ $(1 \leqslant \mu \leqslant m \leqslant n)$ be the m distinct eigen-values of a normal transformation N in $\mathfrak{B}_n$, let $\mathfrak{E}_\mu$ be the corresponding eigen-manifolds and P_μ the orthogonal projectors of $\mathfrak{B}_n$ on the $\mathfrak{E}_\mu$. The spectral representation (16·4·1) then takes the form

$$Nx = \sum_{\mu=1}^{m} l_\mu P_\mu x. \qquad (16{\cdot}7{\cdot}1)$$

Let $f(\zeta)$ be a function of the complex variable ζ continuous in some open set of the complex plane that includes a neighbourhood of each point $\zeta = l_\mu$. (When we speak of a continuous function of the complex variable ζ in this paragraph we mean a function of this kind.) We define the L.T. $f(N)$, using the same form as in (15·2·1), by writing

$$f(N)\,x = \sum_{\mu=1}^{m} f(l_\mu)\,P_\mu x$$

for every x of $\mathfrak{V}_n$, and we justify this definition by reference to Theorem **16·5**, in virtue of which N can be written as $g(H)$, where H is a H.T. with a simple spectrum and $g(t)$ is a polynomial. For, if the distinct eigen-values of H are λ_ν and the corresponding orthogonal projectors are Q_ν $(1 \leqslant \nu \leqslant n)$, we know, by **15·22**, that the numbers l_μ coincide with the values $g(\lambda_\nu)$ and that

$$f(N) = f(g(H)) = \sum_{\nu=1}^{n} f(g(\lambda_\nu))\,Q_\nu = \sum_{\mu=1}^{m} f(l_\mu)\,P_\mu.$$

As in **16·3**, we see that $f(N)$ is a normal transformation, that the values $f(l_\mu)$ are all the eigen-values and that the $\mathfrak{E}_\mu$, or sums of the $\mathfrak{E}_\mu$, are the corresponding eigen-manifolds.

16·71. We readily see that, *mutatis mutandis*, the considerations of **15·3** and **15·31** will apply if we replace H by N. We find that (i) if $f(\zeta)$ and $g(\zeta)$ are continuous and if

$$F(\zeta) = f(\zeta) + g(\zeta), \quad G(\zeta) = f(\zeta)\,g(\zeta),$$

then

$$F(N) = f(N) + g(N) \quad \text{and} \quad G(N) = f(N)\,g(N) = g(N)\,f(N);$$

and (ii) if $\{f_\kappa(\zeta)\}$ is an infinite sequence of continuous functions converging to $f(\zeta)$ in an open set including neighbourhoods of the eigen-values of N, then $\lim_{\kappa \to \infty} f_\kappa(N) = f(N)$.

16·72. As in **15·4**, we write for the resolvent R_λ,

$$f(t) = \frac{1}{t-\lambda}, \quad R_\lambda = (N - \lambda I)^{-1} = \sum_{\mu=1}^{m} \frac{1}{l_\mu - \lambda} P_\mu \quad (\lambda \neq l_\mu).$$

We readily verify the functional equation of **15·41**

$$R_\lambda - R_\mu = (\lambda - \mu)\,R_\lambda R_\mu = (\lambda - \mu)\,R_\mu R_\lambda$$

and the power series developments of **15·42** and **15·43**

$$R_\lambda = -\sum_{\kappa=0}^{\infty} \frac{1}{\lambda^{k+1}} N^\kappa \qquad (|\lambda| > \max\{|l_\mu|\}),$$

$$R_\lambda = \sum_{\kappa=0}^{\infty} (\lambda - l)^\kappa R_l^{\kappa+1} \qquad (|\lambda - l| < \min\{|l - l_\mu|\}),$$

$$R_\lambda = -\frac{1}{\lambda - l_\nu} P_\nu + \sum_{\kappa=0}^{\infty} (\lambda - l_\nu)^\kappa S^{\kappa+1} \quad (|\lambda - l_\nu| < \min_{\mu \neq \nu}\{|l_\mu - l_\nu|\}),$$

where

$$S = \sum_{\mu \neq \nu} \frac{1}{l_\mu - l_\nu} P_\mu.$$

16·73. Another application of the functional calculus for normal transformations leads to the inverse of the Cayley transform and gives the converse of Theorem **16·63**.

THEOREM. *Let H be any H.T. and let $f(t) = -i(t+1)(t-1)^{-1}$. There exists a unitary transformation U with no eigen-value equal to 1 and such that $H = f(U)$.*

PROOF. Let H be written in terms of its distinct (real) eigen-values in the form

$$H = \sum_{\mu=1}^{m} \lambda_\mu P_\mu.$$

Write $l_\mu = (\lambda_\mu - i)(\lambda_\mu + i)^{-1}$, so that the numbers l_μ are distinct and $l_\mu \neq 1$. Then, by **15·5**, the Cayley transform of H,

$$U = \sum_{\mu=1}^{m} \frac{\lambda_\mu - i}{\lambda_\mu + i} P_\mu = \sum_{\mu=1}^{m} l_\mu P_\mu,$$

is a unitary transformation with the numbers l_μ as eigen-values and, by **15·22**, it has the same eigen-manifolds as H. Since, however, $\lambda_\mu = f(l_\mu) = -i(l_\mu + 1)(l_\mu - 1)^{-1}$, we have $H = f(U)$.

16·8. We see that the proofs of Theorems **16·0** and **16·1** still hold if we replace the H.T. H by a normal transformation N, since nowhere in these proofs do we refer to the reality of the numbers λ_κ. We therefore deduce the two following theorems:

THEOREM. *Let the spectral representation of the normal transformation N in $\mathfrak{B}_n$ be*

$$Nx = \sum_{\mu=1}^{m} l_\mu P_\mu x.$$

Then the L.T. A in $\mathfrak{B}_n$ is commutative with N if, and only if, $AP_\mu = P_\mu A$ for $\mu = 1, 2, \ldots, m$.

16·81. Theorem. *Two normal transformations in $\mathfrak{V}_n$ are commutative if, and only if, they have a complete orthonormal system of eigen-solutions in common.*

16·82. Theorem. *Two normal transformations N_1 and N_2 in $\mathfrak{V}_n$ are commutative if, and only if, there exists a H.T. H with a simple spectrum such that $N_1 = f(H)$ and $N_2 = g(H)$, where $f(t)$ and $g(t)$ are continuous functions.*

The proof of Theorem **16·82** is similar to that of Theorem **16·2**. We need only remark that, since the eigen-values of N_1 and N_2 are not necessarily real, the functions $f(t)$ and $g(t)$ cannot be taken as real functions.

16·83. Theorem. *If the normal transformation N is commutative with the L.T. A, then N is also commutative with A^*.*

Proof. If N is commutative with A then, by Theorem **16·8**, $AP_\mu = P_\mu A$ for $\mu = 1, 2, \ldots, m$, and, since P_μ is an orthogonal projector and therefore a H.T., this implies that $P_\mu A^* = A^* P_\mu$. Thus, by Theorem **16·8**, N is commutative with A^*.

16·84. Theorem. *The L.T. A in $\mathfrak{V}_n$ is commutative with a normal transformation N that has a simple spectrum if, and only if, $A = f(N)$, where $f(\zeta)$ is a continuous function. If the condition is satisfied, A is also a normal transformation.*

We omit the proof of this theorem, which is included in Theorem **23·11** for a general L.T. with a simple spectrum. We have already remarked in **16·7** that $f(N)$ is normal if N is normal.

16·85. We readily deduce from Theorem **16·8** that if the normal transformation N has not a simple spectrum then there exist L.T.'s A commutative with N that are not normal transformations. Let

$$\{\phi^{\mu\nu}\} \left(1 \leqslant \mu \leqslant m, 1 \leqslant \nu \leqslant k_\mu; m < n, \sum_{\mu=1}^{m} k_\mu = n\right)$$

be a complete orthonormal system of eigen-solutions of N such that

$$\mathfrak{E}_\mu = [\phi^{\mu,1}, \phi^{\mu,2}, \ldots, \phi^{\mu,k_\mu}].$$

Take a L.T. A uniquely determined by the equations $A\phi^{\mu\nu} = \psi^{\mu\nu}$, where the $\psi^{\mu\nu}$ are any vectors of $\mathfrak{E}_\mu$. Then we have $AP_\mu = P_\mu A$, and hence, by Theorem **16·8**, $AN = NA$. Further, if $k_\mu \geqslant 2$, the $\psi^{\mu\nu}$ in $\mathfrak{E}_\mu$ can be so chosen that A is not normal in $\mathfrak{E}_\mu$, since we can clearly find L.T.'s that are not normal in any subspace $\mathfrak{V}_r$ for $r \geqslant 2$. A L.T. N normal in $\mathfrak{V}_n$, however, must also be normal in every subspace of $\mathfrak{V}_n$ that reduces both N and N^* completely.

16·9. Example. We may illustrate some of the properties of unitary and normal matrices by considering the circulant matrices. A circulant matrix C of order n has the same n elements a_ν arranged in cyclic order in each row and column in the following way:

$$C = \begin{pmatrix} a_1 & a_2 & \ldots & a_{n-1} & a_n \\ a_n & a_1 & \ldots & a_{n-2} & a_{n-1} \\ & \ldots & \ldots & \ldots & \\ a_2 & a_3 & \ldots & a_n & a_1 \end{pmatrix}.$$

We readily verify that the circulant matrix

$$U = \begin{pmatrix} 0 & 0 & \dots & 0 & 1 \\ 1 & 0 & \dots & 0 & 0 \\ \dots & & \dots & & \dots \\ 0 & 0 & \dots & 1 & 0 \end{pmatrix}$$

is a unitary (and therefore a normal) matrix, since we have

$$Uu^n = u^1, \quad Uu^\nu = u^{\nu+1} \quad (1 \leqslant \nu \leqslant n-1), \tag{16·9·1}$$

so that the corresponding L.T. $x' = Ux$ is, in effect, a cyclic rearrangement of coordinates and therefore $(Ux, Ux) = (x, x)$. We also verify that $U^n = I$ and that C may be expressed as a polynomial in U of the form

$$C = a_1 I + a_n U + a_{n-1} U^2 + \dots + a_2 U^{n-1} = p(U). \tag{16·9·2}$$

Thus, by **16·7**, C is a normal matrix. Conversely, since $U^n = I$, any polynomial in U may be written as a sum of powers of U from 0 to $n-1$ and is therefore a circulant matrix of order n.

We deduce at once from **16·71** that any two circulant matrices of order n are commutative and that the product is a circulant matrix.

The eigen-values of U are

$$\omega_\kappa = \cos\frac{2\kappa\pi}{n} + i\sin\frac{2\kappa\pi}{n} \quad (\kappa = 1, 2, \dots, n).$$

They are the distinct roots of the equation $\zeta^n - 1 = 0$ and lie on the unit circle. (This illustrates Theorem **16·6**.) Corresponding eigen-solutions are

$$\psi^\kappa = \omega_\kappa^{n-1} u^1 + \omega_\kappa^{n-2} u^2 + \dots + u^n,$$

as may be verified from (16·9·1), and the vectors $\phi^\kappa = n^{-\frac{1}{2}}\psi^\kappa$ form a complete orthonormal system of eigen-solutions. By **16·7**, the eigen-values of C are $p(\omega_\kappa)$ $(\kappa = 1, 2, \dots, n)$; they are not necessarily distinct. All circulant matrices C have in common the complete orthonormal system of eigen-solutions $\{\phi^\kappa\}$ so that their commutativity provides an illustration of Theorem **16·81**.

The spectral representations for U and C are

$$Ux = \sum_{\kappa=1}^{n} \omega_\kappa (x, \phi^\kappa)\phi^\kappa, \quad C = p(U), \quad Cx = \sum_{\kappa=1}^{n} p(\omega_\kappa)(x, \phi^\kappa)\phi^\kappa.$$

If the circulant matrix C has a simple spectrum, that is, if the values $p(\omega_\kappa)$ are distinct, then, by **16·84**, a matrix A of order n is commutative with C if, and only if, $A = f(C)$, where $f(\zeta)$ is a polynomial, and this is equivalent to the condition that A should be a circulant matrix. Thus the circulant matrices are the only matrices commutative with a circulant matrix that has a simple spectrum.

We notice that the circulant matrices all transform to the diagonal matrix of their eigen-values by the same unitary transformation

$$V = \frac{1}{\sqrt{n}} \begin{pmatrix} \omega_1^{n-1} & \omega_2^{n-1} & \dots & 1 \\ \omega_1^{n-2} & \omega_2^{n-2} & \dots & 1 \\ & \dots & \dots & \\ \omega_1 & \omega_2 & \dots & 1 \\ 1 & 1 & \dots & 1 \end{pmatrix},$$

$$V^* = V^{-1} = \frac{1}{\sqrt{n}} \begin{pmatrix} \omega_1 & \omega_1^2 & \dots & \omega_1^{n-1} & 1 \\ \omega_2 & \omega_2^2 & \dots & \omega_2^{n-1} & 1 \\ & \dots & \dots & \dots & \\ \omega_{n-1} & \omega_{n-1}^2 & \dots & \omega_{n-1}^{n-1} & 1 \\ 1 & 1 & \dots & 1 & 1 \end{pmatrix},$$

the κth column of V being formed by the coordinates of ϕ^κ. Thus, if Ω denotes the diagonal matrix of the ω_κ, we have

$$V^* U^\nu V = \Omega^\nu \quad (\nu = 1, 2, \dots, n)$$

and we deduce from (16·9·2) that

$$V^* C V = a_1 I + a_n \Omega + a_{n-1} \Omega^2 + \dots + a\Omega^{n-1} = p(\Omega).$$

CHAPTER IV

SPECTRAL PROPERTIES OF LINEAR TRANSFORMATIONS IN $\mathfrak{V}_n$

§ 17. Eigen-values and principal manifolds

17·0. Let A be a L.T. in $\mathfrak{V}_n$, of rank r, where $r<n$. Then A determines a sequence $\{\mathfrak{X}^\kappa\}$ of L.M.'s, where $\mathfrak{X}^\kappa$ is defined for any positive integer κ as the null manifold of A^κ, that is, as the L.M. of all vectors $\xi^{(\kappa)}$ such that $A^\kappa\xi^{(\kappa)} = 0$. Since $r<n$, $\mathfrak{X}^1 \neq \mathfrak{O}$; we write $\mathfrak{X}^1 = \mathfrak{X}$. Plainly, $\mathfrak{X}^{\kappa+1} \supseteq \mathfrak{X}^\kappa$ for $\kappa \geqslant 1$. By Theorem **2·6**, therefore, $\mathfrak{X}^{\kappa+1} \supset \mathfrak{X}^\kappa$ if, and only if, rank $\mathfrak{X}^{\kappa+1} >$ rank $\mathfrak{X}^\kappa$; otherwise $\mathfrak{X}^{\kappa+1} = \mathfrak{X}^\kappa$. But rank $\mathfrak{X}^\kappa \leqslant n$ for all κ, so that rank $\mathfrak{X}^\kappa$ cannot increase indefinitely with κ and there must be an infinity of indices μ such that $\mathfrak{X}^{\mu+1} = \mathfrak{X}^\mu$. The following theorem formulates the results precisely:

17·01. Theorem. *Let A and $\mathfrak{X}^\kappa$ have the same meanings as in* **17·0** *and let j be the least index such that $\mathfrak{X}^{j+1} = \mathfrak{X}^j$ (while $\mathfrak{X}^{\kappa+1} \supset \mathfrak{X}^\kappa$ for $1 \leqslant \kappa \leqslant j-1$). Then $\mathfrak{X}^{j+\nu} = \mathfrak{X}^j$ for every positive integer ν.*

Proof. The remark of **17·0** shows that there exists a least index j satisfying the conditions of the theorem, with $j \geqslant 1$. Take any positive integer ν and let $\xi \in \mathfrak{X}^{j+\nu}$. Then $A^{j+\nu}\xi = A^{j+1}A^{\nu-1}\xi = 0$; hence $A^{\nu-1}\xi \in \mathfrak{X}^{j+1}$ and, since $\mathfrak{X}^{j+1} = \mathfrak{X}^j$, $A^{\nu-1}\xi \in \mathfrak{X}^j$. Thus $A^{j+\nu-1}\xi = 0$ and $\xi \in \mathfrak{X}^{j+\nu-1}$. We have now proved that $\xi \in \mathfrak{X}^{j+\nu-1}$ whenever $\xi \in \mathfrak{X}^{j+\nu}$. It follows that $\mathfrak{X}^{j+\nu} = \mathfrak{X}^{j+\nu-1}$ for all $\nu \geqslant 1$ and therefore that $\mathfrak{X}^{j+\nu} = \mathfrak{X}^j$.

Example. If the L.T. A is defined by the equations $Au^\nu = u^{\nu+1}$ for $\nu = 1, 2, \ldots, n-1$ and $Au^n = 0$, then $\mathfrak{X} = [u^n]$,

$$\mathfrak{X}^\kappa = [u^{n-\kappa+1}, u^{n-\kappa+2}, \ldots, u^n]$$

for $\kappa = 2, 3, \ldots, n$, and $\mathfrak{X}^{n+\nu} = \mathfrak{X}^n = \mathfrak{V}_n$ for every positive integer ν. In this case $j = n$. The matrix representing the L.T. of this example is given in (7·83·2).

17·02. Definition of the index and of the principal manifold of a L.T. The number j defined in Theorem **17·01** is called the *index of A* and the corresponding L.M. $\mathfrak{X}^j$ is called the *principal manifold of A*. We denote the principal manifold by $\mathfrak{P}$ and its rank by k.

The principal manifold may be defined as the set of all vectors that are elements either of the null manifold of A or of the null manifold of some positive power A^κ of A. Since we have rank $\mathfrak{X}^{\kappa+1} >$ rank $\mathfrak{X}^\kappa$ for $\kappa \leqslant j-1$ and rank $\mathfrak{X} \geqslant 1$, we see that $k \geqslant j$. If $\mathfrak{P} = \mathfrak{B}_n$, that is, if $k = n$, we say that A is a *nilpotent transformation*, for in this case $A^j = O$. The L.T. A defined in the Example of **17·01** is, clearly, a nilpotent transformation of index n.

17·1. We denote the range of A^κ by $\mathfrak{R}^\kappa$ and we write $\mathfrak{R}^1 = \mathfrak{R}$. We see at once that $\mathfrak{R}^{\kappa+1} \subseteq \mathfrak{R}^\kappa$, since $A^\kappa(Ax) = A^{\kappa+1}x$. In the Example of **17·01** we have

$$\mathfrak{R} = [u^2, u^3, \ldots, u^n], \quad \mathfrak{R}^\kappa = [u^{\kappa+1}, u^{\kappa+2}, \ldots, u^n]$$

for $\kappa = 2, 3, \ldots, n-1$, and $\mathfrak{R}^{n+\nu} = \mathfrak{R}^n = \mathfrak{O}$ for every positive integer ν.

17·11. Theorem. *We have*

$$\mathfrak{P} \, . \, \mathfrak{R}^j = \mathfrak{X}^j \, . \, \mathfrak{R}^j = \mathfrak{O}, \quad \mathfrak{R}^{j+\nu} = \mathfrak{R}^j \quad (\nu = 1, 2, \ldots),$$

where the notation is that of **17·0**, **17·02** *and* **17·1**.

Proof. Let $\xi \in \mathfrak{P} \, . \, \mathfrak{R}^j$; then we may write $\xi = A^j \mathring{x}$, where

$$0 = A^j \xi = A^{2j} \mathring{x}.$$

But, by **17·02**, the equation $A^{2j}\mathring{x} = 0$ implies that $\mathring{x} \in \mathfrak{P}$ and therefore that $A^j \mathring{x} = 0$, since j is the index of A. Thus $\xi = 0$ and therefore $\mathfrak{P} \, . \, \mathfrak{R}^j = \mathfrak{O}$.

Now $\mathfrak{R}^{j+1}$, the range of A^{j+1}, may be interpreted as the image of $\mathfrak{R}^j$ with respect to A. Further, $\mathfrak{X} \, . \, \mathfrak{R}^j = \mathfrak{O}$, since $\mathfrak{X} \subseteq \mathfrak{P}$ and $\mathfrak{P} \, . \, \mathfrak{R}^j = \mathfrak{O}$, so that, by Theorem **6·2**, $\mathfrak{R}^{j+1}$ and $\mathfrak{R}^j$ have the same rank. We have shown in **17·1**, however, that $\mathfrak{R}^{j+1} \subseteq \mathfrak{R}^j$ and therefore, by Theorem **2·6**, $\mathfrak{R}^{j+1} = \mathfrak{R}^j$. An induction argument now completes the proof of the theorem.

17·12. There is a converse of the preceding theorem.

Theorem. *If the L.T. A has index j and if, for some positive integer ν, $\mathfrak{X} \, . \, \mathfrak{R}^\nu = \mathfrak{O}$, where $\mathfrak{R}^\nu$ is the range of A^ν, then $\nu \geqslant j$.*

Proof. We know that $\mathfrak{X}^{\nu+1} \supseteq \mathfrak{X}^\nu$ and, by Theorem **17·01**, it will be enough to prove that $\mathfrak{X}^{\nu+1} = \mathfrak{X}^\nu$. Now, if $\xi^{(\nu+1)}$ is any non-zero element of $\mathfrak{X}^{\nu+1}$, and if we write $\xi = A^\nu \xi^{(\nu+1)}$, we find that $\xi \in \mathfrak{X}$ and $\xi \in \mathfrak{R}^\nu$. Since, however, $\mathfrak{X} \, . \, \mathfrak{R}^\nu = \mathfrak{O}$ we have $\xi = 0$ and therefore $\xi^{(\nu+1)} \in \mathfrak{X}^\nu$. It follows that $\mathfrak{X}^{\nu+1} = \mathfrak{X}^\nu$ and $\nu \geqslant j$.

17·13. There are relations between the $\mathfrak{R}^\nu$ corresponding to the relations between the $\mathfrak{X}^\nu$.

THEOREM. *We have* $\mathfrak{R}^{\nu+1} \subset \mathfrak{R}^\nu$ *for* $1 \leqslant \nu \leqslant j-1$, *where the notation is that of Theorem* **17·12**.

PROOF. We have $\mathfrak{X}\,.\,\mathfrak{R}^\nu \neq \mathfrak{O}$ for $1 \leqslant \nu \leqslant j-1$, by Theorem **17·12**. We can therefore write, by Theorem **4·3**,

$$\mathfrak{R}^\nu = \mathfrak{R}_\nu \oplus \mathfrak{X}\,.\,\mathfrak{R}^\nu,$$

where the L.M. $\mathfrak{R}_\nu$ is of lower rank than $\mathfrak{R}^\nu$ and where $\mathfrak{X}\,.\,\mathfrak{R}_\nu = \mathfrak{O}$. Moreover, the images of $\mathfrak{R}^\nu$ and $\mathfrak{R}_\nu$ with respect to A are clearly the same and, since $\mathfrak{R}^{\nu+1}$ is the image of $\mathfrak{R}^\nu$, $\mathfrak{R}^{\nu+1}$ is the image of $\mathfrak{R}_\nu$. Hence, by Theorem **6·2**, $\mathfrak{R}^{\nu+1}$ is of the same rank as $\mathfrak{R}_\nu$ and is therefore of lower rank than $\mathfrak{R}^\nu$. It follows from **17·1** that

$$\mathfrak{R}^{\nu+1} \subset \mathfrak{R}^\nu \quad \text{for} \quad 1 \leqslant \nu \leqslant j-1.$$

17·2. We write $A_\lambda = A - \lambda I$ for any L.T. A and any complex number λ.

Definition of the index and principal manifold corresponding to any eigen-value of a L.T. and of the multiplicity of the eigen-value. An eigen-value λ of a L.T. A and the corresponding eigen-manifold $\mathfrak{E}$ have already been defined in **8·4** and **8·41**. When λ is an eigen-value of A, the rank of A_λ is less than n and the considerations of **17·0** apply to A_λ. Accordingly, we define $\mathfrak{E}^\kappa$ as the L.M. of all vectors ξ such that $(A_\lambda)^\kappa \xi = 0$. The index j of A_λ is called the *index of A corresponding to λ*; it is determined by the relations $\mathfrak{E}^{j+1} = \mathfrak{E}^j \supset \mathfrak{E}^{j-1}$. Then $\mathfrak{E}^j$ is the principal manifold of A_λ; it is called the *principal manifold of A corresponding to λ. The rank k of $\mathfrak{E}^j$ is called the order, or multiplicity, of the eigen-value λ of A.*

As we have already shown in **17·02**, $k \geqslant j$.

17·21. We have not yet proved that every L.T. in $\mathfrak{B}_n$ has eigen-values, but we do so in § **18**, where we also prove that the number of distinct eigen-values of A does not exceed n.

17·3. THEOREM. *The index of a normal transformation N corresponding to any eigen-value is* 1; *the corresponding eigen-manifold is a principal manifold of N and of N^*.*

PROOF. By Theorem **9·01**, N_λ is a normal transformation for every λ and, if λ is an eigen-value of N then, by Theorem **9·11**, N_λ and $(N_\lambda)^*$ have the same null manifold $\mathfrak{E}$. If now $\mathfrak{R}_\lambda$ denotes the range of N_λ then, by Theorem **6·4**, $\mathfrak{R}_\lambda = \mathfrak{B}_n \ominus \mathfrak{E}$. Thus $\mathfrak{E}\,.\,\mathfrak{R}_\lambda = \mathfrak{O}$

and therefore, by Theorem **17·12**, $j = 1$ and $\mathfrak{E}$ is the principal manifold as well as the eigen-manifold of N corresponding to the eigen-value λ. In the same way we see that it is both the principal manifold and eigen-manifold of N^* corresponding to the eigen-value $\bar{\lambda}$.

NOTE. Since any H.T. H is a normal transformation, Theorem **17·3** is also true for H.T.'s, and we see therefore that Definition **17·2** of the multiplicity of an eigen-value of any L.T. includes Definitions **8·41** and **9·31** for that of an eigen-value of any H.T. and any normal transformation respectively.

17·4. THEOREM. *Let $\mathfrak{P}$, of rank k, be the principal manifold of a L.T. A in $\mathfrak{B}_n$; let j be the index of A and $\mathfrak{R}^j$ the range of A^j. Then $\mathfrak{P} \oplus \mathfrak{R}^j = \mathfrak{B}_n$; further, $\mathfrak{P}$ and $\mathfrak{R}^j$ reduce A completely so that there exists a projector Q of $\mathfrak{B}_n$ on $\mathfrak{P}$ parallel to $\mathfrak{R}^j$ and such that $AQ = QA$. Moreover, A is nilpotent when considered as a L.T. in the space $\mathfrak{B}_k = \mathfrak{P}$ (that is, AQ is nilpotent in $\mathfrak{B}_n$); whereas, when A is considered as a L.T. in the space $\mathfrak{B}_{n-k} = \mathfrak{R}^j$, it is of rank $n-k$ and has an inverse (that is, A is regular in $\mathfrak{B}_{n-k}$, by Definition* **6·51**).

NOTE. This theorem describes the first stage in a process of decomposition of any L.T. A and a corresponding dissection of the space $\mathfrak{B}_n$. We have here the two constituent subspaces in which A is either nilpotent or regular.

PROOF. Since $\mathfrak{P}$, of rank k, is the L.M. of all vectors ξ such that $A^j\xi = 0$, the nullity of A^j equals k and therefore, by Theorem **6·21**, the rank of A^j, which is the rank of $\mathfrak{R}^j$, is $n-k$. We also obtain from Theorem **17·11** that $\mathfrak{P} \,.\, \mathfrak{R}^j = \mathfrak{O}$. Hence,

$$\mathfrak{P} \oplus \mathfrak{R}^j = \mathfrak{X}^j \oplus \mathfrak{R}^j = \mathfrak{B}_n, \tag{17·4·1}$$

since, by Theorem **4·21**, $\mathfrak{P} \oplus \mathfrak{R}^j$ has rank n.

We now show that if any vector x of $\mathfrak{B}_n$ is written in the form $x = p+q$, where $p \in \mathfrak{P}$ and $q \in \mathfrak{R}^j$, then $Ap \in \mathfrak{P}$ and $Aq \in \mathfrak{R}^j$. That $Ap \in \mathfrak{P}$ whenever $p \in \mathfrak{P}$ follows from the equations

$$0 = A^j p = A^{j-1}Ap,$$

which show that $\qquad Ap \in \mathfrak{X}^{j-1} \subset \mathfrak{X}^j = \mathfrak{P};$

and that $Aq \in \mathfrak{R}^j$ whenever $q \in \mathfrak{R}^j$ follows from the equations

$$q = A^j \mathring{x}, \quad Aq = AA^j\mathring{x} = A^jA\mathring{x}.$$

Hence, $\mathfrak{R}^j$ and $\mathfrak{P}$ reduce A completely, so that, by Theorem **10·9**, the projector Q of $\mathfrak{B}_n$ on $\mathfrak{P}$ parallel to $\mathfrak{R}^j$ satisfies the equation $AQ = QA$.

We have seen that the L.T. A maps any vector of $\mathfrak{P}$ on a vector of $\mathfrak{P}$ and any vector of $\mathfrak{R}^j$ on a vector of $\mathfrak{R}^j$. Thus A can be considered as a L.T. defined in the space $\mathfrak{B}_k = \mathfrak{P}$ and also as a L.T. defined in the space $\mathfrak{B}_{n-k} = \mathfrak{R}^j$. But $A^j p = 0$ for every p of $\mathfrak{P}$, so that A is nilpotent of index j with regard to $\mathfrak{P}$. It follows that AQ has the same property with regard to $\mathfrak{B}_n$, since

$$(AQ)^j x = A^j Q^j x = A^j Q x = 0$$

for every x of $\mathfrak{B}_n$.

Further, since $\mathfrak{X} \subseteq \mathfrak{P}$ and $\mathfrak{P} . \mathfrak{R}^j = \mathfrak{O}$, $A\xi = 0$ for ξ in $\mathfrak{R}^j$ if, and only if, $\xi = 0$. Hence A has rank $n-k$ in $\mathfrak{R}^j$ and, by **6·5**, A has an inverse in $\mathfrak{R}^j$.

17·41. Corollary of Theorem **17·4**. *If $\mathfrak{P}$ is the principal manifold corresponding to an eigen-value λ of a L.T. A in $\mathfrak{B}_n$, j the index of A corresponding to λ, $\mathfrak{R}^j$ the range of $(A_\lambda)^j$, then $\mathfrak{P} \oplus \mathfrak{R}^j = \mathfrak{B}_n$. If Q is the projector of $\mathfrak{B}_n$ on $\mathfrak{P}$ parallel to $\mathfrak{R}^j$, we have $A_\lambda Q = QA_\lambda$, $AQ = QA$, and $\mathfrak{P}$ and $\mathfrak{R}^j$ reduce A completely. Moreover, A_λ is regular when considered as a L.T. in $\mathfrak{R}^j$ and is nilpotent when considered as a L.T. in $\mathfrak{P}$; that is, $A_\lambda Q$ is nilpotent in $\mathfrak{B}_n$.*

The proof follows at once on the application of Theorem **17·4** to A_λ.

17·42. The spectral representations (12·43·3), of a H.T. H, and (16·7·1), of a normal transformation N, may be interpreted as giving the structure of H and N in terms of the eigen-manifolds which reduce them completely. Corollary **17·41** suggests that the significance of the principal manifolds of a general L.T. for purposes of spectral analysis will be similar to that of the eigen-manifolds of a H.T. or of a normal transformation. Details of the complete reduction of A by the principal manifolds are given in Theorems **18·3** and **18·51**, and the spectral representation of A is obtained in § **22**.

17·5. We now give a converse of Theorem **17·4**.

Theorem. *Let A be a L.T. in $\mathfrak{B}_n$ and let the L.M.'s $\mathfrak{M}$ and $\mathfrak{N}$ be complementary. If* (i) *$\mathfrak{M}$ and $\mathfrak{N}$ reduce A completely,* (ii) *A is nilpotent of index κ in $\mathfrak{N}$, and* (iii) *$Ax \neq 0$ for every non-zero vector x of $\mathfrak{M}$, then κ is equal to the index j of A in $\mathfrak{B}_n$ and, further, $\mathfrak{M} = \mathfrak{R}^j$, $\mathfrak{N} = \mathfrak{P}$.*

PROOF. Take any element x of $\mathfrak{V}_n$ and write $x = a+b$, where $a \in \mathfrak{M}$ and $b \in \mathfrak{N}$. By hypotheses (i) and (ii), $A^\kappa x \in \mathfrak{M}$ since $A^\kappa x = A^\kappa a$; hence $\mathfrak{R}^\kappa \subseteq \mathfrak{M}$. By hypothesis (iii), however, $\mathfrak{X} . \mathfrak{M} = \mathfrak{O}$, where $\mathfrak{X}$ is the null manifold of A. Therefore, by Theorem **6·2**, A maps $\mathfrak{M}$ on a L.M. $\mathfrak{M}'$ of the same rank and, since $\mathfrak{M}' \subseteq \mathfrak{M}$ by (i), Theorem **2·6** shows that $\mathfrak{M}' = \mathfrak{M}$. It follows that A^κ maps $\mathfrak{M}$ on itself, so that $\mathfrak{M} \subseteq \mathfrak{R}^\kappa$; hence $\mathfrak{M} = \mathfrak{R}^\kappa$ and therefore $\mathfrak{X} . \mathfrak{R}^\kappa = \mathfrak{O}$. Theorem **17·12** now shows that $\kappa \geqslant j$ and Theorem **17·11** that $\mathfrak{M} = \mathfrak{R}^j$.

The principal manifold $\mathfrak{P}$ of A contains the null manifold of every positive power of A, so that, by (ii), $\mathfrak{P} \supseteq \mathfrak{N}$. Thus

$$\mathfrak{R}^j \oplus \mathfrak{P} \supseteq \mathfrak{R}^j \oplus \mathfrak{N} = \mathfrak{M} \oplus \mathfrak{N} = \mathfrak{V}_n,$$

and so, by Theorem **4·3**, rank $\mathfrak{N} =$ rank $\mathfrak{P}$. Hence, by Theorem **2·6**, $\mathfrak{N} = \mathfrak{P}$ and $\kappa = j$.

17·51. If λ is any eigen-value of A, $\mathfrak{E}$ the corresponding eigen-manifold and $\mathfrak{R}_\lambda$ the range of A_λ, then, by Corollary **17·41**, *$\mathfrak{E}$ and $\mathfrak{R}_\lambda$ reduce A completely if $\mathfrak{E}$ is also the principal manifold of A_λ.* If $\mathfrak{E}$ is not the principal manifold of A_λ, then the assumption that there is a L.M. $\mathfrak{M}$ such that $\mathfrak{M} \oplus \mathfrak{E} = \mathfrak{V}_n$ and that $\mathfrak{M}$ and $\mathfrak{E}$ reduce A_λ completely is in contradiction with Theorem **17·5**, for A_λ is nilpotent of index 1 in $\mathfrak{E}$ and $A_\lambda x \neq 0$ for every non-zero x of $\mathfrak{M}$, since $\mathfrak{E} . \mathfrak{M} = \mathfrak{O}$. We have therefore proved the assertion of **8·72** that $\mathfrak{E}$ does not necessarily reduce A completely when A is a general L.T., for there are cases where $\mathfrak{E}$ and $\mathfrak{P}$ do not coincide as, for instance, in the Example **17·01**.

17·6. THEOREM. *Let λ be an eigen-value of the L.T. A and let j, $\mathfrak{P}$, $\mathfrak{R}^j$ and Q have the same meanings as in Corollary* **17·41**. *Then $\bar{\lambda}$ is an eigen-value of A^* with index j and Q^* is the projector of $\mathfrak{V}_n$ on $\mathfrak{P}^*$ parallel to $\mathfrak{R}^{*j}$, where $\mathfrak{P}^*$ is the principal manifold of A^* corresponding to $\bar{\lambda}$ and $\mathfrak{R}^{*j}$ is the range of $(A^*_{\bar{\lambda}})^j$.*

PROOF. We have $(A_\lambda)^* = A^* - \bar{\lambda} I = A^*_{\bar{\lambda}}$, whence it follows, by **6·4** and **7·3**, that, for any positive integer ν, $(A_\lambda)^\nu$ and $(A^*_{\bar{\lambda}})^\nu$ have the same rank. Thus, if λ is an eigen-value of A with index j, then $\bar{\lambda}$ is an eigen-value of A^* with the same index. We now deduce from Theorem **6·4** that

$$\mathfrak{P}^* = \mathfrak{V}_n \ominus \mathfrak{R}^j, \quad \mathfrak{R}^{*j} = \mathfrak{V}_n \ominus \mathfrak{P}. \qquad (17·6·1)$$

Hence, by Theorem **10·3**, Q^* is the projector of $\mathfrak{V}_n$ on $\mathfrak{P}^*$ parallel to R^{*j}.

§ 18. The minimal polynomial

18·0. Definition of a polynomial in a L.T. Let

$$p(\zeta) = \sum_{\kappa=0}^{s} \alpha_\kappa \zeta^\kappa \quad (\alpha_s \neq 0)$$

be any scalar polynomial of degree s in the complex variable ζ and let A be any L.T. in $\mathfrak{V}_n$. Then, as in **15·0**, *we introduce the L.T. $p(A)$ by writing*

$$p(A) = \sum_{\kappa=0}^{s} \alpha_\kappa A^\kappa. \tag{18·0·1}$$

We denote by $\mathfrak{X}[p]$ the L.M. of all vectors ξ such that $p(A)\xi = 0$; thus $\mathfrak{X}[p]$ is the null manifold of $p(A)$.

18·01. It is immediate from Definition **18·0** that, for any two polynomials $p(\zeta)$ and $q(\zeta)$,

$$p(A)\,q(A) = q(A)\,p(A) = pq(A), \tag{18·01·1}$$

where $pq(\zeta)$ is written for the product $p(\zeta)\,q(\zeta)$.

18·1. Weyr's Lemma. *If the polynomials $p_1(\zeta)$ and $p_2(\zeta)$ have no zero in common, then*

$$\mathfrak{X}[p_1]\,.\,\mathfrak{X}[p_2] = \mathfrak{O}, \quad \mathfrak{X}[p_1 p_2] = \mathfrak{X}[p_1] \oplus \mathfrak{X}[p_2].$$

Proof. Since $p_1(\zeta)$ and $p_2(\zeta)$ have no zero in common there exist polynomials $q_1(\zeta)$ and $q_2(\zeta)$ such that

$$q_1(\zeta)\,p_1(\zeta) + q_2(\zeta)\,p_2(\zeta) = 1.$$

Hence

$$q_1(A)\,p_1(A) + q_2(A)\,p_2(A) = I, \tag{18·1·1}$$

and we deduce that $\mathfrak{X}[p_1]$ and $\mathfrak{X}[p_2]$ can have no non-zero element in common. Further, it is clear from (18·01·1) that

$$\mathfrak{X}[p_1] \oplus \mathfrak{X}[p_2] \subseteq \mathfrak{X}[p_1 p_2]; \tag{18·1·2}$$

it remains to establish the equality.

We use the relation (18·1·1) to write any element ξ of $\mathfrak{X}[p_1 p_2]$ in the form $\xi = \xi^1 + \xi^2$, where

$$\xi^1 = q_2 p_2(A)\,\xi, \quad \xi^2 = q_1 p_1(A)\,\xi.$$

Then

$$p_1(A)\,\xi^1 = p_1 q_2 p_2(A)\,\xi = q_2 p_1 p_2(A)\,\xi = 0,$$

$$p_2(A)\,\xi^2 = p_2 q_1 p_1(A)\,\xi = q_1 p_1 p_2(A)\,\xi = 0,$$

so that $\xi^1 \in \mathfrak{X}[p_1]$ and $\xi^2 \in \mathfrak{X}[p_2]$. We have therefore shown that every element of $\mathfrak{X}[p_1 p_2]$ can be expressed as the sum of an element of $\mathfrak{X}[p_1]$ and an element of $\mathfrak{X}[p_2]$, so that

$$\mathfrak{X}[p_1 p_2] \subseteq \mathfrak{X}[p_1] \oplus \mathfrak{X}[p_2]. \tag{18·1·3}$$

The equality $$\mathfrak{X}[p_1 p_2] = \mathfrak{X}[p_1] \oplus \mathfrak{X}[p_2]$$
follows from (18·1·2) and (18·1·3).

18·2. Lemma **18·1** leads to important results about the eigen-values of A which we prove in **18·21**. We give first, however, a simple remark that we need in the proof. Let λ be an eigen-value of A, j the corresponding index, $\mathfrak{E}$ and $\mathfrak{P}$ the corresponding eigen-manifold and principal manifold; form the polynomial

$$p(\zeta) = (\zeta - \lambda)^\nu,$$

and let $\mathfrak{E}^\nu$ have the same meaning as in **17·2**. Then,

$$\mathfrak{X}[p] = \mathfrak{E}^\nu \quad (1 \leqslant \nu \leqslant j-1), \qquad \mathfrak{X}[p] = \mathfrak{P} \quad (\nu \geqslant j).$$

18·21. Corollary of Lemma **18·1**. *If $\lambda_1, \lambda_2, \ldots, \lambda_s$ are distinct eigen-values of a L.T. A in $\mathfrak{B}_n$ and if $\mathfrak{P}_\mu$ is the principal manifold of A corresponding to λ_μ, then*

$$(\mathfrak{P}_1 \oplus \mathfrak{P}_2 \oplus \ldots \oplus \mathfrak{P}_{\mu-1}) \cdot \mathfrak{P}_\mu = \mathfrak{O} \quad (\mu = 2, 3, \ldots, s)$$

and
$$s \leqslant \text{rank} \sum_{\mu=1}^{s} \mathfrak{P}_\mu \oplus \leqslant n.$$

Note. The corollary shows that the number of distinct eigen-values of A is at most n.

Proof. Let j_μ be the index of A corresponding to λ_μ and write

$$e_\mu(\zeta) = (\zeta - \lambda_\mu)^{j_\mu}, \quad q(\zeta) = \prod_{\mu=1}^{s} e_\mu(\zeta).$$

Then, by **18·2**, $\mathfrak{X}[e_\mu] = \mathfrak{P}_\mu$, and we deduce from Lemma **18·1** that

$$\mathfrak{P}_1 \cdot \mathfrak{P}_2 = \mathfrak{O}, \quad (\mathfrak{P}_1 \oplus \mathfrak{P}_2) \cdot \mathfrak{P}_3 = \mathfrak{O}, \quad \mathfrak{P}_\mu \cdot \sum_{\nu=1}^{\mu-1} \mathfrak{P}_\nu \oplus = \mathfrak{O},$$

so that we may form the L.M. $\sum_{\mu=1}^{s} \mathfrak{P}_\mu \oplus$ of which the rank cannot exceed n. By **4·42**, however, the rank of this L.M. is at least s.

18·3. Theorem. *The spectrum of any L.T. A in $\mathfrak{B}_n$ consists of m distinct eigen-values λ_μ, where $1 \leqslant m \leqslant n$, with corresponding indices j_μ and principal manifolds $\mathfrak{P}_\mu$ such that*

$$\sum_{\mu=1}^{m} \mathfrak{P}_\mu \oplus = \mathfrak{B}_n. \tag{18·3·1}$$

If we write $$e_\mu(\zeta) = (\zeta - \lambda_\mu)^{j_\mu}, \quad q_A(\zeta) = \prod_{\mu=1}^{m} e_\mu(\zeta),$$

then we have $q_A(A) = O$. Further, $q_A(\zeta)$ is a factor of every other polynomial $p(\zeta)$ for which $p(A) = O$.

PROOF. (i) We first establish the existence of polynomials $p(\zeta)$ such that $p(A) = O$; that is, such that $\mathfrak{X}[p] = \mathfrak{V}_n$. We recall that any L.T. A in $\mathfrak{V}_n$ is uniquely determined by the n^2 elements $a_{\mu\nu}$ of the corresponding matrix $(a_{\mu\nu})$, and also that the two operations of addition and multiplication by a number are defined in the same way for matrices in terms of the elements as for vectors in terms of the coordinates (see (7·1·1) and (7·0·1)). It follows that, as regards results based on the use of these two operations, we may represent any L.T. A in $\mathfrak{V}_n$ by a vector in $\mathfrak{V}_{n^2}$, and conversely. If now we consider the set of n^2+1 vectors in $\mathfrak{V}_{n^2}$ representing the L.T.'s A^ν, where $\nu = 0, 1, \ldots, n^2$, we know by Corollary **2·31**, for which the scalar product is not used, that this set of elements in $\mathfrak{V}_{n^2}$ is linearly dependent. There exist, therefore, n^2+1 numbers α_ν, not all zero, such that

$$p(A) = \sum_{\nu=0}^{n^2} \alpha_\nu A^\nu = O,$$

and we deduce the existence of a polynomial equation for the L.T. A. This gives at least one polynomial $p(\zeta)$, with degree n^2 at most, such that $\mathfrak{X}[p] = \mathfrak{V}_n$.

(ii) Now let $p(\zeta)$ be any such polynomial. If some of the zeros of $p(\zeta)$ are eigen-values of A, denote them by λ_μ ($\mu = 1, 2, \ldots, s$), and let ω_μ ($\mu = 1, 2, \ldots, s'$) be all the zeros that are not eigen-values of A. Let κ_μ and κ'_μ be the multiplicities of the zeros λ_μ and ω_μ respectively. Write

$$e_\mu(\zeta) = (\zeta - \lambda_\mu)^{\kappa_\mu}, \qquad \epsilon_\mu(\zeta) = (\zeta - \omega_\mu)^{\kappa'_\mu},$$

$$p(\zeta) = \prod_{\mu=1}^{s} e_\mu(\zeta) \prod_{\mu=1}^{s'} \epsilon_\mu(\zeta), \quad p_1(\zeta) = \prod_{\mu=1}^{s} e_\mu(\zeta),$$

where it is understood that one of the sets of zeros λ_μ, ω_μ may be empty. Since ω_μ is not an eigen-value of A, $A - \omega_\mu I$ is of rank n and therefore $\mathfrak{X}[\epsilon_\mu] = \mathfrak{O}$. Further, since λ_μ is an eigen-value of A, $\mathfrak{X}[e_\mu] = \mathfrak{E}_\mu^{\kappa_\mu}$, by **18·2**, where $\mathfrak{E}_\mu$ is the corresponding eigen-manifold. Thus, by Lemma **18·1**,

$$\mathfrak{V}_n = \mathfrak{X}[p] = \sum_{\mu=1}^{s} \mathfrak{E}_\mu^{\kappa_\mu} \oplus = \mathfrak{X}[p_1], \tag{18·3·2}$$

and we now see that the set of zeros λ_μ cannot be empty but that A has at least one eigen-value which is a zero of $p(\zeta)$. Suppose that A has m distinct eigen-values λ_μ, where $m \geqslant s$, with corresponding principal manifolds $\mathfrak{P}_\mu$ and indices j_μ. Then the relation (18·3·2) gives

$$\sum_{\mu=1}^{m} \mathfrak{P}_\mu \oplus \subseteq \mathfrak{V}_n = \sum_{\mu=1}^{s} \mathfrak{E}_\mu^{\kappa_\mu} \oplus \subseteq \sum_{\mu=1}^{m} \mathfrak{P}_\mu \oplus,$$

since $\mathfrak{E}_{\mu}^{\kappa_\mu} \subseteq \mathfrak{P}_\mu$ with equality only if $\kappa_\mu \geqslant j_\mu$. It follows that $m = s$ and that $\kappa_\mu \geqslant j_\mu$. Hence, every eigen-value of A is a zero of $p(\zeta)$, $p(\zeta)$ contains the polynomial

$$q_A(\zeta) = \prod_{\mu=1}^{m} (\zeta - \lambda_\mu)^{j_\mu}$$

as a factor,

$$\mathfrak{B}_n = \sum_{\mu=1}^{m} \mathfrak{P}_\mu \oplus = \mathfrak{X}[q_A]$$

and $q_A(A) = O$.

We have therefore deduced the existence of m distinct eigen-values of A from the existence of polynomials $p(\zeta)$ such that $p(A) = O$ and we have shown that any such polynomial contains the polynomial $q_A(\zeta)$ as a factor.

18·31. The polynomial $q_A(\zeta)$ is called the *minimal polynomial for A*. If k_μ is the rank of $\mathfrak{P}_\mu$, that is, if k_μ is the order of the eigen-value λ_μ, (18·3·1) shows that $\sum_{\mu=1}^{m} k_\mu = n$. Further, since $k_\mu \geqslant j_\mu$, as we have shown in **17·02**, the degree n' of $q_A(\zeta)$, which is given by the sum $n' = \sum_{\mu=1}^{m} j_\mu$, is at most n. Thus, if we write

$$p_A(\zeta) = \prod_{\mu=1}^{m} (\zeta - \lambda_\mu)^{k_\mu},$$

we see that $p_A(\zeta) = g(\zeta)\, q_A(\zeta)$, where $g(\zeta)$ is a polynomial, and that $p_A(A) = O$. This result is the general form of the *Cayley-Hamilton Theorem*. We remark that $p_A(\zeta)$, called the *characteristic polynomial of A*, is the determinant of the matrix $\zeta I - A$.

If the minimal polynomial is of degree n it coincides with the characteristic polynomial, for $\sum_{\mu=1}^{m} j_\mu = n$ if, and only if, $j_\mu = k_\mu$, since $j_\mu \leqslant k_\mu$. We notice in particular that when A has simple eigen-values we have $q_A(\zeta) = p_A(\zeta)$.

18·32. Corollary of Theorem **18·3**. *Let λ be an eigen-value of the L.T. A in $\mathfrak{B}_n$, and let the index and principal manifold of A corresponding to λ be j and $\mathfrak{P}$. If A is considered as a L.T. in $\mathfrak{P}$, then the minimal polynomial of A with regard to $\mathfrak{P}$ is $q_{A,\mathfrak{P}}(\zeta) = (\zeta - \lambda)^j$. If A is nilpotent with index j, then $q_A(\zeta) = \zeta^j$.*

Proof. If A is nilpotent with index j then $\mathfrak{B}_n$ is the principal manifold of A, A has no eigen-value λ other than $\lambda = 0$ and j is the corresponding index. For, if $A\xi = \lambda\xi$ for any non-zero vector

ξ and for any $\lambda \neq 0$, then $A^j\xi = \lambda^j\xi$, contrary to the hypothesis that $A^j\xi = 0$. Further, $A^\nu \neq O$ if $\nu < j$. Hence, $\zeta = 0$ is the only zero of the minimal polynomial $q_A(\zeta)$, and it is, in fact, a j-fold zero.

Now, by Theorem **17·4**, if λ is any eigen-value of the general L.T. A in $\mathfrak{B}_n$ then A_λ is nilpotent with index j when considered as a L.T. in the corresponding principal manifold $\mathfrak{P}$. It appears from the preceding argument that λ is the only eigen-value of A in $\mathfrak{P}$ and that the corresponding index is j. Thus, the minimal polynomial of A with regard to $\mathfrak{P}$ is $q_{A,\mathfrak{P}}(\zeta) = (\zeta - \lambda)^j$.

18·4. If N is a normal transformation in $\mathfrak{B}_n$ then, by Theorem **17·3**, all the indices j_μ corresponding to the m eigen-values λ_μ are 1 and the minimal polynomial is $q_N(\zeta) = \prod_{\mu=1}^{m} (\zeta - \lambda_\mu)$. This is in accordance with the result of **15·01**, which is there given, however, for H.T.'s only.

18·5. By (18·3·1), there exists, for any L.T. in $\mathfrak{B}_n$ with m eigen-values λ_μ, a set of projectors Q_ν of $\mathfrak{B}_n$ on $\mathfrak{P}_\nu$ parallel to $\mathfrak{Q}_\nu$, where

$$\mathfrak{Q}_\nu = \sum_{\mu \neq \nu} \mathfrak{P}_\mu \oplus, \quad \mathfrak{P}_\nu \oplus \mathfrak{Q}_\nu = \mathfrak{B}_n.$$

The projectors Q_ν satisfy the relations

$$Q_\mu Q_\nu = \delta_{\mu\nu} Q_\nu, \quad \sum_{\mu=1}^{m} Q_\mu = I. \qquad (18·5·1)$$

18·51. THEOREM. *Let $\{Q_\nu\}$ be the set of projectors defined for the L.T. A in* **18·5**. *Then $AQ_\nu = Q_\nu A$ and $\mathfrak{Q}_\nu = \mathfrak{R}_\nu^{j_\nu}$, the range of $(A_{\lambda_\nu})^{j_\nu}$.*

PROOF. By Theorem **10·9**, it will be sufficient for the first result to show that if we write any x of $\mathfrak{B}_n$ in the form

$$x = Q_\nu x + (I - Q_\nu)x,$$

then $AQ_\nu x \in \mathfrak{P}_\nu$ and $A(I - Q_\nu)x \in \mathfrak{Q}_\nu$. Now $(I - Q_\nu)x = \sum_{\mu \neq \nu} Q_\mu x$, by (18·5·1), so that it will be sufficient to show that $AQ_\mu x \in \mathfrak{P}_\mu$ for $\mu = 1, 2, \ldots, m$. But $\mathfrak{P}_\mu$ is the principal manifold of A_{λ_μ} and therefore, by Corollary **17·41**, $A_{\lambda_\mu} Q_\mu x \in \mathfrak{P}_\mu$. Thus, since $A = A_{\lambda_\mu} + \lambda_\mu I$, it follows that $AQ_\mu x \in \mathfrak{P}_\mu$, as we wished to prove.

We now see (i) that $\mathfrak{P}_\nu$ and $\mathfrak{Q}_\nu$ reduce A completely, (ii) that A_{λ_ν} is nilpotent with index j_ν when considered as a L.T. in $\mathfrak{P}_\nu$, and (iii) that the relation $\mathfrak{P}_\nu . \mathfrak{Q}_\nu = \mathfrak{O}$ implies that $A_{\lambda_\nu}\xi \neq 0$ for any non-zero ξ of $\mathfrak{Q}_\nu$. We therefore deduce, by Theorem **17·5**, that $\mathfrak{Q}_\nu = \mathfrak{N}_\nu^{j_\nu}$.

NOTE. The representation of Q_ν as a polynomial in A given in **19·22** provides another proof that $AQ_\nu = Q_\nu A$.

§ 19. FUNCTIONAL CALCULUS FOR L.T.'S. THE RESOLVENT

19·0. In the course of § **19** we use an interpolation formula for numerical polynomials which is an immediate generalization of the familiar Newton-Lagrange interpolation formula. We begin by stating the problem and establishing the existence of a solution.

LEMMA. *Let λ_μ be a set of m points in the complex ζ-plane, let j_μ be a set of m positive integers and let*

$$c_{\mu\kappa} \quad (\mu = 1, 2, \ldots, m;\ \kappa = 0, 1, \ldots, j_\mu - 1)$$

be a set of n' complex numbers, where $n' = \sum_{\mu=1}^{m} j_\mu$. Then there exists a uniquely determined polynomial $p(\zeta)$, of degree $n'-1$ at most, such that

$$p^{(\kappa)}(\lambda_\mu) = c_{\mu\kappa} \quad (\mu = 1, 2, \ldots, m;\ \kappa = 0, 1, \ldots, j_\mu - 1), \tag{19·0·1}$$

where $p^{(\kappa)}(\lambda_\mu)$ is written for the κth derivative of $p(\zeta)$ at $\zeta = \lambda_\mu$.

PROOF. Write

$$q(\zeta) = \prod_{\mu=1}^{m} (\zeta - \lambda_\mu)^{j_\mu} \quad q_\nu(\zeta) = \frac{q(\zeta)}{(\zeta - \lambda_\nu)^{j_\nu}},$$

so that $q(\zeta)$ has degree n', $q_\nu(\zeta)$ has degree $n' - j_\nu$, and further

$$q_\mu^{(\kappa)}(\lambda_\nu) = 0 \quad (\nu \neq \mu;\ \kappa = 0, 1, \ldots, j_\nu - 1). \tag{19·0·2}$$

If we assume a solution of the problem in the form

$$p(\zeta) = \sum_{\mu=1}^{m} p_\mu(\zeta)\, q_\mu(\zeta), \tag{19·0·3}$$

where the $p_\mu(\zeta)$ are polynomials, of degree $j_\mu - 1$ at most, to be determined, we obtain by (19·0·1) and (19·0·2)

$$c_{\nu\kappa} = p^{(\kappa)}(\lambda_\nu) = \sum_{\iota=0}^{\kappa} \binom{\kappa}{\iota} p_\nu^{(\iota)}(\lambda_\nu)\, q_\nu^{(\kappa-\iota)}(\lambda_\nu)$$
$$(\nu = 1, 2, \ldots, m;\ \kappa = 0, 1, \ldots, j_\nu - 1),$$

and hence

$$p_\nu(\lambda_\nu) = \frac{c_{\nu 0}}{q_\nu(\lambda_\nu)}, \quad p_\nu^{(\kappa)}(\lambda_\nu) = \frac{1}{q_\nu(\lambda_\nu)}\left(c_{\nu\kappa} - \sum_{\iota=0}^{\kappa-1} \binom{\kappa}{\iota} p_\nu^{(\iota)}(\lambda_\nu)\, q_\nu^{(\kappa-\iota)}(\lambda_\nu)\right)$$
$$(\kappa = 1, 2, \ldots, j_\nu - 1).$$

The formulae above enable us to compute successively the values of $p_\nu(\lambda_\nu), p'_\nu(\lambda_\nu), \ldots, p_\nu^{(j_\nu-1)}(\lambda_\nu)$. We then write

$$p_\nu(\zeta) = \sum_{\kappa=0}^{j_\nu-1} \frac{1}{\kappa!} p_\nu^{(\kappa)}(\lambda_\nu)(\zeta-\lambda_\nu)^\kappa,$$

and finally, by substitution in (19·0·3), we obtain a polynomial $p(\zeta)$, of degree $n'-1$ at most, which clearly satisfies (19·0·1). Further, $p(\zeta)$ is the unique solution of the problem since, if $r(\zeta)$ were a second solution, we should have

$$p^{(\kappa)}(\lambda_\mu) - r^{(\kappa)}(\lambda_\mu) = 0 \quad (\mu = 1, 2, \ldots, m;\ \kappa = 0, 1, \ldots, j_\mu - 1), \qquad (19·0·4)$$

where $p(\zeta)-r(\zeta)$ is a polynomial of degree $n'-1$ at most. But, by (19·0·4), $p(\zeta)-r(\zeta)$ has a zero of order j_μ at each of the points $\zeta = \lambda_\mu$ and is therefore of degree n' at least unless it vanishes identically. Thus, $r(\zeta)$ must coincide with $p(\zeta)$.

19·1. Definition of a regular function of a L.T. Let A be any L.T. in $\mathfrak{B}_n$, let λ_μ $(\mu = 1, 2, \ldots, m)$ be the complete set of distinct eigen-values of A, let j_μ be the corresponding indices and Q_μ the projectors on the corresponding principal manifolds $\mathfrak{P}_\mu$, as defined in **18·5**. Further, let $f(\zeta)$ be an analytic function regular in some open set $\mathfrak{d}$ in the complex ζ-plane (not necessarily connected) containing the m points $\zeta = \lambda_\mu$. For instance, $\mathfrak{d}$ may consist of the interiors of m non-overlapping small circles surrounding the points. Then *we define the L.T. $f(A)$ by writing*

$$f(A) = \sum_{\mu=1}^{m} \sum_{\kappa=0}^{j_\mu-1} \frac{1}{\kappa!} f^{(\kappa)}(\lambda_\mu)(A-\lambda_\mu I)^\kappa Q_\mu. \qquad (19·1·1)$$

We see, by **18·4**, that this definition includes Definition **15·2** when A is a H.T. We have to show that it includes Definition **18·0** when $f(\zeta)$ is a polynomial. We first show, however, that the last part of Theorem **18·3** can be extended to apply to regular functions.

We continue throughout § **19** to use the notation of Definition **19·1**.

19·11. Extension of Theorem **18·3**. *The L.T. $f(A)$ is zero if, and only if, there exists a function $g(\zeta)$, regular in $\mathfrak{d}$, such that*

$$f(\zeta) = g(\zeta)\, q_A(\zeta),$$

where $q_A(\zeta)$ is the minimal polynomial for A defined in **18·3**.

Proof. We deduce from (19·1·1) that $f(A)$ is zero if, and only if, $f^{(\kappa)}(\lambda_\mu) = 0$ for $\mu = 1, 2, \ldots, m$; $\kappa = 0, 1, \ldots, j_\mu - 1$. We see at once that these conditions are sufficient to make $f(A)$ zero in $\mathfrak{B}_n$; by considering $f(A)$ in $\mathfrak{P}_\mu$ we see that they are also necessary. For, if $f(A)$ is zero in $\mathfrak{P}_\mu$ then, by (19·1·1), the polynomial in A,

$$\sum_{\kappa=0}^{j_\mu-1} \frac{1}{\kappa!} f^{(\kappa)}(\lambda_\mu)(A-\lambda_\mu I)^\kappa, \tag{19·11·1}$$

must also be zero in $\mathfrak{P}_\mu$. But, by Corollary **18·32**, the minimal polynomial for A in $\mathfrak{P}_\mu$ has degree j_μ, and therefore the polynomial (19·11·1) of degree $j_\mu - 1$ is zero only if all the coefficients vanish.

Clearly, if $f(\zeta) = g(\zeta) q_A(\zeta)$, where $g(\zeta)$ is regular in $\mathfrak{d}$, then $f(A) = O$. Conversely, if $f(A) = O$, $f^{(\kappa)}(\lambda_\mu) = 0$ for $\kappa = 0, 1, \ldots, j_\mu - 1$ and $f(\zeta)$ has a zero of order j_μ at least for $\zeta = \lambda_\mu$. Thus $f(\zeta)/q_A(\zeta)$ is regular in $\mathfrak{d}$.

19·2. The functional calculus for L.T.'s is based on a simple result concerning sums and products of regular functions.

THEOREM. *Let $f(\zeta)$ and $g(\zeta)$ be two functions regular in $\mathfrak{d}$ and write*

$$F(\zeta) = f(\zeta) + g(\zeta), \qquad G(\zeta) = f(\zeta) g(\zeta).$$

Then $F(A) = f(A) + g(A), \quad G(A) = f(A) g(A) = g(A) f(A).$

PROOF. The expression for $F(A)$ follows at once from (19·1·1). In forming the product $f(A) g(A)$ we remark that, by (18·5·1), $Q_\mu Q_\nu = O$ when $\mu \neq \nu$, and that $(A - \lambda I)^\kappa Q_\mu = Q_\mu (A - \lambda I)^\kappa$, by Theorem **18·51**. Hence

$$f(A) g(A) = \sum_{\mu=1}^{m} \left(\sum_{\kappa=0}^{j_\mu-1} \sum_{\iota=0}^{j_\mu-1} \frac{1}{\kappa!\,\iota!} f^{(\kappa)}(\lambda_\mu) g^{(\iota)}(\lambda_\mu)(A - \lambda_\mu I)^{\kappa+\iota} \right) Q_\mu,$$

and further, since $(A - \lambda_\mu I)^\nu Q_\mu = O$ for $\nu \geq j_\mu$, the substitution $\nu = \kappa + \iota$ gives

$$\begin{aligned} f(A) g(A) &= \sum_{\mu=1}^{m} \sum_{\nu=0}^{j_\mu-1} \frac{1}{\nu!} \left(\sum_{\kappa=0}^{\nu} \binom{\nu}{\kappa} f^{(\kappa)}(\lambda_\mu) g^{(\nu-\kappa)}(\lambda_\mu) \right) (A - \lambda_\mu I)^\nu Q_\mu \\ &= \sum_{\mu=1}^{m} \sum_{\nu=0}^{j_\mu-1} \frac{1}{\nu!} G^{(\nu)}(\lambda_\mu)(A - \lambda_\mu I)^\nu Q_\mu \\ &= G(A), \end{aligned}$$

by (19·1·1).

19·21. Definition **19·1** gives the same results as Definition **18·0** for the functions $f(\zeta) = 1$ and $f(\zeta) = \zeta$, since it implies for $f(\zeta) = 1$, by (18·5·1),

$$f(A) = \sum_{\mu=1}^{m} Q_\mu = I, \tag{19·21·1}$$

and for $f(\zeta) = \zeta$,

$$f(A) = \sum_{\mu=1}^{m} (\lambda_\mu I + (A - \lambda_\mu I))\, Q_\mu = A \sum_{\mu=1}^{m} Q_\mu = A. \quad (19{\cdot}21{\cdot}2)$$

But we can construct any polynomial $p(\zeta)$ from these functions by multiplication and addition and therefore, by Theorem **19·2** and by **18·01**, we see that the two definitions are equivalent for any polynomial $p(\zeta)$.

19·22. The representation (19·1·1) leads to a *representation for any one of the projectors* Q_ν *as a polynomial in* A of degree $n'-1$ at most. For, by Lemma **19·0**, we can determine a polynomial $p(\zeta)$ such that, for a specified integer ν,

$$\left.\begin{aligned} p(\lambda_\nu) &= 1, \quad p^{(\kappa)}(\lambda_\nu) = 0, \\ p(\lambda_\mu) &= 0, \quad p^{(\kappa)}(\lambda_\mu) = 0, \quad (\mu \neq \nu), \end{aligned}\right\} \quad (\kappa = 1, 2, \ldots, j_\mu - 1),$$

and then, by (19·1·1), $p(A) = Q_\nu$. We see, by (19·0·3), that $p(\zeta)$ has the form $p_\nu(\zeta)\, q_\nu(\zeta)$, since $p_\mu(\zeta) = 0$ for $\mu \neq \nu$.

19·23. We do not use the method of approximation by polynomials that we used in **15·2** to justify Definition **19·1** in the case of a general regular function, for now $f(\zeta)$ is defined for non-real as well as for real values of ζ and the approximation of a complex function by polynomials is subject to restrictive conditions. Instead, we use Lemma **19·0**, and we also demand, from the start, that any definition of a regular function $f(A)$ shall satisfy Theorem **19·2**.

Thus, if a regular function $f(\zeta)$ is given, we construct a polynomial $p(\zeta)$, of degree n' at most, such that

$$p^{(\kappa)}(\lambda_\mu) = f^{(\kappa)}(\lambda_\mu) \quad (\mu = 1, 2, \ldots, m;\ \kappa = 0, 1, \ldots, j_\mu - 1), \quad (19{\cdot}23{\cdot}1)$$

and we remark that $f(\zeta) - p(\zeta)$ has a zero, of order j_μ at least, at every point $\zeta = \lambda_\mu$, so that we may write

$$f(\zeta) = g(\zeta)\, q_A(\zeta) + p(\zeta),$$

where $g(\zeta)$ is regular in $\mathfrak{d}$. We then write, in accordance with our demand,

$$f(A) = g(A)\, q_A(A) + p(A),$$

and, since $q_A(A) = O$, we obtain $f(A) = p(A)$. But $p(A)$ is defined by (18·0·1) which, by **19·21**, leads to the expression (19·1·1) for $p(A)$,

$$p(A) = \sum_{\mu=1}^{m} \sum_{\kappa=0}^{j_\mu - 1} \frac{1}{\kappa!} p^{(\kappa)}(\lambda_\mu)\, (A - \lambda_\mu I)^\kappa\, Q_\mu,$$

and (19·23·1) now shows that Definition **19·1** gives the only value of $f(A)$ that satisfies our demands.

We formulate the results of the preceding discussion in the following theorem.

THEOREM. *Let A be a L.T. in $\mathfrak{B}_n$, $f(\zeta)$ an analytic function regular in an open set $\mathfrak{d}$ containing the spectrum of A, and $f(A)$ the L.T. defined by* (19·1·1). *There is a polynomial $p(\zeta)$ of degree not greater than $n'-1$ such that $p(A)=f(A)$, where*

$$n' = \sum_{\mu=1}^{m} j_\mu \leqslant n,$$

and n' is the degree of the minimal polynomial of A.

19·3. THEOREM. *Let A be a L.T. in $\mathfrak{B}_n$ and $\mathfrak{d}$ an open set in the complex ζ-plane containing the spectrum of A. If $\{f_\nu(\zeta)\}$ is an infinite sequence of analytic functions each regular in $\mathfrak{d}$, then the sequence of L.T.'s $\{f_\nu(A)\}$ is uniformly convergent in $\mathfrak{B}_n$ if, and only if, the sequences*

$$\{f_\nu^{(\kappa)}(\lambda_\mu)\} \quad (\mu = 1,2,\ldots,m;\ \kappa = 0,1,\ldots,j_\mu-1)$$

are all convergent. Moreover, $f_\nu(A)\to f(A)$ (uniformly) as $\nu\to\infty$ if, and only if, $f_\nu^{(\kappa)}(\lambda_\mu)\to f^{(\kappa)}(\lambda_\mu)$ as $\nu\to\infty$.

PROOF. It is at once clear that the conditions of the theorem are sufficient for the convergence of $f_\nu(A)x$ to $f(A)x$ for any element x of $\mathfrak{B}_n$, and it follows from Theorem **15·12** that the convergence is uniform in $\mathfrak{B}_n$.

Now suppose that $\lim_{\nu\to\infty} f_\nu(A) = f(A)$ and take any vector ξ of $\mathfrak{E}_\mu$. By (19·1·1) $f_\nu(A)\,\xi = f_\nu(\lambda_\mu)\,\xi$ so that the sequence $f_\nu(\lambda_\mu)$ must be convergent. Assume that the convergence of the sequences

$$\{f_\nu'(\lambda_\mu)\},\quad \{f_\nu''(\lambda_\mu)\},\quad \ldots,\quad \{f_\nu^{(\kappa-1)}(\lambda_\mu)\} \quad (2\leqslant\kappa\leqslant j_\mu-1)$$

has also been established and take any vector ξ contained in $\mathfrak{E}_\mu^{\kappa+1}$ but not in $\mathfrak{E}_\mu^{\kappa}$. We obtain from (19·1·1)

$$f_\nu(A)\,\xi = \sum_{\iota=0}^{\kappa} \frac{1}{\iota!} f_\nu^{(\iota)}(\lambda_\mu)\,(A_{\lambda_\mu})^\iota\,\xi,$$

which means that

$$f_\nu(A)\,\xi - \sum_{\iota=0}^{\kappa-1} \frac{1}{\iota!} f_\nu^{(\iota)}(\lambda_\mu)\,(A_{\lambda_\mu})^\iota\,\xi = \frac{1}{\kappa!} f_\nu^{(\kappa)}(\lambda_\mu)\,(A_{\lambda_\mu})^\kappa\,\xi.$$

Since the left-hand side is, by assumption, convergent, so is the right-hand side, and therefore the sequence $\{f_\nu^{(\kappa)}(\lambda_\mu)\}$ is convergent. The proof of the theorem is now completed by an induction process.

19·4. The resolvent and the resolvent set. If the L.T. A in $\mathfrak{B}_n$ has distinct eigen-values λ_μ ($\mu = 1, 2, \ldots, m$), if $\lambda \neq \lambda_\mu$ and if we write, for $\zeta \neq \lambda$,

$$f(\zeta) = \frac{1}{\zeta-\lambda}, \quad f(A) = R_\lambda,$$

then, by Theorem **19·2**,

$$R_\lambda A_\lambda = A_\lambda R_\lambda = I,$$

since $A_\lambda = g(A)$, where $g(\zeta) = \zeta - \lambda$. Further,

$$f^{(\kappa)}(\zeta) = -\frac{\kappa!}{(\lambda-\zeta)^{\kappa+1}},$$

so that, by (19·1·1),

$$R_\lambda = -\sum_{\mu=1}^{m}\sum_{\kappa=0}^{j_\mu-1}\frac{1}{(\lambda-\lambda_\mu)^{\kappa+1}}(A-\lambda_\mu I)^\kappa Q_\mu. \qquad (19·4·1)$$

The L.T. $R_\lambda = A_\lambda^{-1}$ is defined as above for every complex number λ that does not belong to the spectrum of A. It is a function of λ, called *the resolvent of A. The set of all numbers λ for which A_λ^{-1} exists is called the resolvent set of A*; it cannot contain any point of the spectrum of A, since A_λ is singular for such points. Thus, any complex number λ is contained either in the spectrum or in the resolvent set of A.

19·41. As in **15·41**, we deduce the functional equation for the resolvent

$$R_\lambda - R_\mu = (\lambda-\mu)R_\lambda R_\mu = (\lambda-\mu)R_\mu R_\lambda$$

from the equation

$$\frac{1}{\zeta-\lambda} - \frac{1}{\zeta-\mu} = \frac{(\lambda-\mu)}{(\zeta-\lambda)(\zeta-\mu)}.$$

19·42. As in **15·42**, we obtain two power-series representation for R_λ, corresponding to (15·42·1) and (15·42·2),

$$R_\lambda = -\sum_{\kappa=0}^{\infty}\frac{1}{\lambda^{\kappa+1}}A^\kappa \quad (|\lambda| > |\lambda_\mu|,\ \mu = 1, 2, \ldots, m) \quad (19·42·1)$$

and

$$R_\lambda = \sum_{\kappa=0}^{\infty}(\lambda-l)^\kappa R_l^{\kappa+1} \quad (|\lambda-l| < |\lambda_\mu - l|,\ \mu = 1, 2, \ldots, m),$$

by using the two expansions

$$\frac{1}{\zeta-\lambda} = -\sum_{\kappa=0}^{\infty}\frac{1}{\lambda^{\kappa+1}}\zeta^\kappa, \quad \frac{1}{\zeta-\lambda} = \sum_{\kappa=0}^{\infty}(\lambda-l)^\kappa\frac{1}{(\zeta-l)^{\kappa+1}},$$

and applying Theorem **19·3** with the partial sums of these expansions as the functions $f_\nu(\zeta)$.

19·43. We obtain a power series representation for R_λ in ascending powers of $\lambda-\lambda_\nu$ like that of **15·43**. We write (19·4·1) in the form

$$R_\lambda = -\Sigma_1(\lambda)-\Sigma_2(\lambda),$$

where

$$\left.\begin{aligned}\Sigma_1(\lambda) &= \sum_{\kappa=0}^{j_\nu-1} \frac{1}{(\lambda-\lambda_\nu)^{\kappa+1}}(A-\lambda_\nu I)^\kappa Q_\nu,\\ \Sigma_2(\lambda) &= \sum_{\mu\neq\nu}\sum_{\kappa=0}^{j_\mu-1} \frac{1}{(\lambda-\lambda_\mu)^{\kappa+1}}(A-\lambda_\mu I)^\kappa Q_\mu.\end{aligned}\right\} \qquad (19·43·1)$$

Since $(\lambda-\lambda_\mu)^{-\kappa-1}$ is regular for $\lambda=\lambda_\nu(\kappa\geqslant 0,\ \mu\neq\nu)$, we can write $\Sigma_2(\lambda)$ as a power series,

$$-\Sigma_2(\lambda) = \sum_{\kappa=0}^{\infty}(\lambda-\lambda_\nu)^\kappa S_{\kappa+1}, \qquad (19·43·2)$$

with radius of convergence equal to the smallest distance of λ_ν from the $m-1$ other eigen-values. We use the relation

$$-(\Sigma_1(\lambda)+\Sigma_2(\lambda))\,A_\lambda = I \qquad (19·43·3)$$

to determine the coefficients $S_{\kappa+1}$. We obtain from (19·43·1)

$$\begin{aligned}-\Sigma_1(\lambda)\,A_\lambda &= -\Sigma_1(\lambda)\,(A_{\lambda_\nu}-(\lambda-\lambda_\nu)\,I) = -\frac{1}{(\lambda-\lambda_\nu)^{j_\nu}}(A-\lambda_\nu I)^{j_\nu}Q_\nu+Q_\nu\\ &= Q_\nu,\end{aligned}$$

since $(A-\lambda_\nu I)^{j_\nu}Q_\nu = O$; further, by (19·43·2),

$$\begin{aligned}-\Sigma_2(\lambda)\,A_\lambda &= -\Sigma_2(\lambda)\,(A_{\lambda_\nu}-(\lambda-\lambda_\nu)\,I)\\ &= S_1A_{\lambda_\nu}+\sum_{\kappa=1}^{\infty}(\lambda-\lambda_\nu)^\kappa(S_{\kappa+1}A_{\lambda_\nu}-S_\kappa).\end{aligned}$$

Hence, by (19·43·3),

$$I = R_\lambda A_\lambda = Q_\nu+S_1A_{\lambda_\nu}+\sum_{\kappa=1}^{\infty}(\lambda-\lambda_\nu)^\kappa\,(S_{\kappa+1}A_{\lambda_\nu}-S_\kappa).$$

By Theorem **1·52**, we have, for every x and y of $\mathfrak{B}_n$,

$$\begin{aligned}(x,y) &= \lim_{m\to\infty}\left(\left(Q_\nu+S_1A_{\lambda_\nu}+\sum_{\kappa=1}^{m}(\lambda-\lambda_\nu)^\kappa\,(S_{\kappa+1}A_{\lambda_\nu}-S_\kappa)\right)x,y\right)\\ &= ((Q_\nu+S_1A_{\lambda_\nu})\,x,y)+\sum_{\kappa=1}^{\infty}(\lambda-\lambda_\nu)^\kappa\,((S_{\kappa+1}A_{\lambda_\nu}-S_\kappa)\,x,y),\end{aligned}$$

and so we obtain an identity for numerical power series in which we may equate coefficients of like powers.

Using the Corollary to Theorem **6·06** and recalling that $R_\lambda A_\lambda = A_\lambda R_\lambda$, we obtain the relations

$$I-Q_\nu = S_1A_{\lambda_\nu} = A_{\lambda_\nu}S_1,\quad S_{\kappa+1}A_{\lambda_\nu} = A_{\lambda_\nu}S_{\kappa+1} = S_\kappa\quad (\kappa=1,2,\ldots), \qquad (19·43·4)$$

and we deduce that

$$S_\kappa S_1 = S_{\kappa+1}A_{\lambda_\nu}S_1 = S_{\kappa+1}(I-Q_\nu) = S_{\kappa+1}\quad (\kappa=1,2,\ldots),$$

since, by the defining equation (19·43·1) for $\Sigma_2(\lambda)$, we have $\Sigma_2(\lambda)\,Q_\nu = O$ and therefore $S_{\kappa+1}Q_\nu = O$ for $\kappa=0,1,2,\ldots$. But the equation $S_\kappa S_1 = S_{\kappa+1}$

implies that $S_{\kappa+1} = S_1^{\kappa+1}$, and so we obtain the development for R_λ in the form

$$R_\lambda = -\sum_{\kappa=0}^{j_\nu-1} \frac{1}{(\lambda-\lambda_\nu)^{\kappa+1}} (A-\lambda_\nu I)^\kappa Q_\nu + \sum_{\kappa=0}^{\infty} (\lambda-\lambda_\nu)^\kappa S_1^{\kappa+1}, \quad (19{\cdot}43{\cdot}5)$$

where S_1 satisfies the equations (19·43·4). We may interpret S_1 as a generalized inverse of A_{λ_ν} defined by the equations

$$S_1 A_{\lambda_\nu} x = A_{\lambda_\nu} S_1 x = x \quad \left(x \in \mathfrak{Q}_\nu = \sum_{\mu \neq \nu} \mathfrak{P}_\mu \oplus\right),$$

$$S_1 x = 0 \quad (x \in \mathfrak{P}_\nu),$$

which show that S_1 is the inverse of A_{λ_ν} with regard to the subspace $\mathfrak{Q}_\nu$.

19·5. We compare the principal manifolds of the L.T.'s A and $f(A)$ in **19·6**; we first, however, prove a result complementary to Theorem **17·5**.

THEOREM. *Let $\lambda_1, \lambda_2, \ldots, \lambda_s, \ldots, \lambda_m$ be the distinct eigen-values of a L.T. A in $\mathfrak{B}_n$, where $s \leqslant m$, and let $S_1, S_2, \ldots, S_s$ be a corresponding set of s L.T.'s such that*

(i) $\sum_{\mu=1}^{s} S_\mu = I$; $S_\mu^2 = S_\mu \neq O$ *for* $\mu = 1, 2, \ldots, s$;

(ii) $A_{\lambda_\mu} S_\mu = S_\mu A_{\lambda_\mu}$ *is nilpotent in* $\mathfrak{B}_n$ *for* $\mu = 1, 2, \ldots, s$.

Then $s = m$ and $S_\mu = Q_\mu$, where Q_μ is the projector corresponding to λ_μ

PROOF. By hypothesis (i) and Theorem **10·2**, S_μ is a projector; denote its range by $\mathfrak{S}_\mu$. By the same hypothesis the sum $\sum_{\mu=1}^{s} S_\mu$ is also a projector with range $\mathfrak{B}_n$. Thus, by Theorems **10·81** and **18·3**,

$$\sum_{\mu=1}^{s} \mathfrak{S}_\mu \oplus = \mathfrak{B}_n = \sum_{\mu=1}^{m} \mathfrak{P}_\mu \oplus,$$

where $\mathfrak{P}_\mu$ is the principal manifold corresponding to λ_μ, and therefore, by **4·42**,

$$\sum_{\mu=1}^{s} \operatorname{rank} \mathfrak{S}_\mu = n = \sum_{\mu=1}^{m} \operatorname{rank} \mathfrak{P}_\mu. \quad (19{\cdot}5{\cdot}1)$$

By hypothesis (ii), however, $\mathfrak{S}_\mu \subseteq \mathfrak{P}_\mu$ for $\mu = 1, 2, \ldots, s$, since, according to a remark in **17·02**, $\mathfrak{P}_\mu$ contains the null manifolds of all positive integral powers of A_{λ_μ}. Thus, rank $\mathfrak{S}_\mu \leqslant$ rank $\mathfrak{P}_\mu$ for $\mu = 1, 2, \ldots, s$, and we deduce from (19·5·1) that $s = m$ and rank $\mathfrak{S}_\mu$ = rank $\mathfrak{P}_\mu$ for $\mu = 1, 2, \ldots, m$. It follows by Theorem **2·6** that $\mathfrak{S}_\mu = \mathfrak{P}_\mu$. Finally, since $I - S_\nu = \sum_{\mu \neq \nu} S_\mu$ and the range $\mathfrak{Q}_\nu$ of $I - S_\nu$ is given by $\mathfrak{Q}_\nu = \sum_{\mu \neq \nu} \mathfrak{P}_\mu \oplus$, we obtain $S_\mu = Q_\mu$ as desired.

19·6. Theorem. *Let A, $f(\zeta)$ and $\mathfrak{d}$ satisfy the conditions of Definition* **19·1** *and let $l_1, l_2, \ldots, l_{m'}$ $(m' \leqslant m)$ be the distinct values taken by $f(\lambda_\mu)$ for $\mu = 1, 2, \ldots, m$. Then the set of m' numbers l_ν is the complete spectrum of $f(A)$,*

$$\mathfrak{P}'_\nu = \sum_{f(\lambda_\kappa)=l_\nu} \mathfrak{P}_\kappa \oplus \tag{19·6·1}$$

is the principal manifold of $f(A)$ corresponding to l_ν and

$$S_\nu = \sum_{f(\lambda_\kappa)=l_\nu} Q_\kappa \tag{19·6·2}$$

is the corresponding projector on $\mathfrak{P}'_\nu$, where the summations run over all integers κ such that $f(\lambda_\kappa) = l_\nu$.

Note. The theorem includes and makes more precise a result known as Sylvester's Theorem, namely, that the order k'_ν of the eigen-value l_ν of $f(A)$ is the sum of the orders of the corresponding eigen-values of A. For k'_ν is the rank of $\mathfrak{P}'_\nu$ and therefore, by (19·6·1),

$$k'_\nu = \sum_{f(\lambda_\kappa)=l_\nu} k_\kappa.$$

Proof. Let $l_\nu = f(\lambda_\mu)$ and let ξ be any vector of $\mathfrak{E}_\mu$, the eigen-manifold of A corresponding to λ_μ. Then, by (19·1·1), $f(A)\xi = l_\nu \xi$ and therefore l_ν is an eigen-value of $f(A)$.

We deduce from Theorem **19·5** that the L.T.'s S_ν defined by (19·6·2) are the projectors of $\mathfrak{V}_n$ on the principal manifolds of $f(A)$ corresponding to the eigen-values l_ν by showing that they satisfy the conditions of that theorem. We have

(i) $\sum_{\nu=1}^{m'} S_\nu = \sum_{\mu=1}^{m} Q_\mu = I, \quad S_\nu^2 = \sum_{f(\lambda_\kappa)=l_\nu} Q_\kappa^2 = S_\nu,$

(ii) $(f(A) - l_\nu I) S_\nu = S_\nu (f(A) - l_\nu I)$ is nilpotent in $\mathfrak{V}_n$,

by (19·1·1) and (19·6·2), since $(f(A) - l_\nu I) S_\nu$ can be represented by

$$(f(A) - l_\nu I) S_\nu = \sum_{f(\lambda_\kappa)=l_\nu} \sum_{\mu=1}^{j_\kappa - 1} \frac{1}{\mu!} f^{(\mu)}(\lambda_\kappa)(A - \lambda_\kappa I)^\mu Q_\kappa,$$

and is nilpotent of index not exceeding $\max j_\kappa$, where $\max j_\kappa$ denotes the greatest of the indices j_κ belonging to the λ_κ for which $f(\lambda_\kappa) = l_\nu$. Thus, the eigen-values l_ν form the complete spectrum of $f(A)$ and $\mathfrak{P}'_\nu$, the range of S_ν, is the principal manifold of $f(A)$ corresponding to l_ν and S_ν is the corresponding projector.

§ 20. Canonical bases of a principal manifold

20·0. We continue the discussion, begun in § **17**, of the dissection of the space $\mathfrak{B}_n$ with reference to any L.T. The present Section prepares the way for the next, in which we show that the principal manifold of a L.T. A, which reduces A and in which A is nilpotent, breaks down into a number of constituent L.M.'s, each of which, however, still reduces A completely. These L.M.'s may then be used in obtaining *Jordan's canonical form for a nilpotent* L.T. In § **22** we extend the process to all the principal manifolds of A and obtain Jordan's canonical form for a general L.T.

Let A be a L.T. in $\mathfrak{B}_n$ of rank r, where $r<n$, and of index j; let $\mathfrak{R}$ be the range of A; and let the set of j L.M.'s $\mathfrak{X}^\kappa$ be the set of null manifolds defined in **17·0**, so that the L.M. $\mathfrak{X}^j$, of rank k, is the principal manifold $\mathfrak{P}$ of A.

Definition of the index of any element of $\mathfrak{P}$. By Definition **17·02**, there is associated with every non-zero element ξ of $\mathfrak{P}$ an index ι, where $A^\iota\xi = 0$ while $A^{\iota-1}\xi \neq 0$. We write $\iota = j_\xi$ and call j_ξ the *index of* ξ. The zero element will be considered as the only element of $\mathfrak{P}$ with index 0.

Clearly, *the index indicates the first L.M. of the sequence* $\mathfrak{X}^1, \mathfrak{X}^2, \ldots,$ *of null manifolds to which* ξ *belongs*; any $\mathfrak{X}^\kappa$ may be regarded as the L.M. of all elements ξ of $\mathfrak{P}$ of which the index does not exceed κ; and we have the inequality $0 \leqslant j_\xi \leqslant j$, with $j_\xi = 0$ only for $\xi = 0$.

20·01. Definition of the descent of any element of $\mathfrak{P}$. Let ξ be any element of $\mathfrak{P}$. *If the equation* $A^\iota x = \xi$ *has a solution for* $\iota = 1, 2, \ldots, d_\xi$ *but no solution for* $\iota = d_\xi + 1$, *we say that* ξ *is of descent* d_ξ. If the equation $Ax = \xi$ has no solution we say that ξ is of descent 0.

Let the L.M.'s $\mathfrak{R}^\kappa$ be the ranges defined in **17·1**. Then *the descent of* ξ *indicates the last L.M. of the sequence* $\mathfrak{R}^1, \mathfrak{R}^2, \ldots,$ *to which* ξ *belongs*, and the L.M. $\mathfrak{P} \,.\, \mathfrak{R}^\kappa$ may be regarded as the L.M. of all elements ξ of $\mathfrak{P}$ of descent not less than κ. Since $\mathfrak{P} \,.\, \mathfrak{R}^j = \mathfrak{O}$, by Theorem **17·11**, it follows that the descent d_ξ satisfies the inequality $0 \leqslant d_\xi \leqslant j-1$ for $\xi \neq 0$. The zero element $\xi = 0$, however, is of infinite descent.

20·02. Definition of the order of any element of $\mathfrak{P}$. Let ξ be any non-zero element of $\mathfrak{P}$ of index j_ξ and of descent d_ξ. We call the number a_ξ the *order of* ξ, where $a_\xi = j_\xi + d_\xi$. The element $\xi = 0$ is of infinite order.

Clearly, $A^\kappa\xi$ is of at least the same order a_ξ as ξ if $\xi \neq 0$, since, if j_ξ and d_ξ are the index and descent of ξ, then the index of $A^\kappa\xi$ is $j_\xi - \kappa$ and the descent is at least $d_\xi + \kappa$. Thus, if $\xi = A^{d_\xi}x$, the index of x must be $j_\xi + d_\xi$, which is a_ξ, and the descent must be 0. This shows that, for $\xi \neq 0$, we have $1 \leqslant a_\xi \leqslant j$.

We verify that ξ and $A^\kappa\xi$ need not have the same order by considering, for example, $\xi = \xi^1 + \xi^2$, where ξ^1 has index 1 and descent 0, and ξ^2 has index 2 and descent 1. Then ξ has index 2, descent 0 and order 2, while $A\xi$, which equals $A\xi^2$, has index 1, descent at least 2 and order at least 3.

20·1. Construction of the set $\mathfrak{B}$. We now construct a set $\mathfrak{B}$ of elements of $\mathfrak{P}$ and show by Theorem **20·2** that it forms a basis of $\mathfrak{P}$. The construction leads to further complete reductions of $\mathfrak{P}$ which we obtain in § **21**.

By Theorems **17·11** and **17·12**, the null manifold $\mathfrak{X}$ of A contains elements ξ of descents d_ξ in the range $0 \leqslant d_\xi \leqslant j-1$. We write $\mathfrak{X}$ as the sum of j L.M.'s each consisting of elements (apart from the zero element) of the same descent. We write

$$\mathfrak{X}_1 = \mathfrak{X}, \quad \mathfrak{X}_{\kappa+1} = \mathfrak{X} \, . \, \mathfrak{R}^\kappa,$$

so that, by **20·01**, $\mathfrak{X}_{\kappa+1}$ consists of the elements of $\mathfrak{X}$ that are of descent κ or more; and, since $\mathfrak{R}^1 \supset \mathfrak{R}^2 \supset \ldots \supset \mathfrak{R}^j$, by Theorem **17·13**, $\mathfrak{X} \, . \, \mathfrak{R}^{j-1} \supset \mathfrak{O}$ and $\mathfrak{X} \, . \, \mathfrak{R}^j = \mathfrak{O}$, by Theorem **17·12**, we have

$$\mathfrak{X}_1 \supseteq \mathfrak{X}_2 \supseteq \ldots \supseteq \mathfrak{X}_j \supset \mathfrak{X}_{j+1} = \mathfrak{X} \, . \, \mathfrak{R}^j = \mathfrak{O}.$$

By Theorem **4·3** we can determine L.M.'s $\mathfrak{X}'_\kappa$ $(1 \leqslant \kappa \leqslant j-1)$, such that

$$\mathfrak{X}_{\kappa+1} \oplus \mathfrak{X}'_\kappa = \mathfrak{X}_\kappa,$$

with the possibility that $\mathfrak{X}'_\kappa = \mathfrak{O}$, when $\mathfrak{X}_\kappa = \mathfrak{X}_{\kappa+1}$. Then all the elements of $\mathfrak{X}'_\kappa$, except zero, are of descent $\kappa - 1$. If ρ_κ and ρ'_κ are the ranks of $\mathfrak{X}_\kappa$ and $\mathfrak{X}'_\kappa$ respectively, we have

$$\rho'_\kappa = \rho_\kappa - \rho_{\kappa+1},$$

and we obtain

$$\mathfrak{X}_\iota = \mathfrak{X}_j \oplus \sum_{\kappa=\iota}^{j-1} \mathfrak{X}'_\kappa \oplus, \quad \mathfrak{X} = \mathfrak{X}_j \oplus \sum_{\kappa=1}^{j-1} \mathfrak{X}'_\kappa \oplus, \qquad (20·1·1)$$

and hence

$$\rho_1 = n - r = \sum_{\kappa=1}^{j} \rho'_\kappa,$$

if we write $\rho'_j = \rho_j$. The set of numbers $(\rho_1, \rho_2, \ldots, \rho_j)$ was introduced by Eduard Weyr. It is called the *Weyr characteristic* belonging to the eigen-value $\lambda = 0$ of the L.T. A.

We now determine bases in $\mathfrak{X}'_\kappa$ for $1 \leqslant \kappa \leqslant j-1$ and in $\mathfrak{X}_j$, denoting their elements by the symbols $\binom{\kappa, \mu}{1}$, where $1 \leqslant \kappa \leqslant j$, $1 \leqslant \mu \leqslant \rho'_\kappa$. We thus obtain, by **4·42**, a set of ρ_1 elements which forms a basis of $\mathfrak{X}$. Since these elements are of index 1 and of descent $\kappa-1$ they are of order κ. Hence there exist solutions $\binom{\kappa, \mu}{\kappa}$ of the equations $A^{\kappa-1}\binom{\kappa, \mu}{\kappa} = \binom{\kappa, \mu}{1}$, although they are not uniquely determined. By **20·01**, however, they are elements of $\mathfrak{P}$ of index κ, of descent 0, and of order κ. Finally, we write

$$\binom{\kappa, \mu}{\sigma} = A^{\kappa-\sigma}\binom{\kappa, \mu}{\kappa} \quad (1 \leqslant \kappa \leqslant j, 1 \leqslant \mu \leqslant \rho'_\kappa, 1 \leqslant \sigma \leqslant \kappa). \quad (20{\cdot}1{\cdot}2)$$

The $\binom{\kappa, \mu}{\sigma}$ are elements of $\mathfrak{P}$ of order κ, index σ, and descent $\kappa-\sigma$, for $1 \leqslant \sigma \leqslant \kappa$. For the remarks of **20·02** show that they are of order $\binom{\kappa, \mu}{\kappa}$ at least and $\binom{\kappa, \mu}{1}$ at most, both of which equal κ.

We obtain in this way a set $\mathfrak{B}$ of k' elements $\binom{\kappa, \mu}{\sigma}$ of $\mathfrak{P}$, where

$$k' = \sum_{\kappa=1}^{j} \kappa\rho'_\kappa = \sum_{\kappa=1}^{j} \kappa(\rho_\kappa - \rho_{\kappa+1}) = \sum_{\kappa=1}^{j} \rho_\kappa. \quad (20{\cdot}1{\cdot}3)$$

20·2. Theorem. *The set $\mathfrak{B}$ constructed in* **20·1** *is a basis of $\mathfrak{P}$, so that the number k' of* (20·1·3) *equals the rank k of $\mathfrak{P}$.*

Proof. We show (i) that the k' elements of $\mathfrak{B}$ are linearly independent and (ii) that every element ξ of $\mathfrak{P}$ can be expressed as a linear combination of the elements $\binom{\kappa, \mu}{\sigma}$. We give the two parts of the proof in Lemmas **20·21** and **20·22**.

20·21. Lemma. *The k' elements $\binom{\kappa, \mu}{\sigma}$ of $\mathfrak{B}$ are linearly independent.*

Proof. If the lemma is false, there exists a linear combination of some of the elements of $\mathfrak{B}$ of the form

$$\omega = \sum_\iota c_\iota \binom{\kappa_\iota, \mu_\iota}{\sigma_\iota}, \quad (20{\cdot}21{\cdot}1)$$

where none of the numerical coefficients c_ι are zero and where $\omega = 0$. Let σ' be the greatest of the σ_ι in the sum (20·21·1) and form the expression $A^{\sigma'-1}\omega$. Then all the terms in which $\sigma_\iota \leqslant \sigma'-1$ will disappear, since σ_ι is the index of $\binom{\kappa_\iota, \mu_\iota}{\sigma_\iota}$, and only the terms in which $\sigma_\iota = \sigma'$ will remain. If we denote any one of these terms by $c'_\iota\binom{\kappa'_\iota, \mu'_\iota}{\sigma'}$, where the c'_ι form a subset of the c_ι of (20·21·1), we obtain

$$A^{\sigma'-1}\omega = \sum_\iota c'_\iota\binom{\kappa'_\iota, \mu'_\iota}{1} = 0.$$

The elements $\binom{\kappa'_\iota, \mu'_\iota}{1}$, however, are basis elements of $\mathfrak{X}$ and therefore linearly independent. Hence $c'_\iota = 0$, contrary to the assumption that no c_ι is zero. It follows that the lemma is true.

20·22. LEMMA. *Every element $\xi^{(\iota)}$ of $\mathfrak{X}^\iota$ (that is, every element of $\mathfrak{P}$ of which the index does not exceed ι) can be written in the form*

$$\xi^{(\iota)} = \sum_{\kappa=1}^{j} \sum_{\mu=1}^{\rho'_\kappa} \sum_{\sigma=1}^{\min(\kappa,\iota)} c_{\kappa\mu\sigma}\binom{\kappa, \mu}{\sigma}, \qquad (20·22·1)$$

where the set of numerical coefficients $c_{\kappa\mu\sigma}$ may include zeros. The rank of $\mathfrak{X}^\iota$ is equal to the sum $\sum_{\kappa=1}^{\iota} \rho_\kappa$.

NOTE. If we take $\iota = j$ we obtain from the lemma the second part of the proof of Theorem **20·2**.

PROOF. We prove the lemma by induction with regard to ι. It is certainly true for $\iota = 1$, since, by construction, the elements $\binom{\kappa, \mu}{1}$, for $1 \leqslant \kappa \leqslant j$, $1 \leqslant \mu \leqslant \rho'_\kappa$, form a basis of $\mathfrak{X}$. We assume the possibility of a representation (20·22·1) for a particular integer ι, where $\iota < j$, and deduce the possibility for $\iota+1$. Plainly, we need only consider elements $\xi^{[\iota+1]}$ contained in $\mathfrak{X}^{\iota+1}$ but not in $\mathfrak{X}^\iota$; they are of index $\iota+1$. We write $\xi' = A^\iota\xi^{[\iota+1]}$, and we see that ξ' is of index 1 and of descent not less than ι, so that $\xi' \in \mathfrak{X} \,.\, \mathfrak{R}^\iota = \mathfrak{X}_{\iota+1}$. Hence, by (20·1·1), we may write

$$\xi' = \sum_{\kappa=\iota+1}^{j} \sum_{\mu=1}^{\rho'_\kappa} c_{\kappa\mu}\binom{\kappa, \mu}{1},$$

and the equation $\xi' = A^\iota\xi^{[\iota+1]}$ now yields

$$\xi^{[\iota+1]} = \xi^{(\iota)} + \sum_{\kappa=\iota+1}^{j} \sum_{\mu=1}^{\rho'_\kappa} c_{\kappa\mu}\binom{\kappa, \mu}{\iota+1},$$

where $\xi^{(\iota)}$ satisfies the equation $A^\iota\xi^{(\iota)} = 0$ and is therefore an element of $\mathfrak{X}^\iota$. If we substitute for $\xi^{(\iota)}$ the expression (20·22·1), in accordance with our initial assumption, we obtain for $\xi^{[\iota+1]}$ a representation of the required form. It follows that every element $\xi^{(\iota+1)}$ has similar representation.

By Lemma **20·21**, the set of all elements $\binom{\kappa,\mu}{\sigma}$ for $1 \leqslant \kappa \leqslant j$, $1 \leqslant \mu \leqslant \rho'_\kappa$, $1 \leqslant \sigma \leqslant \min(\kappa, \iota)$, is linearly independent. This set therefore forms a basis of $\mathfrak{X}^\iota$ and the rank of $\mathfrak{X}^\iota$ is accordingly

$$\sum_{\kappa=1}^{\iota-1} \kappa\rho'_\kappa + \iota \sum_{\kappa=\iota}^{j} \rho'_\kappa = \sum_{\kappa=1}^{\iota-1} \kappa(\rho_\kappa - \rho_{\kappa+1}) + \iota\rho_\iota = \sum_{\kappa=1}^{\iota} \rho_\kappa. \quad (20·22·2)$$

Thus the rank k of $\mathfrak{P}$, that is, of $\mathfrak{X}^j$, is $\sum_{\kappa=1}^{j} \rho_\kappa$, and hence, by (20·1·3), $k' = k$.

This completes the proofs of Lemma **20·22** and Theorem **20·2**.

20·3. Definition of a chain. Let ξ be any element of $\mathfrak{P}$ of descent 0 and of index κ (so that ξ is not contained in $\mathfrak{R}$). We call the *set of* κ *elements* $\xi, A\xi, \ldots, A^{\kappa-1}\xi$ *a chain of order* κ *belonging to* A *and contained in* $\mathfrak{P}$, *provided that* $A^{\kappa-1}\xi$ *is also of order* κ.

We readily see that the elements of a chain are linearly independent, since a relation

$$\omega = \sum_{\nu=0}^{\kappa-1} c_\nu A^\nu \xi = 0$$

leads in turn to $A^{\kappa-1-\nu}\omega = 0$, and thence to $c_\nu = 0$, for $(0 \leqslant \nu \leqslant \kappa - 1)$. We also see that, by **20·02**, all the elements of a chain have the same order as the chain.

In the Example of **17·01**, the coordinate vectors u^ν $(\nu = 1, 2, \ldots, n)$ form a chain belonging to the particular L.T. there defined. More generally, if we refer to the set $\mathfrak{B}$ constructed in **20·1**, we see that for any fixed κ and μ the set of κ elements $\binom{\kappa,\mu}{\kappa}, \binom{\kappa,\mu}{\kappa-1}, \ldots, \binom{\kappa,\mu}{1}$ forms a chain of order κ belonging to the L.T. A; we call this the μth chain of order κ in $\mathfrak{B}$.

20·31. Definition of a canonical basis of a principal manifold. Let the j integers ρ'_κ have the same meanings as in **20·1** with reference to the principal manifold $\mathfrak{P}$ of the L.T. A in $\mathfrak{B}_n$, so that $\sum_{\kappa=1}^{j} \rho'_\kappa = \rho_1 = n - r$, where r is the rank of A. *A basis* $\mathfrak{B}$ *of* $\mathfrak{P}$ *is said to be a canonical basis belonging to* A *if* $\mathfrak{B}$ *consists of* $n - r$ *chains belonging to* A, ρ'_κ *of which are of order* κ, *where* $1 \leqslant \kappa \leqslant j$.

The set $\mathfrak{B}$ constructed in **20·1** is readily seen to be a canonical basis of $\mathfrak{P}$ belonging to A, with the ρ_1 elements $\binom{\kappa, \mu}{\kappa}$ as the first elements of the chains. While the numbers ρ'_κ which give the numbers of chains of order κ contained in a canonical basis are uniquely determined with reference to $\mathfrak{P}$ by the equations

$$\rho'_\kappa = \text{rank}\, \mathfrak{X} \,.\, \mathfrak{R}^{\kappa-1} - \text{rank}\, \mathfrak{X} \,.\, \mathfrak{R}^{\kappa}, \quad (1 \leqslant \kappa \leqslant j),$$

the construction described in **20·1** gives an infinity of different canonical bases of $\mathfrak{P}$.

§ 21. Jordan's canonical form for a nilpotent L.T. Commutativity

21·0. We consider a nilpotent L.T. A in $\mathfrak{B}_n$ of rank r (where r is necessarily less than n), and of index j. Then, by Definition **17·02**, $\mathfrak{P} = \mathfrak{B}_n$ and $k = n$, so that, by Theorem **17·4** and Corollary **17·41**, the discussion of A in $\mathfrak{B}_n$ is applicable to the consideration of a general L.T. in any principal manifold. By Corollary **18·32**, A has only one eigen-value, $\lambda = 0$, and the minimal polynomial of A has the form $q_A(\zeta) = \zeta^j$.

We now take a canonical basis of the principal manifold $\mathfrak{B}_n$ belonging to A, constructed according to **20·1**, and denote its elements by b^ν $(\nu = 1, 2, \ldots, n)$, beginning our enumeration with the first element of the first chain of order j and enumerating in turn all chains of that order before passing in succession to those of lower orders. The b^ν are the elements $\binom{\kappa, \mu}{\sigma}$ of **20·1**, where $1 \leqslant \kappa \leqslant j$, $1 \leqslant \mu \leqslant \rho'_\kappa$, $1 \leqslant \sigma \leqslant \kappa$. If we introduce the numbers

$$\left.\begin{aligned} \rho''_\kappa &= \sum_{\nu=\kappa}^{j} \nu \rho'_\nu = \kappa \rho_\kappa + \sum_{\nu=\kappa+1}^{j} \rho_\nu \\ \rho''_{j+1} &= 0, \quad \rho''_1 = \sum_{\nu=1} \rho_\nu = k = n \end{aligned}\right\} \quad (1 \leqslant \kappa \leqslant j), \qquad (21{\cdot}0{\cdot}1)$$

we may write

$$b^\nu = \binom{\kappa, \mu}{\sigma} \quad (\nu = \rho''_{\kappa+1} + \mu\kappa + 1 - \sigma), \qquad (21{\cdot}0{\cdot}2)$$

and so determine the suffix ν corresponding to a set of three suffixes κ, μ, σ. Conversely, to determine the three suffixes κ, μ, σ corresponding to a given suffix ν, we first determine κ by the inequality $\rho''_{\kappa+1} + 1 \leqslant \nu \leqslant \rho''_\kappa$, and then μ and σ by (21·0·2).

We obtain from (20·1·2) the equations

$$\left.\begin{aligned} Ab^{\nu} &= 0 \qquad (\nu = \rho''_{\kappa+1} + \mu\kappa) \\ Ab^{\nu} &= b^{\nu+1} \quad (\nu = \rho''_{\kappa+1} + \mu\kappa + 1 - \sigma,\ 2 \leqslant \sigma \leqslant \kappa) \end{aligned}\right\} \qquad (21{\cdot}0{\cdot}3)$$

where $\qquad 1 \leqslant \kappa \leqslant j, \quad 1 \leqslant \mu \leqslant \rho'_{\kappa}.$

Any basis $\{b'^{\nu}\}$ of $\mathfrak{B}_n$ satisfying the equations (21·0·3) is a canonical basis of the principal manifold $\mathfrak{B}_n$ belonging to A. For, we readily see that the $\{b'^{\nu}\}$ for $\nu = \rho''_{\iota+1} + \mu\iota$ $(\kappa \leqslant \iota \leqslant j-1,\ 1 \leqslant \mu \leqslant \rho'_{\iota})$ form a basis of $\mathfrak{X}.\mathfrak{R}^{\kappa}$. Hence, for $\nu = \rho''_{\kappa} + \mu(\kappa+1)$, $b'^{\nu} \in \mathfrak{R}^{\kappa-1}$, $b'^{\nu} \notin \mathfrak{R}^{\kappa}$, so that b'^{ν} is of order κ exactly.

21·01. We later use yet another notation for the elements of a canonical basis. The elements b^{ν} are enumerated as before; this means that the successive chains have non-increasing orders and that the successive elements in each chain have increasing descents. We then write any element b^{ν} as $\xi^{\iota\kappa}$, where $\kappa - 1$ is the descent of b^{ν} and ι denotes the chain to which it belongs. This use of κ should be distinguished from its use in the notation $\binom{\kappa, \mu}{\sigma}$. Since there are ρ_1 chains belonging to A we have $1 \leqslant \iota \leqslant \rho_1 = n - r$. We denote by $j_{.\iota}$ the order of the ιth chain, so that κ satisfies the inequality $1 \leqslant \kappa \leqslant j_{.\iota}$. (The dot before the suffix in $j_{.\iota}$ marks an empty place that will be filled by a suffix μ when, in §**22**, we construct bases of a principal manifold $\mathfrak{P}_{\mu}$ corresponding to an eigen-value λ_{μ} of a general L.T.) We write

$$j_{.\iota} = \sigma \quad (1 \leqslant \sigma \leqslant j,\ \rho_{\sigma+1} + 1 \leqslant \iota \leqslant \rho_{\sigma},\ \rho_{j+1} = 0), \quad (21{\cdot}01{\cdot}1)$$

for there are ρ'_{σ} chains of order σ. This relation implies that the $j_{.\iota}$ are uniquely determined by the ρ_{σ}, and since, by their definition in **20·1**, the ρ_{σ} are uniquely determined by A independently of the choice of the canonical basis, this is also true of the $j_{.\iota}$.

The equations (21·0·2) and (21·0·3) take the following forms

$$b^{\nu} = \xi^{1\nu} \quad (1 \leqslant \nu \leqslant j) \qquad (21{\cdot}01{\cdot}2)$$

$$b^{\nu} = \xi^{\iota\kappa} \quad \left(\nu = \kappa + \sum_{\sigma=1}^{\iota-1} j_{.\sigma}\right) \quad (j+1 \leqslant \nu \leqslant n,\ 2 \leqslant \iota \leqslant \rho_1,\ 1 \leqslant \kappa \leqslant j_{.\iota})$$

$$\left.\begin{aligned} Ab^{\nu} &= 0 \qquad \left(\nu = \sum_{\sigma=1}^{\iota} j_{.\sigma}\right) \\ Ab^{\nu} &= b^{\nu+1} \quad \left(\nu = \kappa + \sum_{\sigma=1}^{\iota-1} j_{.\sigma}\right) \quad (1 \leqslant \kappa \leqslant j_{.\iota} - 1). \end{aligned}\right\} \qquad (21{\cdot}01{\cdot}3)$$

21·1. We make use of a canonical basis $\{b^{\nu}\}$ of $\mathfrak{B}_n$, described in **21·0** and **21·01**, to express the L.T. A in simple analytical form.

We define a L.T. T in $\mathfrak{B}_n$, with reference to **6·02**, by writing $Tu^\nu = b^\nu$ $(1 \leqslant \nu \leqslant n)$. Then T is of rank n since its range is the L.M. $[b^1, b^2, \ldots, b^n]$ of rank n, T^{-1} exists and $u^\nu = T^{-1}b^\nu$. We write $\mathscr{E} = T^{-1}AT$ and deduce from (21·01·3) that

$$\begin{aligned} \mathscr{E}u^\nu &= T^{-1}Ab^\nu && (1 \leqslant \nu \leqslant n) \\ &= 0 && \left.\begin{array}{l} \left(\nu = \sum_{\sigma=1}^{\iota} j_{.\sigma}\right) \\ \left(\nu \neq \sum_{\sigma=1}^{\iota} j_{.\sigma}\right) \end{array}\right\} (1 \leqslant \iota \leqslant n-r), \\ &= u^{\nu+1} && \end{aligned} \qquad (21·1·1)$$

so that the u^ν form a canonical basis belonging to $\mathscr{E}$ and, like $\mathfrak{B}$, consisting of ρ_1 chains.

We now introduce the matrices of order ι

$$\mathscr{E}_{\lambda,\iota} = \begin{pmatrix} \lambda & 0 & \ldots & 0 & 0 \\ 1 & \lambda & \ldots & 0 & 0 \\ \ldots & & \ldots & & \ldots \\ 0 & 0 & \ldots & 1 & \lambda \end{pmatrix}, \qquad (21·1·2)$$

in which every element of the leading diagonal is λ, and every element immediately below and to the left is 1, while every other element is zero. We see at once that the matrix $\mathscr{E}_{0,n}$ coincides with (7·83·2) and represents the transformation defined in the Example of **17·01** to which there belongs the canonical basis $\{u^\nu\}$ consisting of one chain only. We deduce from (21·1·1) that the transformation $\mathscr{E}$ can be represented by the nth order matrix $\mathscr{E}$ that contains ρ_1 blocks $\mathscr{E}_{0,\,j_{.\iota}}$, corresponding to the ρ_1 chains contained in the canonical basis $\{u^\nu\}$ belonging to $\mathscr{E}$; all the other elements of $\mathscr{E}$ are zeros. The blocks are arranged down the leading diagonal of $\mathscr{E}$ so that there come first ρ'_j blocks $\mathscr{E}_{0,\,j}$ followed by ρ'_{j-1} blocks $\mathscr{E}_{0,\,j-1}$ and, generally, by ρ'_σ blocks $\mathscr{E}_{0,\sigma}$, in accordance with (21·01·1). Thus,

$$\mathscr{E} = \begin{pmatrix} \boxed{\mathscr{E}_{0,\,j_{.1}}} & & & 0 \\ & \boxed{\mathscr{E}_{0,\,j_{.2}}} & & \\ & & \ddots & \\ 0 & & & \boxed{\mathscr{E}_{0,\,j_{.n-r}}} \end{pmatrix}. \qquad (21·1·3)$$

The matrix $\mathscr{E}$ of (21·1·3) is called Jordan's canonical form for A or, briefly, the Jordan matrix for A, and any matrix formed from diagonal blocks $\mathscr{E}_{\lambda,\iota}$ is called a Jordan matrix. We have proved the following theorem.

21·11. THEOREM. *Corresponding to any nilpotent L.T. A in $\mathfrak{V}_n$ of rank r there exists a L.T. T of rank n such that the matrix $T^{-1}AT$ is a Jordan matrix.*

We say that the transformation T *reduces* A to a Jordan matrix.

21·2. We now show that any canonical basis belonging to a nilpotent L.T. A gives rise to a dissection of the principal manifold $\mathfrak{V}_n$ into constituent L.M.'s, each of which reduces A completely.

THEOREM. *Let A be a nilpotent L.T. in $\mathfrak{V}_n$. Then the L.M. $[\xi^1, \xi^2, \ldots, \xi^\sigma]$, where the ξ^ν form a chain belonging to A, reduces A completely.*

PROOF. We first consider the ρ_1 chains of order $j_{.\iota}$ forming a canonical basis $\{\xi^{\iota\kappa}\}$ belonging to A such as we have described in **21·01**. We write

$$\mathfrak{P}_{.\iota} = [\xi^{\iota 1}, \xi^{\iota 2}, \ldots, \xi^{\iota j_{.\iota}}],$$

so that $\mathfrak{P}_{.\iota}$ is the L.M. spanned by the ιth chain. We show that each of the ρ_1 L.M.'s $\mathfrak{P}_{.\iota}$ reduces A completely.

We see at once, first, by **4·43**, that

$$\mathfrak{V}_n = [\{\xi^{\iota\kappa}\}] = \sum_{\iota=1}^{\rho_1} \mathfrak{P}_{.\iota} \oplus,$$

and, secondly, that if we write any element $\xi^{(\iota)}$ of $\mathfrak{P}_{.\iota}$ in the form $\xi^{(\iota)} = \sum_{\kappa=1}^{j_{.\iota}} \alpha_\kappa \xi^{\iota\kappa}$, then

$$A\xi^{(\iota)} = \sum_{\kappa=1}^{j_{.\iota}-1} \alpha_\kappa \xi^{\iota,\kappa+1} \in \mathfrak{P}_{.\iota}.$$

Hence, if we write

$$\mathfrak{V}_n = \mathfrak{P}_{.\iota} \oplus \mathfrak{Q}_{.\iota}, \quad \mathfrak{Q}_{.\iota} = \sum_{\substack{\nu=1 \\ \nu\neq\iota}}^{\rho_1} \mathfrak{P}_{.\nu} \oplus,$$

then, when $x \in \mathfrak{P}_{.\iota}$ and $y \in \mathfrak{Q}_{.\iota}$, we have $Ax \in \mathfrak{P}_{.\iota}$ and $Ay \in \mathfrak{Q}_{.\iota}$. This means, by Definition **8·7**, that $\mathfrak{P}_{.\iota}$ reduces A completely.

Now let $\xi^1, \xi^2, \ldots, \xi^\sigma$ be any chain of order σ belonging to A. We show that there is a canonical basis belonging to A and containing this chain; it then follows from the proof above that the L.M. spanned by the chain reduces A completely.

The element ξ^σ is of descent $\sigma-1$ and index 1. Hence, in the notation of **20·1**, ξ^σ is contained in $\mathfrak{X}_\sigma$ but not in $\mathfrak{X}_{\sigma+1}$. There is, therefore, a L.M. $\mathfrak{X}'_\sigma$ such that

$$\mathfrak{X}_\sigma = \mathfrak{X}_{\sigma+1} \oplus \mathfrak{X}'_\sigma$$

and such that a basis of $\mathfrak{X}'_\sigma$ contains ξ^σ as an element. Using the method of construction described in **20·1**, we can now obtain a canonical basis $\begin{pmatrix}\kappa,\mu\\ \nu\end{pmatrix}$ belonging to A such that

$$\begin{pmatrix}\sigma,1\\ 1\end{pmatrix} = \xi^\sigma, \quad \begin{pmatrix}\sigma,1\\ \sigma\end{pmatrix} = \xi^1, \quad \begin{pmatrix}\sigma,1\\ \sigma+1-\nu\end{pmatrix} = \xi^\nu \quad (1 \leqslant \nu \leqslant \sigma).$$

This completes the proof.

21·21. Theorem. *Let A be a nilpotent L.T., let the elements $\xi^\nu\,(1 \leqslant \nu \leqslant \sigma)$ form a chain of order σ belonging to A, and write $\mathfrak{M} = [\xi^1, \xi^2, \ldots, \xi^\sigma]$. Then A is irreducible in $\mathfrak{M}$ in the sense that $\mathfrak{M}$ cannot be expressed as the sum $\mathfrak{M}_1 \oplus \mathfrak{M}_2$ of two L.M.'s $\mathfrak{M}_1$, $\mathfrak{M}_2$, both different from zero, such that $Aa \in \mathfrak{M}_1$ and $Ab \in \mathfrak{M}_2$ whenever $a \in \mathfrak{M}_1$ and $b \in \mathfrak{M}_2$.*

Proof. Every element ξ of $\mathfrak{M}$ can be written in the form

$$\xi = \sum_{\kappa=1}^{\sigma} \alpha_\kappa \xi^\kappa,$$

so that the index of ξ does not exceed σ. Further, $A\xi = \sum_{\kappa=1}^{\sigma-1} \alpha_\kappa \xi^{\kappa+1}$ and therefore $A\xi = 0$ if, and only if, $\alpha_\kappa = 0$ for $1 \leqslant \kappa \leqslant \sigma-1$, since, by **20·3**, the elements ξ^κ of the chain are linearly independent. Thus, $\mathfrak{X}\,.\,\mathfrak{M} = [\xi^\sigma]$ and is of rank 1.

Now assume the theorem false and suppose that there exist L.M.'s $\mathfrak{M}_1$, $\mathfrak{M}_2$ that reduce A completely in $\mathfrak{M}$. These L.M.'s cannot both contain non-zero solutions of the equation $A\xi = 0$, for this would mean that both contained the L.M. $[\xi^\sigma]$, whereas their only common element is zero. We may therefore suppose that $\mathfrak{M}_1\,.\,\mathfrak{X} = \mathfrak{O}$. If a is any non-zero element of $\mathfrak{M}_1$, then the index σ_0 of a does not exceed σ and we have, successively,

$$Aa \in \mathfrak{M}_1, \quad A^2 a \in \mathfrak{M}_1, \quad \ldots, \quad A^{\sigma_0-1} a \in \mathfrak{M}_1,$$

so that, in particular,

$$a' = A^{\sigma_0-1} a \in \mathfrak{M}_1, \quad a' \neq 0, \quad Aa' = 0.$$

This is contrary to the relation $\mathfrak{M}_1 . \mathfrak{X} = \mathfrak{O}$, and the contradiction establishes the theorem.

21·22. The next theorem, following directly from the last two, describes the dissection of $\mathfrak{B}_n$ with reference to the nilpotent L.T. A and analyses the reducibility of A in $\mathfrak{B}_n$.

THEOREM. *Let A be a nilpotent L.T. in $\mathfrak{B}_n$ of rank r. Then every canonical basis belonging to A leads to a dissection*

$$\mathfrak{B}_n = \sum_{\iota=1}^{n-r} \mathfrak{P}_{.\iota} \oplus,$$

where $\mathfrak{P}_{.\iota}$ is the L.M. spanned by the elements of the ιth chain of the basis. Each L.M. $\mathfrak{P}_{.\iota}$ reduces A completely, while A is irreducible in $\mathfrak{P}_{.\iota}$.

NOTE. The reduction of A by the sum of $n-r$ *L.M.*'s $\mathfrak{P}_{.\iota}$ is not uniquely determined, since every canonical basis belonging to A leads to a different dissection.

A method of determining all canonical bases belonging to a nilpotent A when one canonical basis is known is given in **21·4**.

21·3. We use the canonical bases belonging to a nilpotent L.T. A in considering the L.T.'s S such that $SA = AS$. We say that these L.T.'s are *commutative with* A.

THEOREM. *Let A be a nilpotent L.T. in $\mathfrak{B}_n$ of rank r and let $\{b^\nu\}$ be a canonical basis of $\mathfrak{B}_n$ belonging to A. Then the L.T. S is commutative with A if, and only if, the n elements a^ν, where*

$$a^\nu = Sb^\nu \quad (1 \leqslant \nu \leqslant n)$$

form a system satisfying the equations (21·01·3).

NOTE. The set $\{a^\nu\}$ is not necessarily linearly independent and therefore does not necessarily form a canonical basis of $\mathfrak{B}_n$, although it satisfies the equations (21·01·3).

PROOF. Let T be the L.T. defined by the equations

$$Tu^\nu = b^\nu \quad (1 \leqslant \nu \leqslant n).$$

We see from Theorem **21·11** that $A = T\mathscr{E}T^{-1}$, where $\mathscr{E}$ is the Jordan matrix (21·1·3).

(i) Let $\{a^\nu\}$ be any system of elements satisfying the equations (21·01·3) and let S be the L.T. determined uniquely, according to

6·03, by the equations $Sb^\nu = a^\nu$. Then, since the elements $\{b^\nu\}$ satisfy the equations (21·01·3), we have

$$\begin{aligned} ASb^\nu &= Aa^\nu && (1 \leqslant \nu \leqslant n) \\ &= 0 = SAb^\nu && \left.\begin{aligned}&\left(\nu = \sum_{\sigma=1}^{\iota} j_{.\sigma}\right)\\ &\left(\nu \neq \sum_{\sigma=1}^{\iota} j_{.\sigma}\right)\end{aligned}\right\} \quad (1 \leqslant \iota \leqslant n-r) \\ &= a^{\nu+1} = Sb^{\nu+1} = SAb^\nu && \end{aligned} \qquad (21\cdot3\cdot1)$$

Every vector x of $\mathfrak{B}_n$, however, may be written as $x = \sum_{\nu=1}^{n} \alpha_\nu b^\nu$. Hence

$$ASx = \sum_{\nu=1}^{n} \alpha_\nu ASb^\nu = \sum_{\nu=1}^{n} \alpha_\nu SAb^\nu = SAx.$$

(ii) Conversely, if $AS = SA$ and if we write $Sb^\nu = a^\nu$ and use the equations (21·01·3) for the basis $\{b^\nu\}$ of A, we then have

$$\begin{aligned} Aa^\nu &= ASb^\nu = SAb^\nu \\ &= 0 \\ &= Sb^{\nu+1} = a^{\nu+1} \end{aligned}$$

for the same system of suffixes as in (21·3·1). Thus, the elements a^ν satisfy the equations (21·01·3).

21·31. Consider first the case when the L.T. S above has rank n. The relation $AS = SA$ implies that $S^{-1}AS = A$, and we then say that S *transforms* A *into itself*. Let T be the L.T. defined by the equations $Tu^\nu = b^\nu$ $(1 \leqslant \nu \leqslant n)$. Then $STu^\nu = a^\nu$ and, by **6·11**, ST has rank n if, and only if, the n vectors a^ν are linearly independent. By Theorem **7·7** this is also true of STT^{-1}, since T has rank n. Hence, S has rank n if, and only if, the set of vectors a^ν forms a basis of $\mathfrak{B}_n$. We have proved the following theorem:

THEOREM. *If A is a nilpotent L.T. in $\mathfrak{B}_n$, of rank r, and if $\{b^\nu\}$ is a canonical basis of $\mathfrak{B}_n$ belonging to A, then all L.T.'s of rank n commutative with A, that is, all L.T.'s transforming A into itself, are determined by the conditions $Sb^\nu = b'^\nu$ $(1 \leqslant \nu \leqslant n)$, where $\{b'^\nu\}$ is also a canonical basis of $\mathfrak{B}_n$ belonging to A.*

This theorem raises the problem, already mentioned at the end of **21·22**, of constructing all canonical bases of a principal manifold $\mathfrak{P}$ belonging to a L.T. A if one canonical basis is known. We consider this problem in **21·4**.

21·32. We now try to find all the L.T.'s S, not necessarily of rank n, commutative with A. By Theorem **21·3** they are determined by all the sets of vectors a^ν, not necessarily linearly independent, satisfying the equations (21·01·3). We use the index notation of (21·01·2). We determine the sets of vectors a^ν by writing

$$a^\nu = \eta^{\iota\kappa} = A^{\kappa-1}\eta^{\iota 1},$$

where the set $\{\eta^{\iota 1}\}$ is chosen so that $\eta^{\iota 1}$ belongs to an index not exceeding $j_{.\iota}$, but it is not necessarily a linearly independent set. We then define S as in Theorem **21·3**, and in this way we obtain the most general L.T. S commutative with A. Now, by Lemma **20·22**, the rank of $\mathfrak{X}^\kappa$ is $\sum_{\nu=1}^{\kappa} \rho_\nu$, and this is the maximum number of linearly independent elements of $\mathfrak{V}_n$ of which the indices do not exceed κ. Thus, the element $\eta^{\iota 1}$ $(\rho_{\kappa+1}+1 \leqslant \iota \leqslant \rho_\kappa)$ depends on $\sum_{\nu=1}^{\kappa} \rho_\nu$ arbitrary constants, and hence the matrix S, which is uniquely determined by the ρ_1 elements $\eta^{\iota 1}$, depends on a number of arbitrary constants equal to

$$\sum_{\kappa=1}^{j} (\rho_\kappa - \rho_{\kappa+1}) \sum_{\nu=1}^{\kappa} \rho_\nu = \sum_{\kappa=1}^{j} \rho_\kappa^2.$$

Frobenius gave the number of constants determining S as

$$\sum_{\iota=1}^{\rho_1} (2\iota-1) j_{.\iota},$$

and we see that this agrees with our result if we write, by (21·01·1),

$$\sum_{\iota=1}^{\rho_1} (2\iota-1) j_{.\iota} = \sum_{\kappa=1}^{j} \sum_{\iota=\rho_{\kappa+1}+1}^{\rho_\kappa} (2\iota-1)\kappa = \sum_{\kappa=1}^{j} \kappa(\rho_\kappa^2-\rho_{\kappa+1}^2) = \sum_{\kappa=1}^{j} \rho_\kappa^2.$$

21·4. The problem of the reducibility of a nilpotent L.T. A in $\mathfrak{V}_n$ formulated in **21·22** and the problem of the construction of all L.T.'s S transforming A into itself both lead to the problem of determining all the canonical bases of $\mathfrak{V}_n$ belonging to A. We now give a method of constructing all these bases when one is known, but we omit the proof since we do not refer to the construction again. The proof is easy, but tedious; it depends on an analysis of the method developed in **20·1** combined with an application of Theorem **4·31**. (A reference for a proof is given in the notes at the end of the book.)

THEOREM. *Let A be a nilpotent L.T. in $\mathfrak{V}_n$. Denote the elements of a canonical basis of $\mathfrak{V}_n$ belonging to A, as in* **20·1** *by* $\binom{\kappa,\mu}{\sigma}$, *write*

$$\mathfrak{N}_\kappa = \left[\binom{\kappa,1}{\kappa}, \binom{\kappa,2}{\kappa}, \ldots, \binom{\kappa,\rho'_\kappa}{\kappa}\right],$$

so that $\mathfrak{N}_\kappa$ is the L.M. spanned by those elements of the given basis that are of descent 0 *and of order κ, and let $\{\beta^{\kappa\mu}\}$ $(\mu = 1, 2, \ldots, \rho'_\kappa)$, be any basis of $\mathfrak{N}_\kappa$. Then* *the elements* $\begin{pmatrix}\kappa,\mu\\ \sigma\end{pmatrix}'$ *of every canonical basis belonging to* A *can be written in the following way:*

$$\begin{pmatrix}\kappa,\mu\\ \kappa\end{pmatrix}' = \beta^{\kappa\mu} + \beta^{[\kappa-1],\mu} + y^{[\kappa],\mu}$$

$$\begin{pmatrix}\kappa,\mu\\ \sigma\end{pmatrix}' = A^{\kappa-\sigma}\begin{pmatrix}\kappa,\mu\\ \kappa\end{pmatrix}' \quad (1 \leqslant \sigma \leqslant \kappa),$$

where $\beta^{[\kappa-1],\mu}$ *denotes any element of the L.M.* $\sum_{\iota=1}^{\kappa-1} \mathfrak{N}_\iota \oplus$, *and where* $y^{[\kappa],\mu}$ *denotes any element of* $\mathfrak{N}$ *of which the index does not exceed* κ, *so that it is, in fact, any element of* $\mathfrak{N}.\mathfrak{X}^\kappa$.

§ 22. Jordan's canonical form for any L.T.; elementary divisors and Segre characteristic; similar transformations

22·0. Let A be a L.T. in $\mathfrak{B}_n$; let $\lambda_1, \lambda_2, \ldots, \lambda_m$ be the complete set of distinct eigen-values of A; let j_μ be the index corresponding to λ_μ and $\mathfrak{P}_\mu$ the principal manifold, of rank k_μ, so that, by (18·3·1), $\sum_{\mu=1}^{m} k_\mu = n$. Let r_μ be the rank of A_{λ_μ} and write $s_\mu = n - r_\mu > 0$. Then s_μ is the rank of the eigen-manifold $\mathfrak{E}_\mu$ and the nullity of A_{λ_μ}. Hence, since $\mathfrak{E}_\mu \subseteq \mathfrak{P}_\mu$, by **17·2**, we have $s_\mu \leqslant k_\mu$. Also, by Corollary **17·41**, A_{λ_μ}, considered as a L.T. in the space $\mathfrak{B}_{k_\mu} = \mathfrak{P}_\mu$, is nilpotent of index j_μ. We may therefore apply to A_{λ_μ} the procedure described in **20·1**, **21·0** and **21·01**, obtaining a canonical basis $\{b^{\mu\nu}\}$ of each $\mathfrak{P}_\mu (1 \leqslant \nu \leqslant k_\mu)$ that consists of a set of s_μ chains of order $j_{\mu\iota}$ $(1 \leqslant \iota \leqslant s_\mu)$ belonging to A_{λ_μ} such that

$$j_\mu = j_{\mu1} \geqslant j_{\mu2} \geqslant \ldots \geqslant j_{\mu s_\mu}, \quad \sum_{\iota=1}^{s_\mu} j_{\mu\iota} = k_\mu, \tag{22·0·1}$$

and

$$\left.\begin{aligned} A_{\lambda_\mu} b^{\mu\nu} &= 0 && \left(\nu = \sum_{\sigma=1}^{\iota} j_{\mu\sigma}\right) \\ &= b^{\mu,\nu+1} && \left(\nu \neq \sum_{\sigma=1}^{\iota} j_{\mu\sigma}\right) \end{aligned}\right\} \tag{22·0·2}$$

where $\qquad 1 \leqslant \iota \leqslant s_\mu; \; 1 \leqslant \nu \leqslant k_\mu.$

The set of bases $\{b^{\mu\nu}\}$ of $\mathfrak{P}_\mu$ for $\mu = 1, 2, \ldots, m$ gives a set of n vectors satisfying the equations

$$\left.\begin{aligned} A b^{\mu\nu} &= \lambda_\mu b^{\mu\nu} && \left(\nu = \sum_{\sigma=1}^{\iota} j_{\mu\sigma}\right) \\ &= \lambda_\mu b^{\mu\nu} + b^{\mu,\nu+1} && \left(\nu \neq \sum_{\sigma=1}^{\iota} j_{\mu\sigma}\right) \end{aligned}\right\} \tag{22·0·3}$$

where $\qquad 1 \leqslant \mu \leqslant m; \; 1 \leqslant \iota \leqslant s_\mu; \; 1 \leqslant \nu \leqslant k_\mu,$

and, by (18·3·1), these vectors form a linearly independent set.

We call any set of n linearly independent vectors $\{b'^{\mu\nu}\}$ satisfying the equations (22·0·3) a canonical basis of $\mathfrak{B}_n$ belonging to A.

We notice that, as in **21·01**, the set $\{j_{\mu\iota}\}\,(1 \leqslant \iota \leqslant s_\mu)$ does not depend on the choice of the canonical basis $\{b^{\mu\nu}\}$ but is uniquely determined by A.

We now write

$$\left.\begin{aligned} \mathfrak{P}_{\mu 1} &= [\{b^{\mu\nu}\}] \quad (1 \leqslant \nu \leqslant j_{\mu 1}), \\ \mathfrak{P}_{\mu\iota} &= [\{b^{\mu\nu}\}] \quad \left(\iota \geqslant 2, 1 + \sum_{\sigma=1}^{\iota-1} j_{\mu\sigma} \leqslant \nu \leqslant \sum_{\sigma=1}^{\iota} j_{\mu\sigma}\right). \end{aligned}\right\} \tag{22·0·4}$$

Then the L.M. $\mathfrak{P}_{\mu\iota}$ is of rank $j_{\mu\iota}$ for $1 \leqslant \iota \leqslant s_\mu$; the basis of $\mathfrak{P}_{\mu\iota}$ is a chain of order $j_{\mu\iota}$ belonging to A_{λ_μ} and, by **4·42**,

$$\mathfrak{P}_\mu = \sum_{\iota=1}^{s_\mu} \mathfrak{P}_{\mu\iota} \oplus .$$

By (22·0·3), A maps every element of $\mathfrak{P}_{\mu\iota}$ on an element of $\mathfrak{P}_{\mu\iota}$. Hence, if $Q_{\mu\iota}$ is the projector, zero in every $\mathfrak{P}_\nu$ where $\nu \neq \mu$, that projects $\mathfrak{P}_\mu$ on $\mathfrak{P}_{\mu\iota}$ parallel to $\sum_{\kappa \neq \iota} \mathfrak{P}_{\mu\kappa} \oplus$, we have

$$\sum_{\iota=1}^{s_\mu} Q_{\mu\iota} = Q_\mu, \quad AQ_{\mu\iota} = Q_{\mu\iota} A.$$

Thus, by Theorem **10·9**, $\mathfrak{P}_{\mu\iota}$ reduces A completely. If we now apply Theorem **21·22** to A_{λ_μ}, considered as a nilpotent L.T. in $\mathfrak{P}_\mu$, we conclude that A is irreducible in $\mathfrak{P}_{\mu\iota}$ and that, in writing

$$\mathfrak{B}_n = \sum_{\mu=1}^{m} \mathfrak{P}_\mu \oplus = \sum_{\mu=1}^{m} \sum_{\iota=1}^{s_\mu} \mathfrak{P}_{\mu\iota} \oplus , \tag{22·0·5}$$

we have a final dissection of $\mathfrak{B}_n$ with reference to the L.T. A. We recall, however, the Note in **21·22** to the effect that *this dissection is not, in general, uniquely determined* although each of the constituent L.M.'s reduces A completely. The corresponding decomposition of A is

$$A = \sum_{\mu=1}^{m} AQ_\mu = \sum_{\mu=1}^{m} \sum_{\iota=1}^{s_\mu} AQ_{\mu\iota} = \sum_{\mu=1}^{m} \sum_{\iota=1}^{s_\mu} Q_{\mu\iota} A. \tag{22·0·6}$$

22·1. As in **21·1**, we make use of a canonical basis $\{b^{\mu\nu}\}$ of $\mathfrak{B}_n$ belonging to A to reduce the L.T. A to a simple analytical form. We define a L.T. T in $\mathfrak{B}_n$ by writing $Tu^\kappa = b^{\mu\nu}$, where

$$\kappa = \nu \quad (\mu = 1), \qquad \kappa = \nu + \sum_{\iota=1}^{\mu-1} k_\iota \quad (\mu \geqslant 2), \quad \left(1 \leqslant \kappa \leqslant \sum_{\iota=1}^{m} k_\iota = n\right).$$

Then T is of rank n, since the set of elements $\{b^{\mu\nu}\}$ is linearly independent. We write $\mathscr{E} = T^{-1}AT$, and deduce from (22·0·3) that, for $\mu = 1, 2, \ldots, m$ and $\iota = 1, 2, \ldots, s_\mu$,

$$\left.\begin{aligned}(\mathscr{E}-\lambda I)\,u^\kappa &= T^{-1}(A-\lambda I)\,b^{\mu\nu}\\ &= (\lambda_\mu-\lambda)\,u^\kappa \quad \left(\mu = 1,\ \kappa = \sum_{\sigma=1}^{\iota} j_{1\sigma}\right),\\ &= (\lambda_\mu-\lambda)\,u^\kappa \quad \left(\mu \geqslant 2, \kappa = \sum_{\sigma=1}^{\mu-1} k_\sigma + \sum_{\sigma=1}^{\iota} j_{\mu\sigma}\right),\\ &= (\lambda_\mu-\lambda)\,u^\kappa + u^{\kappa+1} \quad (\text{all other } \kappa).\end{aligned}\right\} \tag{22·1·1}$$

Using the notation (21·1·2) and writing (λ, j) for $\mathscr{E}_{\lambda,j}$, we can represent $\mathscr{E}-\lambda I$ as the nth order matrix containing blocks $\mathscr{E}_{\lambda,j}$ of order j on the leading diagonal and otherwise consisting of zeros, according to the scheme

$$\mathscr{E}-\lambda I = \begin{pmatrix} \square & & & & & 0 \\ & \square & & & & \\ & & \square & & & \\ & & & \ddots & & \\ & & & & \square & \\ 0 & & & & & \square \end{pmatrix}, \tag{22·1·2}$$

where the number of blocks marked above is $\sum_{\mu=1}^{m} s_\mu$ and where the matrices appearing in the blocks, in order down the diagonal, are

$$(\lambda_1-\lambda, j_{11}),\ \ldots,\ (\lambda_1-\lambda, j_{1s_1}),\ \ldots,\ (\lambda_\mu-\lambda, j_{\mu1}),\ \ldots,\ (\lambda_\mu-\lambda, j_{\mu s_\mu}),\ \ldots,$$
$$(\lambda_m-\lambda,\ j_{m1}),\ \ldots,\ (\lambda_m-\lambda,\ j_{m,s_m}), \tag{22·1·3}$$

while all the elements outside the blocks are zeros. The matrix $\mathscr{E}$ of (22·1·2) is again called *Jordan's canonical form* or, briefly, *the Jordan matrix*, for A.

We may express the result just obtained in the following theorem:

THEOREM. *There corresponds to any L.T. A in $\mathfrak{B}_n$ a regular L.T. T such that the matrix $T^{-1}A_\lambda T$ is a Jordan matrix.*

22·2. Elementary divisors. From the course of our discussion in **20·1**, **21·01** and **22·0**, it appears that the sequence of indices $j_{\mu\iota}$ is uniquely determined by the L.T. A and does not depend on the special choice of the canonical basis $\{b^{\mu\nu}\}$. The corresponding sequence of factors $(\lambda_\mu-\lambda)^{j_{\mu\iota}}\,(1 \leqslant \mu \leqslant m;\ 1 \leqslant \iota \leqslant s_\mu)$ has invariant properties in relation to a certain class of transformations of A considered in **22·4** and **22·41**. For reasons concerned with the determinant theory, which is outside the scope of this book, Weierstrass called these factors the *elementary divisors of the pencil* $A-\lambda I$. In what follows we speak, for simplicity, of the elementary divisors of the L.T. A, or of the matrix A, meaning the elementary divisors of the pencil $A-\lambda I$.

It follows at once from (22·1·2) and (22·1·3) that the sequence of elementary divisors defines uniquely the Jordan matrix obtained from A by the process described in **22·1**, since to every elementary divisor $(\lambda_\mu-\lambda)^{j_{\mu\iota}}$ of A there corresponds the block matrix $(\lambda_\mu, j_{\mu\iota})$ of $\mathscr{E}$. On the other hand, we readily see that any Jordan matrix of order n has elementary divisors $(\lambda_\mu-\lambda)^{j_{\mu\iota}}$ determined by its block matrices $(\lambda_\mu, j_{\mu\iota})$. We let s_μ denote the number of blocks corresponding to any one of the diagonal elements λ_μ (we assume that the $j_{\mu\iota}$ are arranged in non-increasing order of magnitude), and write $\sum_{\iota=1}^{s_\mu} j_{\mu\iota} = k_\mu$, so that $\sum_{\mu=1}^{m} k_\mu = n$. Then the equations (22·1·1) hold for $\mathscr{E}$ and show that $\mathscr{E}$ has eigen-values λ_μ; the corresponding principal manifolds are determined by canonical bases formed from the sets of coordinate vectors u^κ, where $1+\sum_{\sigma=1}^{\mu-1} k_\sigma \leqslant \kappa \leqslant \sum_{\sigma=1}^{\mu} k_\sigma$, the first elements of the chains contained in these bases being the coordinate vectors u^κ for

$$\kappa = 1+\sum_{\sigma=1}^{\mu-1} k_\sigma + \sum_{\sigma=1}^{\iota-1} j_{\mu\sigma} \quad (1 \leqslant \iota \leqslant s_\mu).$$

(When $\mu = 1$ or $\iota = 1$, the corresponding sums to $\mu-1$ or $\iota-1$ are to be omitted.) Further, if T is any regular matrix, the matrix $A = T\mathscr{E}T^{-1}$ has the same elementary divisors as $\mathscr{E}$. For, if we define the sets of vectors $\{b^{\mu\nu}\}$ by the equations $Tu^\kappa = b^{\mu\nu}$, $u^\kappa = T^{-1}b^{\mu\nu}$, with the same suffix relations as in **22·1**, we see at once that the equations (22·0·3) are satisfied for A, which therefore has the same eigen-values and indices $j_{\mu\iota}$ as $\mathscr{E}$, and so the same elementary divisors as $\mathscr{E}$. We conclude that if the matrix A is reduced to a Jordan matrix $\mathscr{E}$ by any regular matrix T, whether T has been determined by the process of **22·1** or not, then $\mathscr{E}$ is uniquely determined by A and is independent of T.

22·21. The Segre characteristic. The sequence of indices $j_{\mu\iota}$ that determines the Jordan canonical form for A is called the *Segre characteristic of* A and is written in the following way:

$$[(j_{11}, j_{12}, \ldots, j_{1s_1}), (j_{21}, j_{22}, \ldots, j_{2s_2}), \ldots, (j_{m1}, j_{m2}, \ldots, j_{ms_m})].$$

22·3. Simple elementary divisors. The L.T. A is said to have simple elementary divisors if *all the indices* $j_{\mu\iota}$ $(1 \leqslant \mu \leqslant m;\ 1 \leqslant \iota \leqslant s_\mu)$ *in the Segre characteristic are* 1. *The Jordan matrix* $\mathscr{E}$ *for any L.T.* A *with simple elementary divisors is therefore a diagonal matrix and, conversely, the L.T.* A *has simple elementary divisors if the Jordan matrix* $\mathscr{E}$ *is a diagonal matrix.*

We deduce from the inequalities $1 \leqslant j_{\mu\iota} \leqslant j_{\mu 1} = j_\mu$, where j_μ is the index of the principal manifold $\mathfrak{P}_\mu$, that the condition for any L.T. A to have simple elementary divisors is equivalent to the condition that each principal manifold should have index 1 and should therefore coincide with the corresponding eigen-manifold of A. By Theorem **2·6**, this condition in turn is equivalent to the condition that the ranks s_μ and k_μ of the corresponding eigen-manifolds and principal manifolds should be equal. It is also equivalent, by **17·51**, to the condition that the eigen-manifolds should reduce A completely. *It follows that the L.T.* A *has simple elementary divisors if, and only if, all the eigen-manifolds reduce* A *completely.*

22·31. Theorem. *If the L.T.* A *has simple elementary divisors, then so has the L.T.* $f(A)$, *where* $f(\zeta)$ *is any function satisfying the conditions of Theorem* **19·23.**

Proof. By Theorem **19·23**, $f(A) = p(A)$, where $p(\zeta)$ is a polynomial. Since A has simple elementary divisors, there exists a regular matrix T and a diagonal matrix Λ such that $A = T\Lambda T^{-1}$. Thus, $A^\kappa = T\Lambda^\kappa T^{-1}$, for any positive power κ, and therefore $p(A) = Tp(\Lambda)\,T^{-1}$. This means that T reduces $p(A)$ to a diagonal matrix; thus $p(A)$ has simple elementary divisors.

22·32. Theorem. *If* $p(A) = O$ *for some polynomial* $p(\zeta)$ *that has simple zeros, then the L.T.* A *has simple elementary divisors.*

Proof. Let $q_A(\zeta)$ be the minimal polynomial of A. Now $q_A(\zeta)$ is a factor of $p(\zeta)$, by Theorem **18·3**, and therefore $q_A(\zeta)$ has simple zeros. But the orders of the zeros are the indices j_μ of the principal manifolds of A, and since these are all 1 it follows that A has simple elementary divisors.

22·33. Corollary of Theorem **22·32**. *Any L.T. with simple eigen-values has simple elementary divisors.*

Proof. If A has simple eigen values the minimal polynomial of A has simple zeros and therefore, by Theorem **22·32**, A has simple elementary divisors.

22·4. Definition of similar L.T.'s. *Two L.T.'s A and B in $\mathfrak{V}_n$ are said to be similar if there exists a L.T. S of rank n such that $S^{-1}AS = B$.*

22·41. Theorem. *The L.T.'s A and B in $\mathfrak{V}_n$ are similar if, and only if, they have the same elementary divisors.*

Proof. (i) If A and B have the same elementary divisors, then there exists a Jordan matrix $\mathscr{E}$ and two L.T.'s T and T_1 of rank n such that

$$\mathscr{E} = T^{-1}AT = T_1^{-1}BT_1. \qquad (22{\cdot}41{\cdot}1)$$

If we write $S = TT_1^{-1}$, we have $B = S^{-1}AS$.

(ii) Conversely, if $S^{-1}AS = B$ and if T is the L.T. of Theorem **22·1** transforming A into the Jordan matrix $\mathscr{E}$, we have

$$B = S^{-1}T\mathscr{E}T^{-1}S.$$

Hence, if we write $T_1 = S^{-1}T$, we have $T_1^{-1}BT_1 = \mathscr{E}$, so that A and B both transform into the same Jordan matrix and therefore, by **22·2**, they have the same elementary divisors.

22·42. Theorem. *If A and B are similar L.T.'s in $\mathfrak{V}_n$ such that $B = S^{-1}AS$, and if $\{b^{\mu\nu}\}$ is a canonical basis of $\mathfrak{V}_n$ belonging to A, then $\{S^{-1}b^{\mu\nu}\}$ is a canonical basis belonging to B.*

Proof. We have $B_\lambda S^{-1} = S^{-1}A_\lambda$. Hence, by (22·0·2),

$$\left.\begin{aligned} B_{\lambda_\mu}S^{-1}b^{\mu\nu} = S^{-1}A_{\lambda_\mu}b^{\mu\nu} &= 0 \\ &= S^{-1}b^{\mu,\nu+1} \end{aligned}\right\}$$

for the sets of suffixes given in (22·0·2). This shows that $\{S^{-1}b^{\mu\nu}\}$ is a canonical basis belonging to B, since, by Theorem **22·41**, A and B have the same elementary divisors.

22·43. We have shown in Theorem **13·42** that the trace is invariant throughout a set of equivalent H.T.'s. We now show that the trace of the matrix representation (see Definition **10·8**) is invariant throughout a set of similar L.T.'s.

Theorem. *Let A and B be similar L.T.'s. Then the matrix representations have the same trace, equal to the sum of the eigen-values $\sum_{\mu=1}^{m} k_\mu\lambda_\mu$.*

Proof. By Definition **22·4** we may write $B = S^{-1}AS$. We write the corresponding matrices as $A = (a_{\mu\nu})$, $B = (b_{\mu\nu})$, $S = (s_{\mu\nu})$ and $S^{-1} = (t_{\mu\nu})$, and, using (7·2·1) and (7·42·1), we establish the equality of the traces τ_A and τ_B by the equations

$$\tau_B = \sum_{\mu=1}^{n} b_{\mu\mu} = \sum_{\mu=1}^{n} \sum_{\nu=1}^{n} \sum_{\kappa=1}^{n} t_{\mu\nu} a_{\nu\kappa} s_{\kappa\mu} = \sum_{\nu=1}^{n} \sum_{\kappa=1}^{n} a_{\nu\kappa} \sum_{\mu=1}^{n} s_{\kappa\mu} t_{\mu\nu}$$

$$= \sum_{\nu=1}^{n} \sum_{\kappa=1}^{n} a_{\nu\kappa} \delta_{\kappa\nu} = \sum_{\nu=1}^{n} a_{\nu\nu} = \tau_A.$$

The equation (22·41·1), however, shows that the L.T.'s A and B are similar to the same Jordan matrix $\mathscr{E}$, so that

$$\tau_A = \tau_B = \tau_{\mathscr{E}} = \sum_{\mu=1}^{m} k_\mu \lambda_\mu,$$

for, clearly, the trace of $\mathscr{E}$ is $\sum_{\mu=1}^{m} k_\mu \lambda_\mu$, where the λ_μ are the distinct eigen-values of both A and B and the k_μ are their multiplicities.

22·44. Note. It follows from Theorem **22·43** that the trace of a L.T. can be defined as the sum of its eigen-values, independently of any matrix representation, so that τ_A may be associated in this way with the L.T. A itself and not only with its matrix representation.

22·5. The connections between the eigen-values λ_μ of a L.T. A and those of its adjoint A^* and between the principal manifolds $\mathfrak{P}_\mu$ and $\mathfrak{P}^*_\mu$ are given in Theorem **17·6**. We now give a further connection between A and A^*.

Theorem. *The adjoint A^* of the L.T. A in $\mathfrak{B}_n$ has the same Segre characteristic as A.*

Proof. (i) We first prove the theorem with the additional hypothesis that A is nilpotent. Then, by (21·01·1), the sequence of indices $j_{.\iota}$ $(1 \leqslant \iota \leqslant \rho_1)$ is uniquely determined by the sequence of numbers ρ_κ $(1 \leqslant \kappa \leqslant j)$ that are defined in **20·1** as the ranks of the L.M.'s $\mathfrak{X} . \mathfrak{R}^{\kappa-1}$. Our assertion will therefore be proved for a nilpotent L.T. A if we can show that A and A^* determine the same sequence of numbers ρ_κ. By Lemma **20·22**, however, rank $\mathfrak{X}^\kappa = \sum_{\nu=1}^{\kappa} \rho_\nu$. Now $\mathfrak{X}^\kappa$ is the null manifold of A^κ and hence, by Theorem **6·21**, rank $\mathfrak{X}^\kappa = n - \text{rank}\, A^\kappa$. If $\mathfrak{Y}^\kappa$ is the null manifold of $(A^*)^\kappa$, we have rank $\mathfrak{Y}^\kappa = n - \text{rank}\, (A^*)^\kappa$, and, since rank $(A^*)^\kappa = \text{rank}\, A^\kappa$, by

Theorem **6·4**, we see that rank $\mathfrak{X}^\kappa$ = rank $\mathfrak{Y}^\kappa$, and therefore that A and A^* determine the same sequence ρ_κ.

(ii) Consider any L.T. A in $\mathfrak{B}_n$ and write $A = \sum_{\mu=1}^{m} AQ_\mu$, by (18·5·1), where $AQ_\mu = Q_\mu A$ so that $A^* = \sum_{\mu=1}^{m} A^* Q_\mu^*$. Now $A_{\lambda\mu}$, considered as a L.T. in $\mathfrak{P}_\mu$, coincides with $A_{\lambda_\mu} Q_\mu$ which is nilpotent in $\mathfrak{B}_n$. The Segre characteristic of $A_{\lambda_\mu} Q_\mu$ is made up of the μth round bracket of that of A and $n-k_\mu$ other round brackets containing only 1. Now, by Theorem **17·6**, $\bar{\lambda}_\mu$ is the eigen-value of A^* corresponding to the projector Q_μ^*. Hence the Segre characteristic of $A^*_{\bar{\lambda}_\mu} Q^*_\mu$ is made up of the μth round bracket of that of A^* and $n-k_\mu$ other round brackets containing only 1. Since, by the first part of this proof, $A_{\lambda_\mu} Q_\mu$ and $A^*_{\bar{\lambda}_\mu} Q^*_\mu$ have the same Segre characteristic, we deduce that the μth round brackets of the Segre characteristics of A and A^* coincide.

22·6. In the rest of this Section we investigate the Jordan matrices for certain important classes of L.T.'s. We begin by considering the projectors.

Let Q be the projector of $\mathfrak{B}_n$ on the L.M. $\mathfrak{M}$ parallel to $\mathfrak{N}$, where $\mathfrak{M} \oplus \mathfrak{N} = \mathfrak{B}_n$. Then $\mathfrak{M}$ and $\mathfrak{N}$ are the eigen-manifolds of Q belonging to the eigen-values 1 and 0 respectively. Moreover, since $\mathfrak{M} \oplus \mathfrak{N} = \mathfrak{B}_n$, $\mathfrak{M}$ and $\mathfrak{N}$ are principal manifolds of Q and there is no eigen-value of Q other than 1 and 0. Hence, Q has simple elementary divisors. If the rank of $\mathfrak{M}$ is k_1 and that of $\mathfrak{N}$ is k_2, then $k_1 + k_2 = n$,

$$\mathscr{E} = \begin{pmatrix} \overbrace{1 \;\ddots\; 1}^{k_1} & & 0 \\ & \overbrace{0 \;\ddots\; 0}^{k_2} & \\ 0 & & \end{pmatrix},$$

and a matrix T transforming Q into $\mathscr{E}$ such that $\mathscr{E} = T^{-1}QT$ and $Q = T\mathscr{E}T^{-1}$ is determined by the equations

$$Tu^\nu = b^{1\nu} \quad (1 \leqslant \nu \leqslant k_1) \quad \text{and} \quad Tu^{k_1+\nu} = b^{2\nu} \quad (1 \leqslant \nu \leqslant k_2),$$

where the sets of vectors $\{b^{1\nu}\}$ and $\{b^{2\nu}\}$ form any bases of $\mathfrak{M}$ and $\mathfrak{N}$ respectively. For, since $j_1 = j_2 = 1$, any basis of $\mathfrak{M}$ or $\mathfrak{N}$ is a canonical basis. The representation of Q given in (10·7·4) will be seen to coincide with the matrix product $Q = T\mathscr{E}T^{-1}$, where $T = (t_{\mu\nu})$, $T^{-1} = (s_{\mu\nu})$ and $k_1 = r$.

22·7. The Jordan matrix for a normal transformation N gives the spectral representation (16·4·1) for N and, as a special case, the spectral representation (12·4·1) for any H.T. We can therefore give a new proof for these spectral representations without using the analytical argument of Chapter III.

By Theorem **17·3**, every principal manifold $\mathfrak{P}_\mu$ of a normal transformation N is an eigen-manifold; therefore, by **22·3**, N has simple elementary divisors and the Jordan matrix $\mathscr{E} - \lambda I$ for N becomes a diagonal matrix $\Lambda - \lambda I$

containing k_μ elements $(\lambda_\mu - \lambda)$ in the leading diagonal. Since each index j_μ is 1, we obtain, by (22·0·3), for any basis $\{b^{\mu\nu}\}$ of $\mathfrak{P}_\mu$ the equations

$$Nb^{\mu\nu} = \lambda_\mu b^{\mu\nu} \quad (1 \leqslant \nu \leqslant k_\mu). \tag{22·7·1}$$

Further, by Theorem **9·2**, we have $(b^{\mu\nu}, b^{\iota\kappa}) = 0$ for $\lambda_\mu \neq \lambda_\iota$. If therefore we take any orthonormal basis $\{\phi^{\mu\nu}\}$ $(\nu = 1, 2, \ldots, k_\mu)$ of $\mathfrak{P}_\mu$ as the basis $\{b^{\mu\nu}\}$, the set of n vectors $\{\phi^{\mu\nu}\}\left(\mu = 1, 2, ., m; \nu = 1, 2, \ldots, k_\mu; \sum_{\mu=1}^{m} k_\mu = n\right)$ will be a complete orthonormal system in $\mathfrak{B}_n$ and every x of $\mathfrak{B}_n$ may be written in the form

$$x = \sum_{\mu=1}^{m} \sum_{\nu=1}^{k_\mu} (x, \phi^{\mu\nu})\, \phi^{\mu\nu},$$

and, by (22·7·1),

$$Nx = \sum_{\mu=1}^{m} \lambda_\mu \sum_{\nu=1}^{k_\mu} (x, \phi^{\mu\nu})\, \phi^{\mu\nu}. \tag{22·7·2}$$

The representation (22·7·2) for a normal transformation is essentially the same as (16·4·1) and, for the special case of a H.T. H, as (12·4·1). We already know, by Theorem **8·5**, the proof of which is entirely algebraic, and by the Note to Theorem **16·4**, that a normal transformation is Hermitian if, and only if, the eigen-values λ_μ are all real.

22·71. We notice that the general projector Q considered in **22·6** is an example of a L.T. with simple elementary divisors, which is not a normal transformation unless Q is an orthogonal projector. For, by Theorem **9·2**, Q is normal if, and only if, the two eigen-manifolds $\mathfrak{M}$ and $\mathfrak{N}$ of Q are orthogonal to one another.

22·72. A real symmetric L.T. A can be considered as a special case of a H.T. and therefore has simple elementary divisors, but this is no longer true for a L.T. A defined by a *non-real symmetric* matrix, as we now show by an example. We write

$$A = \begin{pmatrix} 1 & i \\ i & -1 \end{pmatrix}, \quad T = \begin{pmatrix} 0 & i \\ 1 & -1 \end{pmatrix}, \quad T^{-1}AT = \begin{pmatrix} 0 & 0 \\ 1 & 0 \end{pmatrix}.$$

Here, A is nilpotent of index 2 with Segre characteristic [(2)], since the canonical basis belonging to A which is given by $b^{\cdot 1} = (0, 1), b^{\cdot 2} = (i, -1)$ consists of one chain only. We readily see that the most general nilpotent second-order symmetric matrix of index 2 is of the form αA or $\alpha \bar{A}$, where α is any complex constant.

§ 23. Commutativity of L.T.'s

23·0. In seeking conditions under which a L.T. S is commutative with a given L.T. A in $\mathfrak{B}_n$ we find at once the following necessary conditions:

Theorem. *Let A be a L.T. in $\mathfrak{B}_n$ and let $Q_\mu (1 \leqslant \mu \leqslant m)$ be the projectors of $\mathfrak{B}_n$ on the principal manifolds of A defined in* **18·5**. *If $SA = AS$, then $SQ_\mu = Q_\mu S$.*

Proof. The proof is immediate, since, by **19·22**, Q_μ can be written as a polynomial in A.

23·01. Necessary and sufficient conditions under which a L.T. S is commutative with A are given in the following theorem:

THEOREM. *Let A be a L.T. in $\mathfrak{V}_n$ with the complete set of distinct eigen-values $\lambda_\mu (1 \leqslant \mu \leqslant m)$, let the L.M. $\mathfrak{P}_\mu$, of rank k_μ, be the principal manifold corresponding to λ_μ and let $\{b^{\mu\nu}\} (1 \leqslant \mu \leqslant m;\ 1 \leqslant \nu \leqslant k_\mu)$ be a canonical basis of $\mathfrak{V}_n$ belonging to A. Then the L.T. S is commutative with A if, and only if, the elements $a^{\mu\nu}$ defined by the equations $a^{\mu\nu} = Sb^{\mu\nu}$ form a system satisfying the equations* (22·0·2).

PROOF. (i) Let the elements $a^{\mu\nu}$ satisfy the equations (22·0·2). Then we have

$$\begin{aligned} A_{\lambda_\mu} Sb^{\mu\nu} &= A_{\lambda_\mu} a^{\mu\nu} \\ &\left.\begin{aligned} &= 0 = SA_{\lambda_\mu} b^{\mu\nu} \\ &= a^{\mu,\nu+1} = Sb^{\mu,\nu+1} = SA_{\lambda_\mu} b^{\mu\nu} \end{aligned}\right\} \end{aligned}$$

for the same system of suffixes as in (22·0·2). But $\{b^{\mu\nu}\}$ is a basis of $\mathfrak{V}_n$, so that we may write any x of $\mathfrak{V}_n$ in the form $x = \sum_{\mu=1}^{m} \sum_{\nu=1}^{k_\mu} \alpha_{\mu\nu} b^{\mu\nu}$, and we deduce that $ASx = SAx$.

(ii) Conversely, if $AS = SA$ and if $a^{\mu\nu} = Sb^{\mu\nu}$, we have

$$\begin{aligned} A_{\lambda_\mu} a^{\mu\nu} &= A_{\lambda_\mu} Sb^{\mu\nu} = SA_{\lambda_\mu} b^{\mu\nu} \\ &\left.\begin{aligned} &= 0 \\ &= Sb^{\mu,\nu+1} = a^{\mu,\nu+1} \end{aligned}\right\} \end{aligned}$$

for the same system of suffixes as in (22·0·2). Thus, the elements $a^{\mu\nu}$ satisfy the equations (22·0·2).

23·02. The preceding theorem enables us to give a matrix representation for any L.T. S commutative with a given L.T. A in $\mathfrak{V}_n$. Let $\{b^{\mu\nu}\}$ and $\{a^{\mu\nu}\}$ be the two systems of n elements of Theorem **23·01**, so that $Sb^{\mu\nu} = a^{\mu\nu}$, and let B and C be two nth order matrices of which the n columns consist of the coordinates of $b^{\mu\nu}$ and $a^{\mu\nu}$ respectively. Then the equations $Sb^{\mu\nu} = a^{\mu\nu}$ can be written as the matrix equation $SB = C$, where S now denotes the matrix representing the L.T. S. The matrix B, however, has rank n, since the $b^{\mu\nu}$ form a canonical basis belonging to A and are therefore linearly independent. Hence the required matrix representation for S is $S = CB^{-1}$.

23·03. By an argument similar to that of **21·31**, we see that we shall obtain all L.T.'s S of rank n commutative with A, that is, all

L.T.'s S transforming A into itself, if we choose linearly independent elements $a^{\mu\nu}$ to satisfy the equations (22·0·2); these elements will then form a canonical basis of $\mathfrak{B}_n$ belonging to A. We therefore obtain the following theorem:

THEOREM. *Let the set of elements* $\{b^{\mu\nu}\}$ *be a canonical basis of* $\mathfrak{B}_n$ *belonging to the L.T. A. Then all L.T.'s S of rank n commutative with A, that is, all L.T.'s transforming A into itself, are determined by the condition that the set of elements* $\{b'^{\mu\nu}\}$, *where*

$$b'^{\mu\nu} = Sb^{\mu\nu} \quad (1 \leqslant \mu \leqslant m;\ 1 \leqslant \nu \leqslant k_\mu),$$

should also be a canonical basis belonging to A. In the corresponding matrix representation $S = CB^{-1}$ *of* **23·02** *the matrices B and C are both of rank n.*

23·04. We obtain the most general L.T. S commutative with A, not necessarily of rank n, by writing

$$Sb^{\mu\nu} = a^{\mu\nu} = \eta^{\mu\iota\kappa} = (A_{\lambda_\mu})^{\kappa-1}\eta^{\mu\iota 1},$$

where

$$\nu = \kappa \quad (\iota = 1, \nu \leqslant j_{\mu 1}), \qquad \nu = \kappa + \sum_{\sigma=1}^{\iota-1} j_{\mu\sigma} \quad (2 \leqslant \iota \leqslant s_\mu,\ 1 \leqslant \kappa \leqslant j_{\mu\iota}),$$

provided only that we choose for the set $\eta^{\mu\iota 1}$ any elements of $\mathfrak{P}_\mu$ of which the indices do not exceed $j_{\mu\iota}$. The elements $a^{\mu\nu}$ will then be the most general set to satisfy the equations (22·0·2).

We introduce a set of integers $\rho_{\mu\kappa}$ by writing

$$\rho_{\mu 1} = s_\mu = \operatorname{rank} \mathfrak{E}_\mu, \quad \sum_{\nu=1}^{\kappa} \rho_{\mu\nu} = \operatorname{rank} \mathfrak{E}_\mu^\kappa \tag{23·04·1}$$

(see **17·2**), and we readily deduce from **21·32** that the number of arbitrary constants on which the most general L.T. S depends is

$$\sum_{\mu=1}^{m} \sum_{\kappa=1}^{j_\mu} \rho_{\mu\kappa}^2 = \sum_{\mu=1}^{m} \sum_{\iota=1}^{s_\mu} (2\iota - 1) j_{\mu\iota}. \tag{23·04·2}$$

23·1. If A has simple elementary divisors any set of k_μ linearly independent elements $b^{\mu\nu}$ of $\mathfrak{P}_\mu$ forms a canonical basis of $\mathfrak{P}_\mu$ belonging to A, and hence the most general L.T. S commutative with A is given at once by the equations

$$Sb^{\mu\nu} = a^{\mu\nu} = \sum_{\kappa=1}^{k_\mu} \alpha_{\mu\nu\kappa} b^{\mu\kappa} \quad (1 \leqslant \mu \leqslant m,\ 1 \leqslant \nu \leqslant k_\mu), \tag{23·1·1}$$

where the number of constants $\alpha_{\mu\nu\kappa}$ is $\sum_{\mu=1}^{m} k_\mu^2$.

23·11. If A has simple eigen-values, that is, if $k_\mu = 1$ for

$$1 \leqslant \mu \leqslant m = n,$$

every eigen-manifold is a principal manifold $\mathfrak{P}_\mu$ of rank 1, the canonical basis of $\mathfrak{V}_n$ belonging to A is the set of eigen-solutions $\{b^\mu\}$ for which $Ab^\mu = \lambda_\mu b^\mu$, and the equations (23·1·1) take the form $Sb^\mu = a^\mu = \omega_\mu b^\mu$, where ω_μ denotes any complex number. They imply that $SQ_\mu = \omega_\mu Q_\mu$, where Q_μ is the projector corresponding to $\mathfrak{P}_\mu$ (that is, a projector on to b^μ). Moreover, by (18·5·1),

$$A = \sum_{\mu=1}^{n} AQ_\mu = \sum_{\mu=1}^{n} \lambda_\mu Q_\mu.$$

If, therefore, we determine a polynomial $p(\zeta)$, of degree $n-1$ at most, such that $p(\lambda_\mu) = \omega_\mu$ $(1 \leqslant \mu \leqslant n)$, we obtain from (19·1·1)

$$S = \sum_{\mu=1}^{n} SQ_\mu = \sum_{\mu=1}^{n} \omega_\mu Q_\mu = \sum_{\mu=1}^{n} p(\lambda_\mu)\, Q_\mu = p(A).$$

We have proved the following theorem:

THEOREM. *Every L.T. S in $\mathfrak{V}_n$ commutative with a L.T. A that has simple eigen-values can be written in the form $S = p(A)$, where $p(\zeta)$ is a polynomial of degree $n-1$ at most.*

23·12. The L.T. $S = p(A)$ of Theorem **23·11** has simple elementary divisors, by Theorem **22·31**, since the L.T. A has simple elementary divisors. Thus, Theorem **23·11**, which is concerned with a special class of L.T.'s with simple elementary divisors, is a generalization of Theorem **16·84** for normal transformations. We obtain theorems corresponding in a similar way to Theorems **16·8**, **16·81** and **16·82** for normal transformations (and to Theorems **16·0**, **16·1** and **16·2** for H.T.'s), as we now show.

23·13. THEOREM. *Let A be a L.T. in $\mathfrak{V}_n$ with simple elementary divisors. Let the distinct eigen-values of A be λ_μ $(1 \leqslant \mu \leqslant m)$, and let the corresponding projectors of $\mathfrak{V}_n$ on the principal manifolds of A be Q_μ, as in Theorem* **23·0**. *The L.T. S is commutative with A if, and only if, $SQ_\mu = Q_\mu S$ for $1 \leqslant \mu \leqslant m$.*

PROOF. We have already proved the necessity of the condition in Theorem **23·0** with no restrictions on the L.T. A. The sufficiency follows at once when A has simple elementary divisors, since then the principal manifolds of A are the eigen-manifolds and, by (18·5·1),

$$A = \sum_{\mu=1}^{m} AQ_\mu = \sum_{\mu=1}^{m} \lambda_\mu Q_\mu,$$

so that, when $SQ_\mu = Q_\mu S$,

$$SA = \sum_{\mu=1}^{m} \lambda_\mu SQ_\mu = \sum_{\mu=1}^{m} \lambda_\mu Q_\mu S = AS.$$

23·14. THEOREM. *Two L.T.'s in $\mathfrak{B}_n$ have a linearly independent set of n eigen-solutions in common if, and only if, they are commutative L.T.'s with simple elementary divisors.*

PROOF. Let the L.T. A have m distinct eigen-values λ_μ with eigen-manifolds of rank s_μ, principal manifolds $\mathfrak{P}_\mu$ of rank k_μ, and corresponding projectors Q_μ; let B have m' distinct eigen-values λ'_ν, principal manifolds $\mathfrak{P}'_\nu$ and corresponding projectors Q'_ν.

If A has a linearly independent set of n eigen-solutions we have $\sum_{\mu=1}^{m} s_\mu = n$. Then, since $\sum_{\mu=1}^{m} k_\mu = n$, by (18·3·1), and since $k_\mu \geqslant s_\mu$ for $1 \leqslant \mu \leqslant m$, it follows that $k_\mu = s_\mu$ for $1 \leqslant \mu \leqslant m$, and therefore, by **22·3**, that A has simple elementary divisors.

If A and B have the linearly independent set $\{b^\kappa\}$ of n eigen-solutions in common, they both have simple elementary divisors. Denoting the eigen-values corresponding to each b^κ by l_κ and l'_κ, we have $Ab^\kappa = l_\kappa b^\kappa$, $Bb^\kappa = l'_\kappa b^\kappa$ and

$$BAb^\kappa = l_\kappa Bb^\kappa = l_\kappa l'_\kappa b^\kappa = ABb^\kappa \quad (\kappa = 1, 2, \ldots, n).$$

Thus, $AB = BA$, since the set $\{b^\kappa\}$ is a basis of $\mathfrak{B}_n$, and one part of the theorem is proved.

We now let A and B be commutative L.T.'s with simple elementary divisors and show that they have a linearly independent set of eigen-solutions in common. By Theorem **23·0**, $AQ'_\nu = Q'_\nu A$ for $1 \leqslant \nu \leqslant m'$. We write $\mathfrak{P}_{\mu\nu} = \mathfrak{P}_\mu . \mathfrak{P}'_\nu$, with the possibility that $\mathfrak{P}_{\mu\nu}$ may be $\mathfrak{O}$. Clearly, $\sum_{\nu=1}^{m'} \mathfrak{P}_{\mu\nu} \oplus \subseteq \mathfrak{P}_\mu$; we prove that $\mathfrak{P}_\mu \subseteq \sum_{\nu=1}^{m'} \mathfrak{P}_{\mu\nu} \oplus$ and deduce equality. We have, for any element a of $\mathfrak{P}_\mu$,

$$Aa = \lambda_\mu a, \quad AQ'_\nu a = Q'_\nu Aa = \lambda_\mu Q'_\nu a \quad (\nu = 1, 2, \ldots, m'),$$

so that $Q'_\nu a \in \mathfrak{P}_\mu$ and hence $Q'_\nu a \in \mathfrak{P}_{\mu\nu}$. But, since $a = \sum_{\nu=1}^{m'} Q'_\nu a$, we have $a \in \sum_{\nu=1}^{m'} \mathfrak{P}_{\mu\nu} \oplus$ and therefore $\mathfrak{P}_\mu \subseteq \sum_{\nu=1}^{m'} \mathfrak{P}_{\mu\nu} \oplus$. Finally,

$$\mathfrak{B}_n = \sum_{\mu=1}^{m} \mathfrak{P}_\mu \oplus = \sum_{\mu=1}^{m} \sum_{\nu=1}^{m'} \mathfrak{P}_{\mu\nu} \oplus.$$

We take a basis in each of the L.M.'s $\mathfrak{P}_{\mu\nu}$ that is not $\mathfrak{O}$ and so obtain a basis $\{b^\kappa\}$ of $\mathfrak{B}_n$ consisting of eigen-solutions common to A and B, since the principal manifolds are all eigen-manifolds. This proves the other part of the theorem.

23·15. THEOREM. *If the commutative L.T.'s A and B in $\mathfrak{B}_n$ have simple elementary divisors there exists a third L.T. C, with simple eigen-values, such that $A = p(C)$ and $B = q(C)$, where $p(\zeta)$ and $q(\zeta)$ are polynomials of degree $n-1$ at most.*

PROOF. The basis $\{b^\kappa\}$ of $\mathfrak{B}_n$ obtained in the second part of the proof of Theorem **23·14** is a canonical basis of $\mathfrak{B}_n$ belonging to A since it is made up from canonical bases in each $\mathfrak{P}_\mu$; clearly, it is also a canonical basis belonging to B. Now let $\{\omega_\kappa\}$ be any set of n distinct numbers and define a L.T. C by writing $Cb^\kappa = \omega_\kappa b^\kappa$ for $\kappa = 1, 2, \ldots, n$. Then C has simple eigen-values ω_κ with eigen-solutions b^κ. By the first part of Theorem **23·14** we have $AC = CA$ and $BC = CB$, and therefore, by Theorem **23·11**, $A = p(C)$ and $B = q(C)$, where $p(\zeta)$ and $q(\zeta)$ are polynomials of degree $n-1$ at most.

23·2. Theorem **23·11** can be generalized to give the same result under wider conditions for the L.T. A.

THEOREM. *Let A be a L.T. in $\mathfrak{B}_n$ with the distinct eigen-values λ_μ $(1 \leqslant \mu \leqslant m)$, and such that the m numbers s_μ defined in **22·0** are all equal to 1, that is, $k_\mu = j_\mu$ and the Segre characteristic of A is*

$$[j_1, j_2, \ldots, j_m]$$

(the round brackets that would enclose only the one number j_μ being dropped in this case). Then every L.T. S commutative with A can be written in the form $S = p(A)$, where $p(\zeta)$ is a polynomial of degree $n-1$ at most.

PROOF. Let $\{b^{\mu\nu}\}$ be a canonical basis of $\mathfrak{B}_n$ belonging to A. By hypothesis, the canonical bases in $\mathfrak{P}_\mu$ $(1 \leqslant \mu \leqslant m)$ each consist of only one chain of order k_μ belonging to A_{λ_μ}, and the equations (22·0·2) take the form

$$\left.\begin{aligned} A_{\lambda_\mu} b^{\mu\nu} &= 0 & (\nu = j_\mu). \\ &= b^{\mu,\nu+1} = A^\nu_{\lambda_\mu} b^{\mu 1} & (1 \leqslant \nu \leqslant j_\mu - 1) \end{aligned}\right\} \qquad (23\cdot2\cdot1)$$

If now S is a L.T. commutative with A and if we write $Sb^{\mu\nu} = a^{\mu\nu}$, then, by **23·04**, the only condition to be fulfilled is that $a^{\mu 1}$ should be an element of $\mathfrak{P}_\mu$ with index not exceeding j_μ. But j_μ is the index of $\mathfrak{P}_\mu$ so that any element of $\mathfrak{P}_\mu$ satisfies this condition. Further, $\{b^{\mu\nu}\}$ $(1 \leqslant \nu \leqslant j_\mu)$ is a basis of $\mathfrak{P}_\mu$. We may therefore write

$$a^{\mu 1} = \sum_{\kappa=1}^{j_\mu} \alpha_{\mu\kappa} b^{\mu\kappa}, \quad a^{\mu\nu} = A_{\lambda_\mu}^{\nu-1} a^{\mu 1} = \sum_{\kappa=1}^{j_\mu-\nu+1} \alpha_{\mu\kappa} b^{\mu,\kappa+\nu-1}, \tag{23·2·2}$$

where the constants $\alpha_{\mu\kappa}$ are arbitrary complex numbers including zeros. We determine, by Lemma **19·0**, a polynomial $p(\zeta)$ of degree

$$\left(\sum_{\mu=1}^{m} j_\mu\right) - 1 = \left(\sum_{\mu=1}^{m} k_\mu\right) - 1 = n - 1$$

at most, such that

$$\frac{1}{(\kappa-1)!} p^{(\kappa-1)}(\lambda_\mu) = \alpha_{\mu\kappa} \quad (1 \leqslant \kappa \leqslant j_\mu).$$

Then, by (19·1·1),

$$p(A) = \sum_{\mu=1}^{m} \sum_{\kappa=1}^{j_\mu} \alpha_{\mu\kappa} A_{\lambda_\mu}^{\kappa-1} Q_\mu,$$

and, by (23·2·1) and (23·2·2),

$$p(A)\, b^{\mu 1} = \sum_{\kappa=1}^{j_\mu} \alpha_{\mu\kappa} b^{\mu\kappa} = a^{\mu 1},$$

$$p(A)\, b^{\mu\nu} = A_{\lambda_\mu}^{\nu-1} p(A)\, b^{\mu 1} = A_{\lambda_\mu}^{\nu-1} a^{\mu 1} = a^{\mu\nu} \quad (1 \leqslant \nu \leqslant j_\mu).$$

Hence, $p(A)\, b^{\mu\nu} = a^{\mu\nu} = S b^{\mu\nu}$ and therefore, since $\{b^{\mu\nu}\}$ is a basis of $\mathfrak{B}_n$, $p(A) = S$.

23·21. The preceding theorem may also be written in the following form, given by Sylvester:

THEOREM. *If the minimal polynomial of a L.T. A in $\mathfrak{B}_n$ is of degree n, then every L.T. S commutative with A can be written in the form $S = p(A)$, where $p(\zeta)$ is a polynomial of degree $n-1$ at most.*

PROOF. We have shown in **18·31** that the hypothesis is equivalent to the equality of j_μ and k_μ for $\mu = 1, 2, \ldots, m$. Theorem **23·21** is therefore equivalent to Theorem **23·2**.

23·3. It is obvious that any function $f(A)$ that satisfies the conditions of Theorem **19·23**, and that can therefore be written as a polynomial $p(A)$, is commutative with A, but it is not true in general that every S that is commutative with A can be expressed in the form $S = p(A)$. We illustrate this point in **23·42** and **23·43**. We now ask what additional property distinguishes the L.T.'s $p(A)$ from the other L.T.'s commutative with A. Before we can answer this question, however, we need a preliminary lemma.

Lemma. *Let A be any L.T. in $\mathfrak{B}_n$, let $\mathfrak{P}_{\mu\iota}$ $(1 \leqslant \mu \leqslant m;\ 1 \leqslant \iota \leqslant s_\mu)$ be the L.M.'s determined as in (22·0·4) by a canonical basis $\{b^{\mu\nu}\}$ of $\mathfrak{B}_n$ belonging to A, and let $Q_{\mu\iota}$ be the projector of $\mathfrak{B}_n$ on $\mathfrak{P}_{\mu\iota}$ defined as in (22·0·4). There exists a L.T. B satisfying the following three conditions:*

(i) $A = q(B)$,

(ii) $BA = AB, \quad BQ_{\mu\iota} = Q_{\mu\iota}B \quad (1 \leqslant \mu \leqslant m;\ 1 \leqslant \iota \leqslant s_\mu)$,

(iii) *every L.T. S commutative with A as well as with all the $Q_{\mu\iota}$ can be written in the form $S = p(B)$, where $p(\zeta)$ and $q(\zeta)$ are polynomials of degree $n-1$ at most.*

Proof. We write $b^{\mu\nu} = \xi^{\mu\iota\kappa}$, where

$$\nu = \kappa \quad (\iota = 1, \nu \leqslant j_{\mu 1}),$$

$$\nu = \kappa + \sum_{\sigma=1}^{\iota-1} j_{\mu\sigma} \quad \left(2 \leqslant \iota \leqslant s_\mu;\ \sum_{\sigma=1}^{\iota-1} j_{\mu\sigma} < \nu \leqslant \sum_{\sigma=1}^{\iota} j_{\mu\sigma}\right).$$

Then

$$\mathfrak{P}_{\mu\iota} = [\xi^{\mu\iota 1}, \xi^{\mu\iota 2}, \ldots, \xi^{\mu\iota j_{\mu\iota}}] \tag{23·3·1}$$

and

$$\left.\begin{aligned} A\xi^{\mu\iota\kappa} &= \lambda_\mu \xi^{\mu\iota\kappa} + \xi^{\mu\iota,\kappa+1} && (1 \leqslant \kappa \leqslant j_{\mu\iota} - 1) \\ &= \lambda_\mu \xi^{\mu\iota\kappa} && (\kappa = j_{\mu\iota}) \end{aligned}\right\} \tag{23·3·2}$$

where

$$1 \leqslant \mu \leqslant m;\ 1 \leqslant \iota \leqslant s_\mu.$$

We now choose $\sum_{\mu=1}^{m} s_\mu$ different numbers $\omega_{\mu\iota}$ $(1 \leqslant \mu \leqslant m;\ 1 \leqslant \iota \leqslant s_\mu)$, and determine a L.T. B by the equations

$$\left.\begin{aligned} B\xi^{\mu\iota\kappa} &= \omega_{\mu\iota} \xi^{\mu\iota\kappa} + \xi^{\mu\iota,\kappa+1} && (1 \leqslant \kappa \leqslant j_{\mu\iota} - 1) \\ &= \omega_{\mu\iota} \xi^{\mu\iota\kappa} && (\kappa = j_{\mu\iota}). \end{aligned}\right\} \tag{23·3·3}$$

Then $AB = BA$, since, by (23·3·3), $B\xi^{\mu\iota 1}$ is an element of $\mathfrak{P}_{\mu\iota}$ with index not exceeding $j_{\mu\iota}$, and since

$$B\xi^{\mu\iota\kappa} = A_{\lambda_\mu}^{\kappa-1}(\omega_{\mu\iota}\xi^{\mu\iota 1} + \xi^{\mu\iota 2}) = A_{\lambda_\mu}^{\kappa-1} B\xi^{\mu\iota 1},$$

so that $B\xi^{\mu\iota\kappa}$ satisfies the conditions of **23·04**.

We see from (23·3·3) that the canonical basis $\{\xi^{\mu\iota\kappa}\}$ of $\mathfrak{B}_n$ belonging to A is also a canonical basis belonging to B and that the chains of this basis belonging to A also belong to B. Each L.M. $\mathfrak{P}_{\mu\iota}$ is, however, a principal manifold of B corresponding to the eigen-value $\omega_{\mu\iota}$. Thus, by Corollary **17·41**, $BQ_{\mu\iota} = Q_{\mu\iota}B$. Further, $j_{\mu\iota}$ is both rank and index of $\mathfrak{P}_{\mu\iota}$ and therefore the relation $AB = BA$ implies, by Theorem **23·2**, that $A = q(B)$. We have now shown that conditions (i) and (ii) of the lemma are satisfied.

We show that (iii) is satisfied by proving that $BS = SB$ whenever S is commutative with A and with every $Q_{\mu\iota}$, for the relation $BS = SB$ will then show, again by Theorem **23·2**, that $S = p(B)$.

Let $AS = SA$ and $Q_{\mu\iota}S = SQ_{\mu\iota}$ $(1 \leqslant \mu \leqslant m;\ 1 \leqslant \iota \leqslant s_\mu)$, and write

$$\eta^{\mu\iota\kappa} = S\xi^{\mu\iota\kappa} \quad (1 \leqslant \mu \leqslant m;\ 1 \leqslant \iota \leqslant s_\mu;\ 1 \leqslant \kappa \leqslant j_{\mu\iota}).$$

Then

$$\eta^{\mu\iota\kappa} = S\xi^{\mu\iota\kappa} = A_{\lambda_\mu}^{\kappa-1} S\xi^{\mu\iota 1} = A_{\lambda_\mu}^{\kappa-1} \eta^{\mu\iota 1}, \qquad (23\cdot3\cdot4)$$

since

$$\xi^{\mu\iota\kappa} = A_{\lambda_\mu}^{\kappa-1} \xi^{\mu\iota 1};$$

further, $\eta^{\mu\iota\kappa} \in \mathfrak{P}_{\mu\iota}$ since $\eta^{\mu\iota\kappa} = SQ_{\mu\iota}\xi^{\mu\iota\kappa} = Q_{\mu\iota}S\xi^{\mu\iota\kappa}$. Thus, by (23·3·1),

$$\eta^{\mu\iota 1} = \sum_{\nu=1}^{j_{\mu\iota}} \alpha_{\mu\iota\nu} \xi^{\mu\iota\nu}. \qquad (23\cdot3\cdot5)$$

We now deduce from (23·3·2) and (23·3·3) that

$$\left.\begin{aligned} B_{\omega_{\mu\iota}}\xi^{\mu\iota\kappa} &= A_{\lambda_\mu}\xi^{\mu\iota\kappa} \\ &= \xi^{\mu\iota,\kappa+1} \quad (1 \leqslant \kappa \leqslant j_{\mu\iota}-1) \\ &= 0 \quad (\kappa = j_{\mu\iota}), \end{aligned}\right\} \qquad (23\cdot3\cdot6)$$

and therefore, by (23·3·5), that

$$B_{\omega_{\mu\iota}}\eta^{\mu\iota 1} = A_{\lambda_\mu}\eta^{\mu\iota 1}.$$

After multiplying by $A_{\lambda_\mu}^{\kappa-1}$ and using the relations $AB = BA$ and (23·3·4) we have

$$\left.\begin{aligned} B_{\omega_{\mu\iota}}\eta^{\mu\iota\kappa} &= A_{\lambda_\mu}^{\kappa}\eta^{\mu\iota 1} \\ &= \eta^{\mu\iota,\kappa+1} \quad (1 \leqslant \kappa \leqslant j_{\mu\iota}-1) \\ &= 0 \quad (\kappa = j_{\mu\iota}), \end{aligned}\right\}$$

that is,

$$\eta^{\mu\iota\kappa} = B_{\omega_{\mu\iota}}^{\kappa-1}\eta^{\mu\iota 1}.$$

But $\{\xi^{\mu\iota\kappa}\}$ is a canonical basis of $\mathfrak{V}_n$ belonging to B, $\eta^{\mu\iota\kappa} = S\xi^{\mu\iota\kappa}$ and $\eta^{\mu\iota 1} \in \mathfrak{P}_{\mu\iota}$. Thus, by **23·04**, $BS = SB$. This completes the proof of the lemma.

23·4. THEOREM. *Any L.T. S in $\mathfrak{V}_n$ that is commutative with A and is completely reduced by every pair of complementary L.M.'s that reduce A completely can be written as a polynomial in A.*

NOTE. By Theorem **10·9**, we can state Theorem **23·4** in the following equivalent form, which is the form we prove.

Any L.T. S in $\mathfrak{V}_n$ that is commutative not only with the L.T. A but also with every projector commutative with A can be written as a polynomial in A.

PROOF. Let $\{\xi^{\mu\iota\kappa}\}$ be a canonical basis of $\mathfrak{V}_n$ belonging to A, let $\mathfrak{P}_{\mu\iota}$ be the L.M. defined by (23·3·1) and let $Q_{\mu\iota}$ be the corresponding projector. If S is any L.T. commutative with every projector that is commutative with A, then $SQ_{\mu\iota} = Q_{\mu\iota}S$ and we can apply

Lemma **23·3**. We see from (19·1·1) that, if B is the L.T. defined by (23·3·3), then

$$S = p_0(B) = \sum_{\mu=1}^{m} \sum_{\iota=1}^{s_\mu} \sum_{\nu=0}^{j_{\mu\iota}-1} \frac{1}{\nu!} p_0^{(\nu)}(\omega_{\mu\iota})\, B^\nu_{\omega_{\mu\iota}} Q_{\mu\iota},$$

where $p_0(\zeta)$ is a polynomial of degree $n-1$ at most. Further, since (23·3·6) implies that $B^\nu_{\omega_{\mu\iota}} \xi^{\mu\iota\kappa} = A^\nu_{\lambda_\mu} \xi^{\mu\iota\kappa}$ $(1 \leqslant \kappa \leqslant j_{\mu\iota};\ \nu = 1, 2, \ldots)$, and therefore that $B^\nu_{\omega_{\mu\iota}} Q_{\mu\iota} = A^\nu_{\lambda_\mu} Q_{\mu\iota}$, we have

$$S = \sum_{\mu=1}^{m} \sum_{\iota=1}^{s_\mu} \sum_{\nu=0}^{j_{\mu\iota}-1} \frac{1}{\nu!} p_0^{(\nu)}(\omega_{\mu\iota})\, A^\nu_{\lambda_\mu} Q_{\mu\iota}. \qquad (23·4·1)$$

We now assume that at least one of the numbers s_μ, say s_1, is at least 2, since otherwise the truth of the theorem would follow at once from Theorem **23·2**; we also write j_{11} and j_{12}, the orders of the first two chains in the basis $\{\xi^{\mu\iota\kappa}\}$, as j and j' respectively $(j' \leqslant j)$. We consider the L.T. Q_0 defined by the equations

$$\left.\begin{aligned} Q_0 \xi^{\mu\iota\kappa} &= 0 && (\mu \neq 1),\\ Q_0 \xi^{11\kappa} &= A^{\kappa-1}_{\lambda_1}(\xi^{111} + \xi^{121}) = \xi^{11\kappa} + \xi^{12\kappa} && (1 \leqslant \kappa \leqslant j'),\\ &= \xi^{11\kappa} && (j'+1 \leqslant \kappa \leqslant j),\\ Q_0 \xi^{1\iota\kappa} &= 0 && (\iota \geqslant 2). \end{aligned}\right\} \qquad (23·4·2)$$

We readily verify that $Q_0^2 \xi^{\mu\iota\kappa} = Q_0 \xi^{\mu\iota\kappa} = A^{\kappa-1}_{\lambda_\mu} Q_0 \xi^{\mu\iota 1}$ for all $\xi^{\mu\iota\kappa}$. We deduce from the second equality, by **23·04**, that $AQ_0 = Q_0 A$ and from the first, by Theorem **10·2**, that Q_0 is a projector. The range of Q_0 is the L.M.

$$[\xi^{111} + \xi^{121}, \ldots, \xi^{11j'} + \xi^{12j'},\ \xi^{11,j'+1},\ \ldots,\ \xi^{11j}],$$

and its null manifold consists of the sum of all the $\mathfrak{P}_{\mu\iota}$ except $\mathfrak{P}_{11}$. By the hypothesis of the theorem, $SQ_0 = Q_0 S$. We deduce from (23·4·1), however, that

$$\begin{aligned} SQ_0 \xi^{111} &= \sum_{\nu=0}^{j-1} \frac{1}{\nu!} p_0^{(\nu)}(\omega_{11})\, A^\nu_{\lambda_1} \xi^{111} + \sum_{\nu=0}^{j'-1} \frac{1}{\nu!} p_0^{(\nu)}(\omega_{12})\, A^\nu_{\lambda_1} \xi^{121}\\ &= Q_0 S \xi^{111} = \sum_{\nu=0}^{j-1} \frac{1}{\nu!} p_0^{(\nu)}(\omega_{11})\, A^\nu_{\lambda_1} (\xi^{111} + \xi^{121}), \end{aligned}$$

and hence that

$$p_0^{(\nu)}(\omega_{12}) = p_0^{(\nu)}(\omega_{11}) \quad (0 \leqslant \nu \leqslant j' - 1 = j_{12} - 1),$$

since the $j + j'$ elements

$$A^\nu_{\lambda_1} \xi^{111} = \xi^{11,\nu+1}, \quad A^\nu_{\lambda_1} \xi^{121} = \xi^{12,\nu+1}$$

are linearly independent.

In a similar way we show that

$$p_0^{(\nu)}(\omega_{1\iota}) = p_0^{(\nu)}(\omega_{11}) \quad (3 \leqslant \iota \leqslant s_1;\ 0 \leqslant \nu \leqslant j_{1\iota}-1),$$

and, further, that for every μ where $s_\mu \geqslant 2$

$$p_0^{(\nu)}(\omega_{\mu\iota}) = p_0^{(\nu)}(\omega_{\mu 1}) \quad (2 \leqslant \iota \leqslant s_\mu;\ 0 \leqslant \nu \leqslant j_{\mu\iota}-1). \qquad (23{\cdot}4{\cdot}3)$$

We now determine, by Lemma **19·0**, a polynomial $p(\zeta)$ of degree $n'-1$ at most such that

$$p^{(\nu)}(\lambda_\mu) = p_0^{(\nu)}(\omega_{\mu 1}) \quad (1 \leqslant \mu \leqslant m;\ 0 \leqslant \nu \leqslant j_\mu - 1 = j_{\mu 1}-1).$$

Then, by (23·4·3) and since $\sum_{\iota=1}^{s_\mu} Q_{\mu\iota} = Q_\mu$, the equation (23·4·1) becomes

$$S = \sum_{\mu=1}^{m} \sum_{\nu=0}^{j_\mu - 1} \frac{1}{\nu!} p^{(\nu)}(\lambda_\mu) A_{\lambda_\mu}^{\nu} Q_\mu,$$

and hence, by (19·1·1), $\quad S = p(A)$.

23·41. Since $p(A)$ is commutative with every L.T. that is commutative with A, there follow at once from Theorem **23·4** the following corollaries:

Corollaries of Theorem **23·4**. (i) *Any L.T. in $\mathfrak{B}_n$ that is commutative with the L.T. A and is completely reduced by every L.M. that reduces A completely is also commutative with every L.T. commutative with A.*

(ii) *Any L.T. in $\mathfrak{B}_n$ that is commutative with the L.T. A and with every projector commutative with A is also commutative with every L.T. commutative with A.*

23·42. If at least one of the numbers s_μ belonging to the L.T. A exceeds 1, then the corresponding $Q_{\mu 1}$ cannot be expressed as a polynomial in A. For, let $\{\xi^{\mu\iota\kappa}\}$ be a canonical basis of $\mathfrak{B}_n$ belonging to A, let Q_0 be the L.T. defined in (23·4·2), so that $AQ_0 = Q_0 A$, and suppose that $s_1 > 1$; then

$$Q_0 Q_{11} \xi^{111} = Q_0 \xi^{111} = \xi^{111} + \xi^{121}, \quad Q_{11} Q_0 \xi^{111} = Q_{11}(\xi^{111} + \xi^{121}) = \xi^{111},$$

so that $Q_0 Q_{11} \neq Q_{11} Q_0$; whereas if Q_{11} were a polynomial in A we should have $Q_0 Q_{11} = Q_{11} Q_0$. In the same way Q_0 cannot be a polynomial in A for this also would imply that $Q_0 Q_{11} = Q_{11} Q_0$. Again, we readily see that the L.T. B of Lemma **23·3** cannot be expressed in the form $B = p(A)$, since $BQ_0 \xi^{111} \neq Q_0 B \xi^{111}$, although $A = q(B)$ and $AB = BA$.

These examples, and the two equivalent forms of Theorem **23·4**, suggest a connection between the fact that not every L.T. commutative with A is of the form $p(A)$ and the statements in Note **21·22** and in **22·0** that the dissection of the principal manifolds $\mathfrak{P}_\mu$ into the L.M.'s $\mathfrak{P}_{\mu\iota}$ which reduce A completely and in which A is irreducible is not uniquely determined.

23·43. The property corresponding to Theorem **23·15** is not true for commutative L.T.'s A and B in general; that is, there does not always exist a L.T. C such that $A = p(C)$ and $B = q(C)$. We give an example of two third-order matrices to show this. We write

$$A = \begin{pmatrix} 0 & 1 & 0 \\ 0 & 0 & 0 \\ 0 & 0 & 0 \end{pmatrix}, \quad B = \begin{pmatrix} 0 & 0 & 1 \\ 0 & 0 & 0 \\ 0 & 0 & 0 \end{pmatrix};$$

then

$$A^2 = B^2 = AB = BA = O. \tag{23·43·1}$$

If there were a third-order matrix C such that $A = p(C)$ and $B = q(C)$ then, by Theorem **19·23** and since $n' \leqslant n = 3$, p and q could be taken as polynomials of degree 2 at most and we should have

$$A = \alpha_2 C^2 + \alpha_1 C + \alpha_0 I, \quad B = \beta_2 C^2 + \beta_1 C + \beta_0 I. \tag{23·43·2}$$

If now at least one of the coefficients α_2, β_2 were not zero we could form the matrix $\beta_2 A - \alpha_2 B$ and obtain by (23·43·1) and (23·43·2)

$$\begin{aligned} O = (\beta_2 A - \alpha_2 B)^2 &= (\beta_2(\alpha_1 C + \alpha_0 I) - \alpha_2(\beta_1 C + \beta_0 I))^2 \\ &= a^2 C^2 + 2abC + b^2 I, \end{aligned} \tag{23·43·3}$$

where $\quad a = \beta_2 \alpha_1 - \alpha_2 \beta_1, \quad b = \beta_2 \alpha_0 - \alpha_2 \beta_0.$

If $a = 0$, then $b = 0$ by (23·43·3) and $\beta_2 A - \alpha_2 B = O$ contrary to the assumption that α_2, β_2 were not both zero; thus $a \neq 0$ and, by (23·43·3),

$$C^2 = -\frac{2b}{a} C - \frac{b^2}{a^2} I.$$

Substitution of this value for C^2 in (23·43·2) would give A and B as linear polynomials in C,

$$A = a_1 C + a_0 I, \quad B = b_1 C + b_0 I,$$

where neither a_1 nor b_1 could be zero, and, by (23·43·1),

$$O = (b_1 A - a_1 B)^2 = (b_1 a_0 - a_1 b_0)^2 I.$$

But $b_1 a_0 - a_1 b_0 = 0$ would mean that $b_1 A - a_1 B = O$, and this is impossible in view of the special forms of A and B. It follows that there is no matrix C such that $A = p(C)$ and $B = q(C)$.

23·44. The matrices A and B of the preceding example serve to illustrate a number of our results.

We readily verify that both A and B have the single eigen-value zero of order 3 and the Segre characteristic $[(2, 1)]$. Thus they fail to satisfy the conditions of Theorems **23·11** and **23·2**, and also of Theorem **23·15**, which are sufficient for the existence of a suitable matrix C.

Further, we find by inspection that the projector

$$\begin{pmatrix} 1 & 0 & 0 \\ 0 & 1 & 0 \\ 0 & 0 & 0 \end{pmatrix}$$

is commutative with A and not with B, while the projector

$$\begin{pmatrix} 1 & 0 & 0 \\ 0 & 0 & 0 \\ 0 & 0 & 1 \end{pmatrix}$$

is commutative with B and not with A. This illustrates Theorem **23·4**, by which we know that such projectors must exist since neither of A and B is a polynomial in the other.

Finally, the whole space is the principal manifold of the L.T.'s A and B corresponding to the eigen-value zero; the eigen-manifold of A is $[u^1, u^3]$ and that of B is $[u^1, u^2]$; the range of each L.T. is $[u^1]$ and it is contained in the eigen-manifolds. Thus we verify, both for A and for B, in illustration of **17·51**, that the eigen-manifold, which is distinct from the principal manifold, does not reduce the L.T. completely. The projectors given above illustrate the result of Theorem **10·9**. For the first of them, which is not commutative with B, is the orthogonal projector on to the eigen-manifold of B which does not reduce B completely, and the second behaves in a similar way for A.

CHAPTER V

VECTOR SPACES WITH POSITIVE HERMITIAN METRIC FORMS

§ 24. The spaces $\mathfrak{V}'_n$ and $\mathfrak{V}_{n0}$

24·0. In § **12** we discuss the pencil of H.T.'s $H-\lambda I$; we obtain the eigen-values of H as the values of λ for which $H-\lambda I$ is a singular L.T., and we deduce the spectral representation (12·43·4) for the pencil in terms of the eigen-values. Problems of mathematical physics, however, lead to the consideration of the more general pencil $H-\lambda G$, where G is a positive definite H.T., and to the determination of those values of λ, again called the eigen-values, for which $H-\lambda G$ is a singular L.T. (We may mention, in particular, the familiar problem of the small oscillations of a dynamical system with which we deal in § **27**.) We could easily generalize the method developed in § **12** to apply to the pencil $H-\lambda G$, but we give an alternative method that makes use of a vector space $\mathfrak{V}'_n$ differing from $\mathfrak{V}_n$ only in the form of the scalar product. By this method the discussion of the pencil $H-\lambda G$ is reduced to the discussion of a corresponding pencil $K_0-\lambda I$, and the results of § **12** are then taken over as they stand.

The space $\mathfrak{V}'_n$ provides an example of a generalization of the space $\mathfrak{V}_n$. Its introduction links the elementary considerations of Chapter I with discussion of the abstract n-dimensional unitary spaces $\mathfrak{U}_n$ which are defined in terms of certain abstract properties that belong to the space $\mathfrak{V}_n$ and of which both the spaces $\mathfrak{V}_n$ and $\mathfrak{V}'_n$ are special examples, or 'realizations'.

In the present Section we give the definition of the space $\mathfrak{V}'_n$ and develop its simplest properties, thereby preparing the way for the discussion in § **25** of the pencil $H-\lambda G$. In § **26** we use the space $\mathfrak{V}'_n$ to obtain a new characterization of L.T.'s with simple elementary divisors.

24·1. Vectors in $\mathfrak{V}'_n$; multiplication by a number and addition. The space $\mathfrak{V}'_n$ is an n-dimensional vector space in which a scalar product is defined; different spaces $\mathfrak{V}'_n$ are characterized by the metric form that determines the scalar product, and any space $\mathfrak{V}'_n$ is not distinguishable from $\mathfrak{V}_n$ until the definition of the scalar product has been given. Thus, all the considerations of **1·1** to **1·33** hold for $\mathfrak{B}'_n$ as well as for $\mathfrak{B}_n$. In particular, we define a vector x of $\mathfrak{B}'_n$, as we defined a vector x of $\mathfrak{B}_n$ in **1·1**, as an ordered set of n complex numbers $x = (x_1, x_2, \ldots, x_n)$, where the numbers x_ν are called the coordinates of x; we define multiplication of a vector x by a number α as we defined it in **1·2**, and the sum of two vectors x and y as in **1·3**. The laws of addition described in **1·31** and **1·32** for $\mathfrak{B}_n$ then hold for $\mathfrak{B}'_n$ also. We introduce coordinate vectors u^ν in $\mathfrak{B}'_n$ by the definition of **1·33** and we obtain the representation of any vector x as a sum $x = \sum_{\nu=1}^{n} x_\nu u^\nu$.

24·11. The scalar product in $\mathfrak{B}'_n$. We have spoken of both $\mathfrak{B}_n$ and $\mathfrak{B}'_n$ as n-dimensional vector spaces, by which we merely mean that their elements are ordered sets of n complex numbers. We may further say that both spaces are *vectorial*, or *linear*, *spaces*; by which we mean that the *operations of addition of elements and multiplication of an element by a number are defined* so as to satisfy the laws of addition and multiplication set out in **1·2** and **1·31**. We now go on to *define a scalar product* for any two elements of $\mathfrak{B}'_n$ in such a way that $\mathfrak{B}'_n$ is, like $\mathfrak{B}_n$, an n-dimensional *unitary space*; by which we mean a *linear space in which a scalar product is suitably defined.*

We distinguish the scalar product of two vectors x and y of $\mathfrak{B}'_n$ from that of vectors x and y of $\mathfrak{B}_n$ by the use of square brackets instead of round ones. Thus, we write $[x, y]$ for the scalar product in $\mathfrak{B}'_n$.

We begin by defining the scalar product of any two vectors x and y in $\mathfrak{B}'_n$ as a complex number which, like (x, y) in **1·4**, satisfies the following three conditions for any vectors x, y, z and any complex number α:

(i) $[\alpha x, y] = \alpha[x, y]$, (ii) $[x+y, z] = [x, z] + [y, z]$,

(iii) $[y, x] = \overline{[x, y]}$.

These conditions imply the further conditions:

$$[x, \alpha y] = \bar{\alpha}[x, y], \quad [x, y+z] = [x, y] + [x, z].$$

The space $\mathfrak{B}'_n$ will be a unitary space if we satisfy the additional condition that $[x, x] \geqslant 0$ for every vector x of $\mathfrak{B}'_n$, with $[x, x] = 0$ only for $x = 0$. We satisfy this last condition by defining the scalar product for the coordinate vectors u^ν of $\mathfrak{B}'_n$ in terms of a positive definite Hermitian matrix $G = (g_{\mu\nu})$, writing

(iv)′ $[u^\nu, u^\mu] = g_{\mu\nu}$ $(\mu, \nu = 1, 2, \ldots, n)$.

The choice of G characterizes the space $\mathfrak{B}_n'$. When G is the unit matrix I, (iv)$'$ becomes the condition (iv) of **1·4** and $\mathfrak{B}_n'$ coincides with $\mathfrak{B}_n$.

If we write $x = \sum_{\nu=1}^{n} x_\nu u^\nu$, $y = \sum_{\mu=1}^{n} y_\mu u^\mu$, we obtain from conditions (i), (ii), (iii) and (iv)$'$ above an expression for the scalar product in $\mathfrak{B}_n'$

$$[x, y] = \sum_{\nu=1}^{n} \sum_{\mu=1}^{n} g_{\mu\nu} x_\nu \overline{y_\mu} = (Gx, y), \qquad (24·11·1)$$

where (Gx, y) denotes the bilinear form defined by (6·04·1). Then, since G is a positive definite H.T. in $\mathfrak{B}_n$, we have $(Gx, x) = 0$ if $x = 0$ and otherwise $(Gx, x) > 0$, so that $[x, x] = 0$ if $x = 0$ and otherwise $[x, x] > 0$.

The expression (24·11·1) is readily seen to satisfy the conditions we have laid down for the scalar product in $\mathfrak{B}_n'$, and it may therefore be taken as defining this product.

24·12. The absolute value of a vector in $\mathfrak{B}_n'$. We define the absolute value $|x|$ in $\mathfrak{B}_n'$ in terms of the scalar product, as we defined $\|x\|$ in $\mathfrak{B}_n$ in **1·41**, by writing

$$|x| = [x, x]^{\frac{1}{2}} = (Gx, x)^{\frac{1}{2}},$$

and we have $|x| = 0$ if and only if $x = 0$, with $|x| \geqslant 0$ for every x of $\mathfrak{B}_n'$.

The important inequalities for $\mathfrak{B}_n'$ which correspond to the inequalities of **1·42** and **1·43** are deduced in **24·22**.

24·13. Orthogonality in $\mathfrak{B}_n'$. We say that two vectors x and y of $\mathfrak{B}_n'$ are orthogonal if their scalar product in $\mathfrak{B}_n'$ vanishes; that is, if $[x, y] = (Gx, y) = 0$.

Condition (iv)$'$ of **24·11** shows that the system of coordinate vectors in $\mathfrak{B}_n'$ is not an orthonormal system unless $G = I$ and $\mathfrak{B}_n'$ coincides with $\mathfrak{B}_n$. The geometry of $\mathfrak{B}_n'$ may be interpreted as the geometry of a general affine (oblique) coordinate system.

24·2. Distributive mapping and congruent mapping. Any one-one correspondence between the elements x of $\mathfrak{B}_n$ and x' of $\mathfrak{B}_n'$ defines a mapping of the space $\mathfrak{B}_n$ on the space $\mathfrak{B}_n'$; we call x' in $\mathfrak{B}_n'$ the image of the corresponding x in $\mathfrak{B}_n$. For example, we obtain a mapping of $\mathfrak{B}_n$ on $\mathfrak{B}_n'$ by interpreting all sets of n complex numbers $(x_1, x_2, \ldots, x_n)$ both as vectors x in $\mathfrak{B}_n$ and as vectors x' in $\mathfrak{B}_n'$. In this mapping a vector and its image have the same coordinates.

Definition of distributive mapping. *A one-one correspondence between the vectors of two linear n-dimensional vector spaces* $\mathfrak{V}_{n1}$ *and* $\mathfrak{V}_{n2}$ *is said to be a distributive mapping of* $\mathfrak{V}_{n1}$ *on* $\mathfrak{V}_{n2}$ *and of* $\mathfrak{V}_{n2}$ *on* $\mathfrak{V}_{n1}$ *if the vector* $z = \alpha x + \beta y$ *of* $\mathfrak{V}_{n1}$ *corresponds to the vector* $z' = \alpha x' + \beta y'$ *of* $\mathfrak{V}_{n2}$ *whenever* x *and* y *of* $\mathfrak{V}_{n1}$ *correspond to* x' *and* y' *of* $\mathfrak{V}_{n2}$. Such a mapping is written as $\mathfrak{V}_{n1} \sim \mathfrak{V}_{n2}$.

It follows immediately from the definition that the zero vector $z = 0$ of $\mathfrak{V}_{n1}$ corresponds to the zero vector $z' = 0$ of $\mathfrak{V}_{n2}$ in a distributive mapping of $\mathfrak{V}_{n1}$ on $\mathfrak{V}_{n2}$.

Definition of congruent mapping. *Any one-one correspondence between the vectors of two unitary vector spaces* $\mathfrak{V}_{n1}$ *and* $\mathfrak{V}_{n2}$ *is said to be a congruent mapping of* $\mathfrak{V}_{n1}$ *on* $\mathfrak{V}_{n2}$ *and of* $\mathfrak{V}_{n2}$ *on* $\mathfrak{V}_{n1}$ *if it is a distributive mapping in which the scalar product of any two vectors of* $\mathfrak{V}_{n1}$ *equals the scalar product of the image vectors in* $\mathfrak{V}_{n2}$. A congruent mapping is written as $\mathfrak{V}_{n1} \cong \mathfrak{V}_{n2}$.

The mapping of $\mathfrak{V}_n$ on $\mathfrak{V}'_n$ described above, in which a vector and its image have the same coordinates, is a distributive mapping, but is not a congruent mapping except in the trivial case when $G = I$. Throughout the rest of this chapter we use the correspondence sign $\mathfrak{V}_n \sim \mathfrak{V}'_n$ to refer to this particular distributive mapping of $\mathfrak{V}_n$ on $\mathfrak{V}'_n$. In **24·21** and **24·22** we set up a congruent mapping of $\mathfrak{V}'_n$ on a unitary space $\mathfrak{V}_{n0}$ in which the scalar product is defined as in **1·4**, and we write $\mathfrak{V}'_n \cong \mathfrak{V}_{n0}$.

24·21. The first step in the construction of the space $\mathfrak{V}_{n0}$ is the determination of a basis $\{v^\nu\}$ orthonormal with regard to $\mathfrak{V}'_n$, that is, an orthonormal coordinate system for $\mathfrak{V}'_n$. We obtain $\{v^\nu\}$ by applying Schmidt's procedure to the set $u^1, u^2, \ldots, u^n$ in the way described in **3·3**, **3·31** and **3·4**, except that we replace the round brackets of the scalar products by square brackets. At each stage in the construction we obtain v^μ as a linear combination of $u^1, u^2, \ldots, u^\mu$, and we have

$$[v^\nu, v^\mu] = \delta_{\mu\nu}, \quad \gamma_{\mu\mu} v^\mu = u^\mu - \sum_{\nu=1}^{\mu-1} \gamma_{\nu\mu} v^\nu$$

with

$$\gamma_{11} = |u^1| > 0,$$

$$\gamma_{\nu\mu} = [u^\mu, v^\nu] = (Gu^\mu, v^\nu) \quad (1 \leqslant \nu \leqslant \mu - 1).$$

$$\gamma_{\mu\mu} = \left| u^\mu - \sum_{\nu=1}^{\mu-1} \gamma_{\nu\mu} v^\nu \right| > 0$$

Let any vector x in $\mathfrak{B}'_n$ have coordinates $(x_1, x_2, \ldots, x_n)$ and write

$$x = \sum_{\nu=1}^{n} x'_\nu v^\nu = \sum_{\mu=1}^{n} x_\mu u^\mu = \sum_{\mu=1}^{n} \sum_{\nu=1}^{\mu} x_\mu \gamma_{\nu\mu} v^\nu.$$

Then $$x'_\nu = \sum_{\mu=\nu}^{n} \gamma_{\nu\mu} x_\mu = [x, v^\nu] = (Gx, v^\nu). \tag{24·21·1}$$

If we also write $y = \sum_{\nu=1}^{n} y'_\nu v^\nu$, we have

$$[x, y] = \sum_{\nu=1}^{n} \sum_{\mu=1}^{n} x'_\nu \overline{y'_\mu} [v^\nu, v^\mu] = \sum_{\nu=1}^{n} x'_\nu \overline{y'_\nu}. \tag{24·21·2}$$

Now let Γ denote the matrix $(\gamma_{\mu\nu})$, where $\gamma_{\mu\nu} = 0$ when $\mu > \nu$, and let x' and y' be the systems of n numbers $(x'_1, x'_2, \ldots, x'_n)$ and $(y'_1, y'_2, \ldots, y'_n)$ respectively. We can then write (24·21·1) and (24·21·2) in the forms

$$x' = \Gamma x, \tag{24·21·3}$$

$$[x, y] = (x', y') = (\Gamma x, \Gamma y) = (\Gamma^* \Gamma x, y) = (Gx, y), \tag{24·21·4}$$

and if we consider the last equality in (24·21·4) for x and y in $\mathfrak{B}_n$, we see that $G = \Gamma^*\Gamma$. We deduce that Γ and Γ^* in $\mathfrak{B}_n$ have the same rank n as G and therefore that Γ^{-1} and $(\Gamma^*)^{-1}$ exist and that

$$x = \Gamma^{-1} x'. \tag{24·21·5}$$

24·22. The space $\mathfrak{B}_{n0}$. If we regard both x and x' as vectors of $\mathfrak{B}_n$ we may interpret (24·21·3) and (24·21·5) as describing a distributive mapping by the L.T. Γ, of rank n, of the space $\mathfrak{B}_n$ on itself, x' being the image of x by Γ. We may also interpret these relations as giving a one-one correspondence between the vectors x of $\mathfrak{B}'_n$ and the vectors x' of an n-dimensional space $\mathfrak{B}_{n0}$ in which x' is referred to an orthonormal system of coordinate vectors $\{v^\nu\}$ and in which, consequently, the scalar product is defined as in $\mathfrak{B}_n$. We may then interpret (24·21·4) as showing that the scalar product $[x, y]$ in $\mathfrak{B}'_n$ is equal to the scalar product (x', y') of the corresponding vectors in $\mathfrak{B}_{n0}$. Thus we have a congruent mapping of $\mathfrak{B}'_n$ on $\mathfrak{B}_{n0}$. We write $\mathfrak{B}'_n \cong \mathfrak{B}_{n0}$ and we confine the use of this correspondence sign in the rest of the chapter to the congruent mapping described by (24·21·3) and (24·21·4).

We notice that (24·21·3) also describes a distributive mapping of $\mathfrak{B}_n$ on $\mathfrak{B}_{n0}$.

We deduce from (24·21·4) that the scalar product in $\mathfrak{B}'_n$ has the properties **1·4** and **1·43**, since

$$[x,y] = (x',y') \leqslant \| x' \| \, \| y' \| = |x|\,|y|$$

and $$|x+y| = \| x'+y' \| \leqslant \| x' \| + \| y' \| = |x| + |y|.$$

24·23. We notice that there is one set of n vectors that is an orthogonal set in both the spaces $\mathfrak{B}_n$ and $\mathfrak{B}'_n$, namely, a set of principal axes for (Gx, x) in $\mathfrak{B}_n$. For if, with the notation of (12·4·1), $\{\phi^\nu\}$ is a complete orthonormal set of eigen-solutions corresponding to the eigen-values λ_ν of G with regard to $\mathfrak{B}_n$, we have

$$[\phi^\nu, \phi^\mu] = (G\phi^\nu, \phi^\mu) = \lambda_\nu(\phi^\nu, \phi^\mu) = \lambda_\nu \delta_{\mu\nu}.$$

We see, however, that the vectors ϕ^ν are not all unit vectors in $\mathfrak{B}'_n$ unless $G = I$ and $\mathfrak{B}'_n$ coincides with $\mathfrak{B}_n$.

24·3. L.M.'s in $\mathfrak{B}'_n$ and $\mathfrak{B}_{n0}$. Since $\mathfrak{B}'_n \sim \mathfrak{B}_n$, the definitions and theorems developed in § **2** for L.M.'s in $\mathfrak{B}_n$ hold unchanged in $\mathfrak{B}'_n$, for they are based only on the operations of addition of vectors and multiplication of a vector by a number. Vectors of $\mathfrak{B}_n$ that are linearly dependent or linearly independent have the same property when they are considered as vectors of $\mathfrak{B}'_n$, and so have the vectors of $\mathfrak{B}_{n0}$ that correspond to these vectors of $\mathfrak{B}'_n$ by the mapping $\mathfrak{B}'_n \simeq \mathfrak{B}_{n0}$. A set of vectors forms a L.M. in $\mathfrak{B}'_n$ if it forms a L.M. in $\mathfrak{B}_n$, having the same sets of vectors as bases and having the same rank in the two spaces, and the corresponding set of vectors in $\mathfrak{B}_{n0}$ also forms a L.M. of the same rank. In particular, all three spaces $\mathfrak{B}_n$, $\mathfrak{B}'_n$ and $\mathfrak{B}_{n0}$ have rank n. We use the same symbol for L.M.'s formed from the same vectors in $\mathfrak{B}_n$ and $\mathfrak{B}'_n$. We write $\mathfrak{M}_0 = \Gamma\mathfrak{M}$ for the L.M. in $\mathfrak{B}_{n0}$ corresponding to the L.M. $\mathfrak{M}$ in $\mathfrak{B}'_n$, since, by (24·21·3), $\mathfrak{M}_0$ may be regarded as the image of $\mathfrak{M}$ by Γ.

The operations $\mathfrak{M}.\mathfrak{N}$ and $\mathfrak{M} \oplus \mathfrak{N}$ defined in § **4** have the same meaning in $\mathfrak{B}_n$ and $\mathfrak{B}'_n$. An equation $\mathfrak{M} \oplus \mathfrak{N} = \mathfrak{B}_n$ implies an equation $\mathfrak{M} \oplus \mathfrak{N} = \mathfrak{B}'_n$, and conversely. An equation $\mathfrak{N}_1 \oplus \mathfrak{N}_2 = \mathfrak{M}$ holds in both $\mathfrak{B}_n$ and $\mathfrak{B}'_n$ if it holds in either, and the corresponding equation in $\mathfrak{B}_{n0}$ takes the form $\Gamma\mathfrak{N}_1 \oplus \Gamma\mathfrak{N}_2 = \Gamma\mathfrak{M}$.

24·31. To find an orthonormal basis $\{g^\nu\}$ of a L.M. $\mathfrak{M}$ in $\mathfrak{B}'_n$ we may first determine an orthonormal basis $\{g'^\nu\}$ of $\mathfrak{M}_0$ in $\mathfrak{B}_{n0}$, then write $g^\nu = \Gamma^{-1} g'^\nu$, $g'^\nu = \Gamma g^\nu$, and obtain from (24·21·4)

$$[g^\nu, g^\mu] = (Gg^\nu, g^\mu) = (\Gamma g^\nu, \Gamma g^\mu) = (g'^\nu, g'^\mu) = \delta_{\mu\nu}.$$

Alternatively, we may apply Schmidt's procedure to any basis of $\mathfrak{M}$ in $\mathfrak{B}'_n$ by the method described in **24·21**, and so obtain a system

$\{g^\nu\}$ directly. Any element x of $\mathfrak{M}$ may then be represented by the sum

$$x = \sum_{\nu=1}^{r} [x, g^\nu] g^\nu, \qquad (24\cdot31\cdot1)$$

or, if we interpret x as a vector in $\mathfrak{B}_n$,

$$x = \sum_{\nu=1}^{r} (Gx, g^\nu) g^\nu, \qquad (24\cdot31\cdot2)$$

where the basis $\{g^\nu\}$ of $\mathfrak{M}$, considered as a system of vectors in $\mathfrak{B}_n$, is no longer an orthonormal basis.

We notice that the formulae (24·31·1) and (24·31·2) also hold, with $r = n$, for $\mathfrak{M} = \mathfrak{B}_n'$ or $\mathfrak{M} = \mathfrak{B}_n$ respectively, when they generalize the formula (24·21·1).

24·4. Let $\mathfrak{M}$ and $\mathfrak{N}$ be two L.M.'s considered in $\mathfrak{B}_n'$ and such that $\mathfrak{N} \subset \mathfrak{M}$. We denote the result of subtraction with regard to $\mathfrak{B}_n'$ by the symbol $\mathfrak{M} \ominus' \mathfrak{N}$, which we define as representing the set of all vectors p of $\mathfrak{M}$ such that

$$[p, q] = (p, Gq) = (\Gamma p, \Gamma q) = 0$$

for every vector q of $\mathfrak{N}$. Thus,

$$\mathfrak{M} \ominus' \mathfrak{N} = \mathfrak{M} . (\mathfrak{B} \ominus G\mathfrak{N}) = \Gamma^{-1}(\Gamma\mathfrak{M} \ominus \Gamma\mathfrak{N}), \qquad (24\cdot4\cdot1)$$

where the subtraction on the right refers to $\mathfrak{B}_n$.

24·5. L.T.'s in $\mathfrak{B}_n'$. We define a L.T. $z = Ax$ in $\mathfrak{B}_n'$ by the conditions (i) and (ii) of **6·0**. To a L.T. A defined in either of the spaces $\mathfrak{B}_n$ or $\mathfrak{B}_n'$ there corresponds by the distributive mapping $\mathfrak{B}_n \sim \mathfrak{B}_n'$ a L.T. in the other space which we also denote by A and which we do not distinguish from the original L.T. A, for the mapping ensures that A has the same analytical form (6·02·2) in $\mathfrak{B}_n$ and $\mathfrak{B}_n'$, the same range and null manifold, and the same rank. The adjoints, however, A^* in $\mathfrak{B}_n$ and $A^{[*]}$ in $\mathfrak{B}_n'$, are different L.T.'s. We defined A^* in **6·3** by the equation $(Ax, y) = (x, A^*y)$ for every x and y of $\mathfrak{B}_n$; we now define $A^{[*]}$ by the equation

$$[Ax, y] = [x, A^{[*]}y] \qquad (24\cdot5\cdot1)$$

for every x and y of $\mathfrak{B}_n'$. The definition means that

$$(GAx, y) = (Gx, A^{[*]}y), \quad (x, A^*Gy) = (x, GA^{[*]}y),$$

so that

$$A^*G = GA^{[*]}, \quad A^{[*]} = G^{-1}A^*G. \qquad (24\cdot5\cdot2)$$

Since G has rank n, $A^{[*]}$ and A^* have the same rank and therefore, by Theorem **6·4**, $A^{[*]}$ has the same rank as A.

By the mapping $\mathfrak{V}'_n \cong \mathfrak{V}_{n0}$ we obtain from the L.T. $z = Ax$ in $\mathfrak{V}'_n$ a L.T. in $\mathfrak{V}_{n0}$ defined by the equations

$$z' = \Gamma z = \Gamma A x = \Gamma A \Gamma^{-1} x'.$$

Thus the corresponding L.T. in $\mathfrak{V}_{n0}$ is $z' = A_0 x'$, where $A_0 = \Gamma A \Gamma^{-1}$. Further, by (24·5·2), since $G = \Gamma^* \Gamma$ and $G^{-1} = \Gamma^{-1}(\Gamma^*)^{-1}$, we have

$$A_0^* = (\Gamma^*)^{-1} A^* \Gamma^* = \Gamma A^{[*]} \Gamma^{-1}. \qquad (24\cdot5\cdot3)$$

This relation verifies that A_0^* in $\mathfrak{V}_{n0}$ corresponds to $A^{[*]}$ in $\mathfrak{V}'_n$.

24·51. By (24·5·1) we have

$$[A^{[*]}y, x] = [y, Ax]$$

for every x and y of $\mathfrak{V}'_n$ so that A is the adjoint of $A^{[*]}$ in $\mathfrak{V}'_n$.

24·52. It also follows from (24·5·1) that, if $r < n$ and if $\mathfrak{Y}'$ is the L.M. of all vectors y of $\mathfrak{V}'_n$ such that $A^{[*]}y = 0$, then $[Ax, y] = 0$ for every x of $\mathfrak{V}'_n$ and every y of $\mathfrak{Y}'$. Conversely, if $[Ax, y] = 0$ for every x of $\mathfrak{V}'_n$, then $A^{[*]}y = 0$. Thus the range $\mathfrak{R}$ of A and the null manifold $\mathfrak{Y}'$ of $A^{[*]}$ in $\mathfrak{V}'_n$ are related by the equation

$$\mathfrak{R} = \mathfrak{V}'_n \ominus' \mathfrak{Y}'.$$

This, however, yields, by (24·4·1),

$$\mathfrak{R} = \mathfrak{V}'_n \ominus G\mathfrak{Y}',$$

where, by (24·5·2), $G\mathfrak{Y}'$ is the null manifold of A^*.

24·6. Normal and Hermitian transformations in $\mathfrak{V}'_n$. We say that a L.T. K is normal with regard to $\mathfrak{V}'_n$ if $KK^{[*]} = K^{[*]}K$, and that K is Hermitian with regard to $\mathfrak{V}'_n$ if $K^{[*]} = K$. By (24·5·2), this last equation is equivalent to the equations

$$GK = K^*G, \quad K = G^{-1}K^*G. \qquad (24\cdot6\cdot1)$$

Clearly, the L.T. I is a H.T. with regard to $\mathfrak{V}'_n$ as well as with regard to $\mathfrak{V}_n$.

Let K be a H.T. with regard to $\mathfrak{V}'_n$ and write $H = GK$. Then

$$H^* = K^*G = GK = H,$$

so that H is a H.T. with regard to $\mathfrak{V}_n$. Let K_0 be the L.T. in $\mathfrak{V}_{n0}$ corresponding to K in $\mathfrak{V}'_n$. Then $K_0 = \Gamma K \Gamma^{-1}$ and, by (24·5·3), $K_0^* = K_0$, so that K_0 is a H.T. with regard to $\mathfrak{V}_{n0}$. Finally, since $G = \Gamma^*\Gamma$, we have

$$H = \Gamma^*\Gamma K = \Gamma^* K_0 \Gamma. \qquad (24\cdot6\cdot2)$$

We have proved the following theorem:

THEOREM. *If K is a H.T. with regard to $\mathfrak{B}'_n$, then GK is a H.T. with regard to $\mathfrak{B}_n$ and $\Gamma K \Gamma^{-1}$ is a H.T. with regard to $\mathfrak{B}_{n0}$.*

24·7. Projectors in $\mathfrak{B}'_n$. We define a general projector in $\mathfrak{B}'_n$ in the terms of Definition **10·1**. It follows immediately, by the distributive mapping $\mathfrak{B}_n \sim \mathfrak{B}'_n$, that if the L.T. Q is a general projector in either of the spaces $\mathfrak{B}_n$ and $\mathfrak{B}'_n$, then it is a general projector in the other, and, by Theorem **10·2**, that Q is a general projector in both spaces if, and only if, $Q^2 = Q$.

We say that a general projector P' in $\mathfrak{B}'_n$ is an orthogonal projector if its range $\mathfrak{M}$ and null manifold $\mathfrak{N}$ satisfy the relation $\mathfrak{N} = \mathfrak{B}'_n \ominus' \mathfrak{M}$. It follows by the congruent mapping $\mathfrak{B}'_n \cong \mathfrak{B}_{n0}$ that P' is an orthogonal projector in $\mathfrak{B}'_n$ if, and only if, the L.T.

$$P_0 = \Gamma P' \Gamma^{-1}$$

is an orthogonal projector in $\mathfrak{B}_{n0}$, and therefore, by Theorem **10·2**, if, and only if, both $P_0^2 = P_0$ and P_0 is Hermitian with regard to $\mathfrak{B}_{n0}$. Using Theorem **24·6** we see that P' is an orthogonal projector in $\mathfrak{B}'_n$ if, and only if, both $P'^2 = P'$ and P' is Hermitian with regard to $\mathfrak{B}'_n$ or, alternatively, if $P'^2 = P'$ and GP' is Hermitian with regard to $\mathfrak{B}_n$, which means that

$$GP' = (P')^* G. \tag{24·7·1}$$

24·8. Unitary transformations in $\mathfrak{B}'_n$. Any L.T. V is said to be a unitary transformation with regard to $\mathfrak{B}'_n$ if it satisfies the condition

$$[x, y] = [Vx, Vy] \tag{24·8·1}$$

for every x and y of $\mathfrak{B}'_n$, whence it readily appears that a unitary transformation in $\mathfrak{B}'_n$ determines a congruent mapping of $\mathfrak{B}'_n$ on itself.

§ 25. HERMITIAN FORMS IN $\mathfrak{B}'_n$ AND $\mathfrak{B}_{n0}$ AND THE PENCIL $H - \lambda G$ IN $\mathfrak{B}_n$

25·0. Let K be a H.T. with regard to $\mathfrak{B}'_n$ and consider the bilinear form $[Kx, y]$ in $\mathfrak{B}'_n$. By (24·6·2), we have

$$[Kx, y] = (GKx, y) = (Hx, y) = (\Gamma^* K_0 \Gamma x, y) = (K_0 x', y'), \tag{25·0·1}$$

where $GK = H$ and $K_0 = \Gamma K \Gamma^{-1}$, so that (Hx, y) and $(K_0 x', y')$ are corresponding forms in $\mathfrak{B}_n$ and $\mathfrak{B}_{n0}$ respectively. By Theorem **24·6**, H and K_0 are H.T.'s with regard to $\mathfrak{B}_n$ and $\mathfrak{B}_{n0}$ respectively. It follows that the Hermitian form $[Kx, x]$ in $\mathfrak{B}'_n$, like the Hermitian forms (Hx, x) in $\mathfrak{B}_n$ and $(K_0 x', x')$ in $\mathfrak{B}_{n0}$, takes only real values.

25·1. In accordance with Definition **8·4**, we say that λ_0 is an eigen-value of the H.T. K in $\mathfrak{B}'_n$ if there exists a non-zero vector ϕ of $\mathfrak{B}'_n$ such that

$$K\phi - \lambda_0\phi = 0, \qquad (25\cdot1\cdot1)$$

and ϕ is then said to be an eigen-solution corresponding to λ_0. Alternatively, using the interpretation of Definition **6·51** in $\mathfrak{B}'_n$, we say that λ_0 is an eigen-value of K if $K-\lambda_0 I$ is a singular H.T. with regard to $\mathfrak{B}'_n$.

By **24·6** we have
$$G(K-\lambda I) = H-\lambda G,$$
and, since G has rank n, it follows that $H-\lambda G$ and $K-\lambda I$ have the same rank for any value of λ. Thus $H-\lambda_0 G$ is a singular H.T. in $\mathfrak{B}_n$ if, and only if, $K-\lambda_0 I$ is singular in $\mathfrak{B}'_n$. When this condition is fulfilled, we say that λ_0 is an eigen-value of the pencil $H-\lambda G$ of H.T.'s in $\mathfrak{B}_n$. Thus, K in $\mathfrak{B}'_n$ and the pencil $H-\lambda G$ in $\mathfrak{B}_n$ have the same set of eigen-values. Alternatively, we may define an eigen-value of the pencil as a value λ_0 for which there exists a non-zero vector ϕ in $\mathfrak{B}_n$ such that

$$G(K-\lambda_0 I)\phi = (H-\lambda_0 G)\phi = 0. \qquad (25\cdot1\cdot2)$$

Any non-zero vector ϕ satisfying (25·1·2) is called an eigen-solution corresponding to λ_0. Now the equations (25·1·1) and (25·1·2) are equivalent, since G has rank n. Thus the eigen-solutions corresponding to an eigen-value λ_0 are the same vectors ϕ for K in $\mathfrak{B}'_n$ and for the pencil $H-\lambda G$ in $\mathfrak{B}_n$.

By the congruent mapping $\mathfrak{B}'_n \cong \mathfrak{B}_{n0}$, the H.T. $K-\lambda I$ in $\mathfrak{B}'_n$ corresponds to $K_0-\lambda I$ in $\mathfrak{B}_{n0}$, where $K_0 = \Gamma K \Gamma^{-1}$. Thus the eigen-values of $K_0-\lambda I$ in $\mathfrak{B}_{n0}$ coincide with those of K in $\mathfrak{B}'_n$ while the eigen-solutions ϕ' of K_0 are given by the vectors $\Gamma\phi$, where the vectors ϕ are the eigen-solutions of K. It follows that we obtain all the eigen-values and eigen-solutions of K and of the pencil $H-\lambda G$ by considering K_0. But K_0 is a H.T. with regard to $\mathfrak{B}_{n0}$ for which all the discussions of Chapter III hold. In particular, we recall that the eigen-values λ_μ of K_0 are obtained as the maxima of $(K_0 x', x')$ on a series of intersections of certain L.M.'s with the surface $(x', x') = 1$. We deduce by (25·0·1) that the eigen-values λ_μ of the pencil $H-\lambda G$ are obtained as the maxima of (Hx, x) on a series of similar intersections with the surface $(\Gamma x, \Gamma x) = (Gx, x) = 1$.

25·2. We write the spectral representation for K_0 in $\mathfrak{B}_{n0}$ in the form

$$(K_0-\lambda I)x' = \sum_{\nu=1}^{n} (\lambda_\nu - \lambda)(x', \phi'^\nu)\phi'^\nu, \qquad (25\cdot2\cdot1)$$

where $\{\phi'^{\nu}\}$ is a complete orthonormal set of eigen-solutions corresponding to the eigen-values λ_ν. Now, since $H = GK$, $G = \Gamma^*\Gamma$ and $K_0 = \Gamma K \Gamma^{-1}$, we have, by (24·6·2),

$$H - \lambda G = \Gamma^*(K_0 - \lambda I)\Gamma, \quad K - \lambda I = \Gamma^{-1}(K_0 - \lambda I)\Gamma,$$

and we deduce from (25·2·1) and (24·21·5) the spectral representation for $(H - \lambda G)$ in $\mathfrak{V}_n$ in the form

$$\begin{aligned}(H-\lambda G)x = (H-\lambda G)\Gamma^{-1}x' &= \Gamma^*(K_0 - \lambda I)x' \\ &= \sum_{\nu=1}^{n} (\lambda_\nu - \lambda)(x', \phi'^{\nu})\Gamma^*\phi'^{\nu} \\ &= \sum_{\nu=1}^{n} (\lambda_\nu - \lambda)(Gx, \phi^{\nu})G\phi^{\nu}, \quad (25{\cdot}2{\cdot}2)\end{aligned}$$

where we have written

$$(x', \phi'^{\nu}) = (\Gamma x, \Gamma\phi^{\nu}) = (Gx, \phi^{\nu}), \quad \Gamma^*\phi'^{\nu} = \Gamma^*\Gamma\phi^{\nu} = G\phi^{\nu},$$

so that $\{\phi^{\nu}\}$ is the set of eigen-solutions of $H - \lambda G$ in $\mathfrak{V}_n$ corresponding to the set $\{\phi'^{\nu}\}$ of eigen-solutions of K_0 in $\mathfrak{V}_{n0}$. The spectral representation for K in $\mathfrak{V}_n'$ takes the form

$$\begin{aligned}(K-\lambda I)x = (K-\lambda I)\Gamma^{-1}x' &= \sum_{\nu=1}^{n} (\lambda_\nu - \lambda)(x', \phi'^{\nu})\Gamma^{-1}\phi'^{\nu} \\ &= \sum_{\nu=1}^{n} (\lambda_\nu - \lambda)[x, \phi^{\nu}]\phi^{\nu}, \quad (25{\cdot}2{\cdot}3)\end{aligned}$$

and the orthonormal property of the eigen-solutions becomes

$$(\phi'^{\nu}, \phi'^{\mu}) = (G\phi^{\nu}, \phi^{\mu}) = [\phi^{\nu}, \phi^{\mu}] = \delta_{\mu\nu}. \quad (25{\cdot}2{\cdot}4)$$

By writing $\lambda = 0$ in (25·2·2) we obtain the representations

$$Hx = \sum_{\nu=1}^{n} \lambda_\nu (Gx, \phi^{\nu})G\phi^{\nu}, \quad Gx = \sum_{\nu=1}^{n} (Gx, \phi^{\nu})G\phi^{\nu}, \quad (25{\cdot}2{\cdot}5)$$

which we use in the applications of § **27**.

25·21. We obtain from (25·2·1), (25·2·3) and (25·2·2) the forms

$$((K_0 - \lambda I)x', x') = \sum_{\nu=1}^{n} (\lambda_\nu - \lambda)(x', \phi'^{\nu})(\phi'^{\nu}, x'),$$

$$[(K-\lambda I)x, x] = \sum_{\nu=1}^{n} (\lambda_\nu - \lambda)[x, \phi^{\nu}][\phi^{\nu}, x], \quad (25{\cdot}21{\cdot}1)$$

$$((H-\lambda G)x, x) = \sum_{\nu=1}^{n} (\lambda_\nu - \lambda)(Gx, \phi^{\nu})(\phi^{\nu}, Gx), \quad (25{\cdot}21{\cdot}2)$$

the first of which, by a unitary transformation of the orthonormal system $\{\phi'^{\nu}\}$ to the coordinate system $\{v^{\nu}\}$, gives the Hermitian form $(K_0 x', x')$ in $\mathfrak{B}_{n0}$ referred to principal axes. We notice that there is no corresponding unitary transformation for $[Kx, x]$ in $\mathfrak{B}'_n$, since (24·8·1) shows that no unitary transformation can map the system $\{\phi^\nu\}$, which is orthonormal in $\mathfrak{B}'_n$, on the system $\{u^\nu\}$, which is not orthonormal in $\mathfrak{B}'_n$. Neither is there a corresponding unitary transformation for the pencil $H-\lambda G$ in $\mathfrak{B}_n$, since the system $\{u^\nu\}$ is orthonormal in $\mathfrak{B}_n$, but the system $\{\phi^\nu\}$ is not orthonormal in $\mathfrak{B}_n$. Now the equation (25·2·4) for $\nu \neq \mu$ may be interpreted as showing that the vectors ϕ^ν and ϕ^μ give the directions of conjugate diameters of the surface $(Gx, x) = 1$ in $\mathfrak{B}_n$. We may therefore regard (25·21·2) as giving the representation for the pencil of forms $((H-\lambda G)x, x)$ with regard to a set of axes which are conjugate with regard to both (Hx, x) and (Gx, x). We deduce the representations for the separate forms (Hx, x) and (Gx, x), since we obtain from (25·21·2)

$$(Hx, x) = \sum_{\nu=1}^{n} \lambda_\nu |(Gx, \phi^\nu)|^2, \quad (Gx, x) = \sum_{\nu=1}^{n} |(Gx, \phi^\nu)|^2, \tag{25·21·3}$$

where, by (24·31·2), $\qquad x = \sum_{\nu=1}^{n} (Gx, \phi^\nu)\phi^\nu.$

25·3. It is of interest with reference to the computation of eigen-values to remark that the inequalities formulated in Theorems **14·2** and **14·4** also hold for the eigen-values of the pencil $H-\lambda G$, since Theorem **14·1** can be applied at once to K_0 in $\mathfrak{B}_{n0}$ and can therefore be enunciated for K in $\mathfrak{B}'_n$ and for $H-\lambda G$ in $\mathfrak{B}_n$ in the following form:

THEOREM. *If the eigen-values of the H.T. K in $\mathfrak{B}'_n$ (or of the pencil $H-\lambda G$ in $\mathfrak{B}_n$) are arranged in descending order of magnitude as $\lambda_1 \geq \lambda_2 \geq \ldots \geq \lambda_n$, then λ_{r+1} is the minimum of the maxima of $[Kx, x]$ on the surface $[x, x] = 1$ in $\mathfrak{B}'_n$ (or of (Hx, x) on the surface $(Gx, x) = 1$ in $\mathfrak{B}_n$) within all L.M.'s of rank $n-r$.*

25·31. The inequalities for the eigen-values deduced in Theorems **14·2** and **14·4** from Theorem **14·1** follow at once for K_0 in $\mathfrak{B}_{n0}$. Theorem **14·2** takes the following form for K in $\mathfrak{B}'_n$:

THEOREM. *Let $\mathfrak{M}$ be any L.M. of rank $n-r$ and let $P'_{\mathfrak{M}}$ be the projector, orthogonal with regard to $\mathfrak{B}'_n$, of $\mathfrak{B}'_n$ on $\mathfrak{M}$; let K be a H.T. in $\mathfrak{B}'_n$, write $K_1 = P'_{\mathfrak{M}} K P'_{\mathfrak{M}}$ and consider the Hermitian form $[K_1 x, x]$ within $\mathfrak{M}$. If the eigen-values of K in $\mathfrak{B}'_n$ are written in descending* *order of magnitude as* $\lambda_1 \geqslant \lambda_2 \geqslant \ldots \geqslant \lambda_n$ *and those of* K_1 *in* $\mathfrak{M}$ *as* $\lambda'_1 \geqslant \lambda'_2 \geqslant \ldots \geqslant \lambda'_{n-r}$, *then* $\lambda_s \geqslant \lambda'_s \geqslant \lambda_{s+r}$ *for* $s = 1, 2, \ldots, n-r$.

NOTE 1. If we take $[u^1, u^2, \ldots, u^{n-r}]$ for $\mathfrak{M}$ in Theorem **25·31**, as we did in **14·21**, we are not led by the formation of K_1 to the reduced forms of either K or H. For we have

$$x = \sum_{\mu=1}^{n} x_\mu u^\mu, \quad P'_{\mathfrak{M}} x = \sum_{\mu=1}^{n-r} x_\mu u^\mu + \sum_{\mu=n-r+1}^{n} x_\mu P'_{\mathfrak{M}} u^\mu,$$

where
$$P'_{\mathfrak{M}} u^\nu = \sum_{\mu=1}^{n-r} \alpha_{\nu\mu} u^\mu \quad (n-r+1 \leqslant \nu \leqslant n),$$

and this need not be zero since $[u^\nu, u^\mu] = g_{\mu\nu}$. If we wish to approximate to the eigen-values of K by eigen-values of a reduced form, we must use the reduced forms of K_0, since the theory developed in § **14** can be applied at once to K_0 in $\mathfrak{B}_{n0}$.

NOTE 2. The eigen-values of K_1 in the L.M. $\mathfrak{M}$ in $\mathfrak{B}'_n$ are the same as those of the pencil $(P'_{\mathfrak{M}})^* HP'_{\mathfrak{M}} - \lambda GP'_{\mathfrak{M}}$ in the L.M. $\mathfrak{M}$ in $\mathfrak{B}_n$ since, by (24·6·1) and (24·7·1),

$$\begin{aligned} G(P'_{\mathfrak{M}} KP'_{\mathfrak{M}} - \lambda P'_{\mathfrak{M}}) &= (P'_{\mathfrak{M}})^* GKP'_{\mathfrak{M}} - \lambda GP'_{\mathfrak{M}} \\ &= (P'_{\mathfrak{M}})^* HP'_{\mathfrak{M}} - \lambda GP'_{\mathfrak{M}}. \end{aligned}$$

Let the vectors $\{\psi^\nu\}$ be a set of eigen-solutions of K_1 in $\mathfrak{M}$, orthogonal with regard to $\mathfrak{B}'_n$ and corresponding to eigen-values λ'_ν. By (25·2·3), we have

$$(K_1 - \lambda P'_{\mathfrak{M}})\, x = P'_{\mathfrak{M}}(K - \lambda I)\, P'_{\mathfrak{M}} x = \sum_{\nu=1}^{n-r} (\lambda'_\nu - \lambda)\, [P'_{\mathfrak{M}} x, \psi^\nu]\, P'_{\mathfrak{M}} \psi^\nu,$$

from which we deduce the representation

$$[(K_1 - \lambda P'_{\mathfrak{M}})\, x, x] = \sum_{\nu=1}^{n-r} (\lambda'_\nu - \lambda)\, |(GP'_{\mathfrak{M}} x, \psi^\nu)|^2,$$

and the two further representations, corresponding to those of (25·21·3),

$$\left.\begin{aligned} ((P'_{\mathfrak{M}})^* HP'_{\mathfrak{M}} x, x) &= \sum_{\nu=1}^{n-r} \lambda'_\nu\, |(GP'_{\mathfrak{M}} x, \psi^\nu)|^2, \\ (GP'_{\mathfrak{M}} x, x) &= \sum_{\nu=1}^{n-r} |(GP'_{\mathfrak{M}} x, \psi^\nu)|^2. \end{aligned}\right\} \qquad (25{\cdot}31{\cdot}1)$$

25·32. Theorem **14·4** takes the following form for K in $\mathfrak{B}'_n$:

THEOREM. *Let* $\mathfrak{M}$ *be any L.M. of rank* $n-r$ *considered in* $\mathfrak{B}'_n$, *write* $\mathfrak{N} = \mathfrak{B}'_n \ominus' \mathfrak{M}$ *and denote the projectors, orthogonal with regard to* $\mathfrak{B}'_n$, *of* $\mathfrak{B}'_n$ *on* $\mathfrak{M}$ *and* $\mathfrak{N}$ *by* $P'_{\mathfrak{M}}$ *and* $P'_{\mathfrak{N}}$ *respectively, where*

$$P'_{\mathfrak{N}} = I - P'_{\mathfrak{M}}.$$

Let K be a positive definite H.T. in $\mathfrak{V}'_n$, *write* $K_1 = P'_{\mathfrak{M}} K P'_{\mathfrak{M}}$, $K_2 = P'_{\mathfrak{N}} K P'_{\mathfrak{N}}$ *and consider the Hermitian forms* $[K_1 x, x]$ *and* $[K_2 x, x]$ *in* $\mathfrak{M}$ *and* $\mathfrak{N}$ *respectively. If the eigen-values of K are written in descending order of magnitude as* $\lambda_1 \geqslant \lambda_2 \geqslant \dots \geqslant \lambda_n$, *those of* K_1 *as* $\lambda'_1 \geqslant \lambda'_2 \geqslant \dots \geqslant \lambda'_{n-r}$ *and those of* K_2 *as* $\lambda''_1 \geqslant \lambda''_2 \geqslant \dots \geqslant \lambda''_r$, *then*

$$\lambda'_{s+1} + \lambda''_{t+1} \geqslant \lambda_{s+t+1}$$

for $0 \leqslant s \leqslant n-r-1$, $0 \leqslant t \leqslant r-1$.

NOTE. Notes 1 and 2 of Theorem **25·31** also apply with regard to Theorem **25·32**.

§ 26. L.T.'s that are Hermitian or normal in some $\mathfrak{V}'_n$

26·0. We now seek necessary and sufficient conditions for the existence of a positive definite H.T. G in $\mathfrak{V}_n$ such that a given L.T. A is Hermitian or normal with regard to the space $\mathfrak{V}'_n$ defined by the metric form $[x, y] = (Gx, y)$.

26·1. A necessary condition for A is readily obtained; namely, that A should have simple elementary divisors. For, if A is normal with regard to $\mathfrak{V}'_n$, then the similar transformation $A_0 = \Gamma A \Gamma^{-1}$ is normal with regard to $\mathfrak{V}_{n0}$ since, by (24·5·3), $A_0^* = \Gamma A^{[*]} \Gamma^{-1}$. By **22·7**, therefore, $\Gamma A \Gamma^{-1}$ has simple elementary divisors and, by Theorem **22·41**, A also has simple elementary divisors when considered in $\mathfrak{V}_n$. But the elementary divisors of A are the same whether we consider A in $\mathfrak{V}_n$ or in $\mathfrak{V}'_n$, since the definition given in **22·2** is independent of the scalar product. Indeed, we may see directly that a L.T. with simple elementary divisors in either of the spaces $\mathfrak{V}_n$ and $\mathfrak{V}'_n$ has the same property in the other, since, as we have remarked in **22·3**, the property is equivalent to the identity of the eigen-manifolds and principal manifolds corresponding to any eigen-value, and these manifolds are the same in both spaces.

We have shown in **22·71**, however, that there are L.T.'s with simple elementary divisors that are not normal transformations with regard to $\mathfrak{V}_n$. We go on to show that if A has simple elementary divisors and is not normal with regard to $\mathfrak{V}_n$, there is a space $\mathfrak{V}'_n$ with regard to which it is normal.

26·2. THEOREM. *A necessary and sufficient condition for the existence of a positive definite H.T. G corresponding to a L.T. A in* $\mathfrak{V}_n$ *and such that* $AA^{[*]} = A^{[*]}A$, *where* $A^{[*]}$ *is the adjoint of A with* *regard to a space $\mathfrak{V}_n'$ defined by the scalar product $[x,y] = (Gx,y)$, is that A should have simple elementary divisors. Further, if all the eigen-values of A are real, then A is Hermitian with regard to the space $\mathfrak{V}_n'$.*

Proof. Let A have simple elementary divisors. By Theorem **22·1**, we can write the Jordan matrix for A in the form $\mathscr{E} = T^{-1}AT$, where T has rank n, and $\mathscr{E}$ will be a diagonal matrix Λ. We have therefore

$$A = T\Lambda T^{-1}, \quad A^* = (T^{-1})^*\bar{\Lambda}T^*. \qquad (26\cdot2\cdot1)$$

If T is a unitary transformation, that is, if $T^{-1} = T^*$ and $(T^{-1})^* = T$, then A is normal with regard to $\mathfrak{V}_n$ since, by (26·2·1),

$$AA^* = T\Lambda T^*T\bar{\Lambda}T^* = T\Lambda\bar{\Lambda}T^* = T\bar{\Lambda}\Lambda T^* = A^*A.$$

If T is not a unitary transformation, we write

$$G = (T^*)^{-1}T^{-1}, \quad G^{-1} = TT^*, \qquad (26\cdot2\cdot2)$$

so that G, by **8·22**, is a positive definite H.T. Then, if $\mathfrak{V}_n'$ is the space defined by the metric form

$$[x,y] = (Gx,y) = (T^{-1}x, T^{-1}y),$$

and if $A^{[*]}$ is the adjoint of A with regard to $\mathfrak{V}_n'$, we obtain from (24·5·2) and (26·2·1)

$$A^{[*]} = TT^*A^*(T^*)^{-1}T^{-1} = T\bar{\Lambda}T^{-1}.$$

Hence, by (26·2·1),

$$AA^{[*]} = T\Lambda\bar{\Lambda}T^{-1},$$
$$A^{[*]}A = T\bar{\Lambda}\Lambda T^{-1} = T\Lambda\bar{\Lambda}T^{-1} = AA^{[*]},$$

since $\Lambda\bar{\Lambda} = \bar{\Lambda}\Lambda$, by **7·41**, so that A is normal with regard to $\mathfrak{V}_n'$. Further, by the Note to Theorem **16·4**, A is Hermitian with regard to $\mathfrak{V}_n'$ if its eigen-values are all real.

Conversely, as we have already proved in **26·1**, if A is normal with regard to a space $\mathfrak{V}_n'$ it must have simple elementary divisors.

26·21. Corollary of Theorem **26·2**. *Any L.T. Q that is a general projector in the space $\mathfrak{V}_n$ is an orthogonal projector in some space $\mathfrak{V}_n'$.*

Proof. By **22·6**, Q has simple elementary divisors and real eigen-values 0 and 1. Thus, by Theorem **26·2**, there is a space $\mathfrak{V}_n'$ with regard to which Q is Hermitian. But $Q^2 = Q$, since Q is a general projector in $\mathfrak{V}_n$. Thus, by **24·7**, Q is an orthogonal projector in $\mathfrak{V}_n'$.

26·3. THEOREM. *Let A and B be commutative L.T.'s in $\mathfrak{B}_n$ with simple elementary divisors. There is a space $\mathfrak{B}'_n$ with regard to which they are both normal transformations.*

PROOF. By Theorem **23·14**, A and B have a linearly independent set of n eigen-solutions in common. If then we take for T the matrix of which the columns consist of the coordinates of these n eigen-solutions we obtain

$$AT = T\Lambda, \quad BT = T\Lambda',$$

where Λ and Λ' are diagonal matrices. The matrix T defines a positive definite H.T. $G = (T^*)^{-1} T^{-1}$ which determines the metric form in a space $\mathfrak{B}'_n$ and, by Theorem **26·2**, both A and B are normal with regard to $\mathfrak{B}'_n$.

§ 27. APPLICATION TO THE DYNAMICAL THEORY OF SMALL OSCILLATIONS

(References: P. Appell, *Traité de mécanique rationnelle* (vol. 2, ed. 4, Paris, 1923), 330–348. R. Courant and D. Hilbert, [x], 210–212, 240–245. T. Levi-Civita and U. Amaldi, *Lezioni di meccanica razionale* (vol. 2, Parte prima, Bologna, 1926), 437–445. E. T. Whittaker, *Analytical Dynamics* (ed. 3, Cambridge, 1927), 177–195.)

27·0. We consider the Lagrange equations determining the motion of a dynamical system with n degrees of freedom,

$$\frac{d}{dt}\left(\frac{\partial T}{\partial \dot{q}_\nu}\right) - \frac{\partial T}{\partial q_\nu} = -\frac{\partial V}{\partial q_\nu} \quad (\nu = 1, 2, \ldots, n) \tag{27·0·1}$$

(see, for example, E. T. Whittaker, loc. cit. 39), where the q_ν are the 'generalized coordinates' determining a configuration of the system and the $\dot{q}_\nu$ are their derivatives with respect to the time t; $V = V(q_1, q_2, \ldots, q_n)$ is the potential energy of the system and $T = \frac{1}{2} \sum_{\mu=1}^{n} \sum_{\nu=1}^{n} g_{\mu\nu} \dot{q}_\mu \dot{q}_\nu$ is the kinetic energy. The coefficients $g_{\mu\nu}$ are real differentiable functions of the q_ν such that the matrix $G = (g_{\mu\nu})$ is symmetric and, since the kinetic energy is positive unless all the velocities vanish, the quadratic form for T is positive definite. When we develop (27·0·1) we obtain the equations

$$\sum_{\kappa=1}^{n} g_{\nu\kappa} \ddot{q}_\kappa + \sum_{\iota,\kappa=1}^{n} \begin{bmatrix} \iota, \kappa \\ \nu \end{bmatrix} \dot{q}_\iota \dot{q}_\kappa = -\frac{\partial V}{\partial q_\nu} \quad (\nu = 1, 2, \ldots, n), \tag{27·0·2}$$

where $\begin{bmatrix} \iota, \kappa \\ \nu \end{bmatrix}$ is the Christoffel symbol

$$\begin{bmatrix} \iota, \kappa \\ \nu \end{bmatrix} = \frac{1}{2}\left(\frac{\partial g_{\iota\nu}}{\partial q_\kappa} + \frac{\partial g_{\kappa\nu}}{\partial q_\iota} - \frac{\partial g_{\iota\kappa}}{\partial q_\nu}\right).$$

We now interpret the q_ν as the coordinates of vectors q in a real space $\mathfrak{B}_n$, and the $\dot{q}_\nu$ and $\ddot{q}_\nu$ as the coordinates of vectors $\dot{q}$ and $\ddot{q}$ respectively. We let

$\mathring{q} = (\mathring{q}_1, \mathring{q}_2, \ldots, \mathring{q}_n)$ be any vector independent of t of which the coordinates satisfy the equations (27·0·2) so that

$$\left[\frac{\partial V}{\partial q_\nu}\right]_{q=\mathring{q}} = 0 \quad (\nu = 1, 2, \ldots, n). \tag{27·0·3}$$

We say that $\mathring{q}$ is a position of equilibrium of the system. We may assume, without loss of generality, that $\mathring{q}$ coincides with the zero vector in $\mathfrak{V}_n$, and under this assumption we investigate the integrals of the system of differential equations (27·0·2) for small initial values of all the coordinates q_ν and q_ν. If we neglect small terms of order higher than the first we omit the quadratic form in the $\dot{q}_\iota$ in (27·0·2), and we obtain $\partial V/\partial q_\nu$ as a first-order term by using (27·0·3) to write

$$V = V_0 + \frac{1}{2} \sum_{\mu,\nu=1}^{n} a_{\mu\nu} q_\mu q_\nu, \quad \frac{\partial V}{\partial q_\nu} = \sum_{\mu=1}^{n} a_{\mu\nu} q_\mu, \tag{27·0·4}$$

where V_0 is the value of V for $q = 0$ and where $H = (a_{\mu\nu})$ is a real symmetric matrix of constant elements. We rewrite (27·0·2) in the form

$$G\ddot{q} + Hq = 0, \tag{27·0·5}$$

where G is now the matrix of the elements $g_{\mu\nu}$, evaluated at $q = 0$. The transformation G in $\mathfrak{V}_n$ is positive definite, so that we can use for Hq and $G\ddot{q}$ the representations (25·2·5) to obtain

$$Hq = \sum_{\nu=1}^{n} \lambda_\nu (Gq, \phi^\nu) G\phi^\nu, \quad G\ddot{q} = \sum_{\nu=1}^{n} (G\ddot{q}, \phi^\nu) G\phi^\nu, \tag{27·0·6}$$

where the λ_ν and the ϕ^ν are the real eigen-values and eigen-solutions of the pencil $H - \lambda G$, and where the ϕ^ν satisfy the conditions (25·2·4) of orthonormality with respect to the real space $\mathfrak{V}'_n$ associated with $\mathfrak{V}_n$ and determined by the metric form G. The substitution of (27·0·6) in (27·0·5) yields the equations

$$\sum_{\nu=1}^{n} (G(\ddot{q} + \lambda_\nu q), \phi^\nu) G\phi^\nu = 0$$

whence we obtain, by the linear independence of the n vectors $G\phi^\nu$.

$$(G(\ddot{q} + \lambda_\nu q), \phi^\nu) = 0 \quad (\nu = 1, 2, \ldots, n),$$

and, finally,

$$(\ddot{q}, G\phi^\nu) + \lambda_\nu (q, G\phi^\nu) = 0 \quad (\nu = 1, 2, \ldots, n). \tag{27·0·7}$$

We now write

$$q'_\nu = (q, G\phi^\nu) = (Gq, \phi^\nu), \quad \lambda_\nu = 4\pi^2\sigma_\nu^2 \quad (\nu = 1, 2, \ldots, n),$$

and obtain the integrals of the equations (27·0·7) in the form

$$q'_\nu = \alpha_\nu e^{2\pi i \sigma_\nu t} + \beta_\nu e^{-2\pi i \sigma_\nu t} \quad (\nu = 1, 2, \ldots, n), \tag{27·0·8}$$

where the coefficients α_ν and β_ν are determined by the values $q'_{\nu 0}$ and $\dot{q}'_{\nu 0}$ of q'_ν and $\dot{q}'_\nu$ for $t = 0$ as

$$\alpha_\nu = \frac{1}{2}\left(q'_{\nu 0} - i\frac{\dot{q}'_{\nu 0}}{2\pi\sigma_\nu}\right), \quad \beta_\nu = \frac{1}{2}\left(q'_{\nu 0} + i\frac{\dot{q}'_{\nu 0}}{2\pi\sigma_\nu}\right).$$

Since the initial values of q_ν and $\dot{q}_\nu$ are small terms of the first order, it follows that α_ν and β_ν are also of the first order. By (24·31·2), the final solution of the equations (27·0·7) is of the form

$$q = \sum_{\nu=1}^{n} q'_\nu \phi^\nu, \tag{27·0·9}$$

where q'_ν is given by (27·0·8).

27·01. By (25·21·3), the condition that all the eigen-values λ_ν are positive is equivalent to the condition that H is a positive definite H.T. We see from (27·0·4) that, when this condition is satisfied, $V > V_0$ in the neighbourhood of $q = 0$, that is, V has an isolated minimum value at $q = 0$; then the values $\sigma_\nu = \frac{1}{2\pi}\sqrt{\lambda_\nu}$ are real and positive, and the q'_ν, defined by (27·0·8), are of the first order for all values of t, oscillating with frequency σ_ν. By (27·0·9), the vector q is the sum of n small oscillating components q'_ν in the directions defined by the vectors ϕ^ν, which are independent of t, and, since q remains of the first order, the approximating differential equations (27·0·5) describe the variations of q for all values of t. Thus, when the eigen-values λ_ν are positive, q and $\dot{q}$ describe small first-order oscillations about the position $q = 0$, provided that their initial values are of the first order. We then say that the position of equilibrium $q = 0$ is stable in the sense of the following definition.

Definition of stable equilibrium. The position of equilibrium $q = 0$ determined by the equations (27·0·2) and (27·0·3) is said to be stable if there corresponds to any small positive number ϵ a positive number δ such that every system of integrals $\{q_\nu(t)\}$ of (27·0·2) satisfies the inequalities

$$|q_\nu(t)| < \epsilon, \quad |\dot{q}_\nu(t)| < \epsilon \quad (1 \leqslant \nu \leqslant n, t > 0)$$

whenever the initial values $q_\nu(0)$, $\dot{q}_\nu(0)$ satisfy the inequalities

$$|q_\nu(0)| < \delta, \quad |\dot{q}_\nu(0)| < \delta.$$

27·02. Smooth constraints. (References: Courant-Hilbert, loc. cit. 230; Whittaker, loc. cit. 191–193.) We now consider the modifications that occur when the system is subject to smooth constraints imposing r conditions on q independent of t. Since we consider these conditions only in the neighbourhood of $q = 0$ we need only consider their linear approximations, taking into account that they must be satisfied for $q = 0$ itself, and we may therefore take them in the form

$$(b^\mu, q) = 0 \quad (\mu = 1, 2, \ldots, r), \tag{27·02·1}$$

where the b^μ are a set of r linearly independent vectors in $\mathfrak{V}_n$, independent of q and t. We write $\mathfrak{N}_1 = [b^1, b^2, \ldots, b^r]$, $\mathfrak{M} = \mathfrak{V}_n \ominus \mathfrak{N}_1$, and, since $(b^\mu, \ddot{q}) = 0$, we see that we have to consider the kinetic and potential energies of the system in the subspace $\mathfrak{M} = \mathfrak{V}_{n-r}$. We deduce the Lagrange equations (27·0·1) and their approximations (27·0·5), where q, $\dot{q}$ and $\ddot{q}$ are now vectors in the subspace $\mathfrak{M}$.

Let $P'_{\mathfrak{M}}$ be the general projector of $\mathfrak{V}_n$ on $\mathfrak{M}$, orthogonal with regard to $\mathfrak{V}'_n$, and denote the quadratic approximations of the kinetic and potential energies of the system in the subspace $\mathfrak{M}$ by $T_{\mathfrak{M}}$ and $V_{\mathfrak{M}}$ respectively. Then

$$T_{\mathfrak{M}} = \tfrac{1}{2}(GP'_{\mathfrak{M}}\dot{q}, P'_{\mathfrak{M}}\dot{q}), \quad V_{\mathfrak{M}} = V_0 + \tfrac{1}{2}(HP'_{\mathfrak{M}}q, P'_{\mathfrak{M}}q).$$

By (24·6·1), however,

$$(P'_{\mathfrak{M}})^* GP'_{\mathfrak{M}} = G(P'_{\mathfrak{M}})^2 = GP'_{\mathfrak{M}},$$

and therefore

$$T_{\mathfrak{M}} = \tfrac{1}{2}(GP'_{\mathfrak{M}}\dot{q}, \dot{q}), \quad V_{\mathfrak{M}} = V_0 + \tfrac{1}{2}((P'_{\mathfrak{M}})^* HP'_{\mathfrak{M}}q, q),$$

where $GP'_{\mathfrak{M}}$ and $(P'_{\mathfrak{M}})^* HP'_{\mathfrak{M}}$ are H.T.'s of the same form as those considered in Note **2** of Theorem **25·31**. The representations (25·31·1) give

$$T_{\mathfrak{M}} = \frac{1}{2}\sum_{\nu=1}^{n-r} |(GP'_{\mathfrak{M}}\dot{q}, \psi^\nu)|^2, \quad V_{\mathfrak{M}} = V_0 + \frac{1}{2}\sum_{\nu=1}^{n-r} \lambda'_\nu |(GP'_{\mathfrak{M}}q, \psi^\nu)|^2,$$

(27·02·2)

where the λ'_ν are the eigen-values of the pencil $(P'_{\mathfrak{M}})^* HP'_{\mathfrak{M}} - \lambda GP'_{\mathfrak{M}}$ in the subspace $\mathfrak{M}$ and $\{\psi^\nu\}$ is a corresponding set of eigen-solutions. The connexion between the eigen-values λ'_ν of the constrained system and the eigen-values λ_ν of the free system is given by Theorem **25·31**. Thus, every $\lambda'_\nu > 0$ when every $\lambda_\nu > 0$. Writing

$$q'_\nu = (GP'_{\mathfrak{M}}q, \psi^\nu),$$

we deduce the Lagrange equations, by (27·02·2), in the form

$$\ddot{q}'_\nu + \lambda'_\nu q'_\nu = 0 \quad (\nu = 1, 2, ..., n-r), \tag{27·02·3}$$

with the integrals

$$q'_\nu = \alpha_\nu e^{2\pi i \sigma'_\nu t} + \beta_\nu e^{-2\pi i \sigma'_\nu t} \quad (\nu = 1, 2, ..., n-r), \tag{27·02·4}$$

and the final solution

$$q = \sum_{\nu=1}^{n-r} q'_\nu \psi^\nu, \tag{27·02·5}$$

where $\lambda'_\nu = 4\pi^2 \sigma'^2_\nu$ and where, as in **27·0**, the coefficients α_ν, β_ν are small provided that the initial values of q and $\dot{q}$ are small. If every $\lambda'_\nu > 0$ the σ'_ν may be taken positive and they then represent the frequencies of the oscillations of the q'_ν. Further, the approximations (27·02·2) and (27·02·3) for the kinetic and potential energies and for the Lagrange equations are applicable to the motion of the system for every value of t.

We now write $P'_{\mathfrak{N}} = I - P'_{\mathfrak{M}}$ and $\mathfrak{N} = \mathfrak{V}'_n \ominus' \mathfrak{M}$, so that $\mathfrak{M} = \mathfrak{V}'_n \ominus' \mathfrak{N}$ and, by (24·4·1), $\mathfrak{M} = \mathfrak{V}_n \ominus G\mathfrak{M}$; since $\mathfrak{M} = \mathfrak{V}_n \ominus \mathfrak{N}_1$, we have $\mathfrak{N} = G^{-1}\mathfrak{N}_1$. Then $\mathfrak{M}, \mathfrak{N}, P'_{\mathfrak{M}}$ and $P'_{\mathfrak{N}}$ may be taken as the L.M.'s and the projectors of Theorem **25·32**. Using the notation of that theorem we write the eigen-values of the pencil $(P'_{\mathfrak{N}})^* HP'_{\mathfrak{N}} - \lambda GP'_{\mathfrak{N}}$ as $\lambda''_1 \geqslant \lambda''_2 \geqslant ... \geqslant \lambda''_r$, where the λ''_ν are all positive.

We also write $\sigma''_\nu = \frac{1}{2\pi}\sqrt{\lambda''_\nu}$, and we interpret the σ''_ν as the frequencies of a constrained motion of the system that is determined by conditions

$$(c^\mu, q) = 0 \quad (\mu = 1, 2, ..., n-r),$$

where the vectors c^μ form a basis of the L.M. $\mathfrak{M}_1 = G\mathfrak{M} = \mathfrak{V}_n \ominus \mathfrak{N}$, just as the vectors b^μ of the conditions (27·02·1) form a basis of the L.M. $\mathfrak{N}_1 = G\mathfrak{N}$. We obtain from Theorems **25·31** and **25·32** the following inequalities for the frequencies of the free and constrained motions:

$$\sigma_{s+r} \leqslant \sigma'_s \leqslant \sigma_s \quad (s = 1, 2, ..., n-r)$$

$$\sigma^2_{s+t+1} \leqslant (\sigma'_{s+1})^2 + (\sigma''_{t+1})^2 \quad (0 \leqslant s \leqslant n-r-1,\ 0 \leqslant t \leqslant r-1).$$

The first of these inequalities is often quoted in the form: *If the system has r constraints the $n-r$ frequencies of the constrained oscillations lie in the intervals between the frequencies of the free oscillations and, in particular, for $r = 1$, the $n-1$ frequencies of the oscillations of a system with one constraint separate the n frequencies of the free oscillations.*

NOTES

CHAPTER I

§ **1.** The first explicit development of a calculus of vectors appeared in the 1840's, in widely differing presentations, in the work of Hamilton and Grassmann.

Hamilton uses 3-dimensional vectors in illustrating his theory of quaternions. His first note on the theory was published in 1843 ([25], vol. 2);* in later notes he introduces the terms 'vector' and 'scalar' ([25], vol. 3, 3 and 8) and represents a quaternion q as a sum $a+\alpha$, where a, the 'scalar' part, is a real number and α, the 'vector' part, is a vector $ix+jy+kz$ in 3-dimensional space with real coördinates x, y, z referred to unit vectors i, j, k that satisfy the laws of multiplication

$$jk = -kj = i, \quad ki = -ik = j, \quad ij = -ji = k;$$
$$i^2 = j^2 = k^2 = -1.$$

The products that we now call the scalar and vector products are introduced when he forms the product of q with a second quaternion $q' = b+\beta$, where $\beta = ix'+jy'+kz'$. He writes

$$(a+\alpha)(b+\beta) = ab+a\beta+\alpha b+\alpha\beta,$$

where $\alpha\beta$ is again a quaternion with a scalar and a vector part,

$$\alpha\beta = -(xx'+yy'+zz')+i(yz'-y'z)+j(zx'-z'x)+k(xy'-x'y),$$

so that, in effect, $\qquad \alpha\beta = -(\alpha, \beta)+\alpha\times\beta,$

where (α, β) is the scalar product and $\alpha\times\beta$ the vector product of α and β. Hamilton writes the scalar product as $AB\cos(A, B)$ and the vector product as $\gamma AB\sin(A, B)$, where A and B are the lengths of the vectors α and β, (A, B) is the angle between them and γ is a unit vector orthogonal to both of them. Using the relation $\alpha\times\beta = -\beta\times\alpha$, he obtains the relations

$$\alpha\beta+\beta\alpha = -2(\alpha, \beta), \quad \alpha\beta-\beta\alpha = 2(\alpha\times\beta)$$

([25], vol. 3, 11, formulae (a) and (b); [26], vol. 29, 30–31, Art. 21). Hamilton considers only vectors in real 3-dimensional space. He does not illustrate his theory of quaternions, as one might have expected nowadays, in terms of 4-dimensional space. Instead, he

* Numbers in square brackets refer to the List of References at the end of the book. Where page references are given in the List to an author's collected works the references in these notes are also to the collected works and not to the originals.

interprets the scalar part of the quaternion in terms of an 'extra-spatial' or 'scalar direction' to which all directions in (3-dimensional) space are equally related ([25], vol. 3, 8).

Grassmann's work, published in 1844, is more ambitious; it may be described as an attempt to present a theory of abstract n-dimensional space. Mathematics in 1844, however, was not ready for this point of view, which made progress only after axiomatic methods had been developed by Hilbert and others over 50 years later. Grassmann uses an argument that is more philosophical than mathematical in his description of an abstract space ([I], xviii–xxxii and 1–14). He then introduces vectors, which he calls 'Grössen erster Stufe' or 'Strecke' ([I], 15–19), and defines addition of vectors and multiplication by a number ([I], 22–25). His work was hardly noticed by contemporary mathematicians; F. A. Möbius was among the very few who recognized at once the originality of his approach and the importance of his ideas in geometry and mechanics. He persuaded him, however, to present them in a more concrete geometrical form. In a publication of 1847 ([22]), Grassmann confines his attention to a 3-dimensional vector space; he gives there the definition of the scalar product which he calls 'inneres Produkt' ([22], 17–26). The limitations that have been introduced in this memoir are emphasized by the accompanying note of Möbius.

In 1862 Grassmann published a completely new presentation of his work; when we speak of Grassmann's theory to-day we usually mean this second presentation. It is, in effect, a discussion of a concrete n-dimensional vector space. It contains the definitions of vectors, of the addition of vectors and multiplication by scalars ([II], 1–6), and of the scalar product ([II], 109, Art. 141–143). It will be seen that there are frequent references to Grassmann's work throughout our notes on many of the important points.

§**2.** L.M.'s of rank r are introduced by Grassmann ([I], §20, 30–32 and [II], 16, Art. 14); they are called 'Systeme' in [I] and 'Gebiete r-ter Stufe' in [II]. The main properties of bases are dealt with in ([II], 9–12, Art. 19–24).

For §§**1** and **2** see also ([IX], 307–314) and ([XV], I, 14–30). In [III] and [V] the scalar product of vectors is introduced only after the discussion of the invariant affine properties of L.M.'s and L.T.'s.

§3. Schmidt's orthogonalization process is discussed in ([40], 442–443). It is characteristic of the analytical origin of the process, which may be regarded as the first step in the transformation of a quadratic form to principal axes (see our Chapter III), that Schmidt develops it, not for a vector space, but for a function space $\mathscr{L}_2$ of functions of which the square of the absolute value is Lebesgue integrable. Gram, before Schmidt, gives formulae for the orthogonalization of a system of functions, ([21], 44–45), but these formulae use 'Gram's determinants'; they are not recursive and have not the simple geometrical appeal that distinguishes the Schmidt process.

Grassmann remarks that every L.M. has an orthonormal basis ([II], 118–119, Art. 163). See also ([III], 98); ([V], 138–144) and ([IX], 314–316).

§§**4** and **5**. The symbols used for products, sums and differences of L.M.'s are those used in the book by M. H. Stone, *Linear Transformations in Hilbert Space*, American Mathematical Society Colloquium Publications, xv (New York, 1932), 20–21.

5·0. Grassmann introduces the orthogonal complement ('allseitig normales Gebiet') ([II], 112–113, Art. 152). The method of construction follows from Art. 159 (115–116) and Art. 163 (118–119).

5·2. See ([IX], 316–317, 329–330).

§**6.** The equivalent of formula (6·03·1) is used by Grassmann for the definition of a L.T., which he calls 'Quotient'. He writes, in effect,

$$Q = \frac{b^1, b^2, \ldots, b^n}{v^1, v^2, \ldots, v^n}, \quad Qv^\nu = b^\nu$$

([II], 241, Art. 377).

6·0 to **6·21.** See also ([IX], 335–338).

6·71. See ([XV], I, 36–38, Satz 1 and Satz 2).

§**7.** The development of a calculus of L.T.'s in the form of a calculus of matrices is Cayley's achievement ([8], 476–480). He defines, for $n = 3$, addition of matrices, multiplication by a scalar, multiplication of matrices and the inverse matrix; it is immediate that his definitions and theorems, which cover the content of our **7·0** to **7·6**, also hold for general n.

7·8. Sylvester's law of nullity is stated in ([46], 134). See also ([IX], 339–340); and for further references ([VI], 11).

CHAPTER II

§**8.** H.T.'s first appear as Hermitian forms for $n = 2$ in ([28], 237–238) and for general n in [29].

8·5. The reality of the eigen-values of a real symmetric transformation was first noticed in the special case $n = 3$ by Lagrange in 1773 ([33], 603–605), and for general n by Cauchy in 1829 ([5], 180). Hermite extended Cauchy's result to H.T.'s ([29]). For the proof given in **8·5** see Weyr ([56], 224–225); for further references see ([VI], 26).

8·6. For the proof see Schmidt ([40], 444–445).

8·7. The idea of complete reducibility is found in a paper by Frobenius ([18], 19) who refers to a remark by Kronecker. See also ([III], 48–50).

§**9.** Normal transformations are defined by Toeplitz ([50], 190). See also the note to **16·3.**

9·0 to **9·3.** See also ([III], §64, 130–133).

9·4. Unitary transformations are introduced by Autonne ([1 (*a*)]).

§**10.** Grassmann considers projections in ([I], 116–119). He takes up the subject again in [II] and discusses general projections ([II], 17, Art. 33) and orthogonal projections ([II], 120, Art. 164). See also ([III], 51–57 and 112–116).

10·7. The matrix representation of the projector Q (10·7·4) is given by Frobenius ([18], 55–56).

10·8. We have used a remark in ([III], 116) for the proofs of Theorems **10·81** and **10·82**.

CHAPTER III

§§**11–13.** The transformation of a real quadratic form to principal axes was given by Lagrange in 1773 for the case $n = 3$ ([33], 600–608); by Cauchy in 1829 ([5]), and Jacobi in 1834 ([32], 191–228) for the case when the form has n distinct (simple) eigen-values; and by Weierstrass in 1858 ([53]) for the general case with multiple eigen-values. For further references see ([VI], 75).

The analytical method developed in §**12** is Hilbert's ([31], 148–150). It is one of Hilbert's outstanding achievements to have recognized that the eigen-values of quadratic forms have a common origin with the eigen-values that occur in the boundary problems of linear differential equations. In his second Note on Integral Equations he reduces these boundary problems to associated problems for integral equations, which have already been discussed in his first Note as the limits of ordinary symmetric transformations in n-dimensional vector space. The point of view developed in the present book, however, is inspired by the methods of the fourth Note which contains, in addition to the analytical method of our § **12**, a systematic discussion of a complete theory of quadratic forms in a vector space of an infinite number of dimensions. By applying its results to a function space in his fifth Note, Hilbert obtains again all the results of his first Note on integral equations, and much more.

12·0–12·1. A first remark by Lagrange on a maximum property of the eigen-values ([XIV], 381) appears to have passed unnoticed. The first formulation of the maximum properties seems to be in a paper by H. Weber on the boundary problem of a special partial differential equation ([52], 23–26). (It is significant in regard to the history of this method that Weber's work concerns a function space and not an n-dimensional vector space.) The properties are stated and used for quadratic forms by Fischer 36 years later ([17], 245). See also ([V], 191–195) and ([X], 19–22).

13·5. See, for example, ([X], 33–34).

§ **14.** Theorem **14·1** was first given by Fischer ([17], 249); it was rediscovered by Courant who deduced from it the inequalities of Theorem **14·2** ([11], [12]). See also ([III], 151–152), ([V], 196–199) and ([X], 27–28). The inequalities had already been noticed by Cauchy for the reduced forms of real symmetric transformations ([5], 187, Théorème 1).

Further applications of the maximum-minimum methods developed in **14·1** and **14·2** to eigen-value problems arising in connection with various functional equations are given by Courant ([14]). He also discusses certain problems of mathematical physics to which these equations lead.

Aronszajn's inequalities have been published without proof ([1], 476, Theorem 1, Corollary 1′). He very kindly communicated the proof of them to us in 1943.

§ **15.** For notes on functions of a H.T. see the notes to § **19.** For **15·4** and **15·41** see ([X], 24–25).

15·41. See, for example, ([V], 99–100).

15·42. The development (15·42·1), which is the algebraic form of the familiar Neumann resolvent of potential theory, was first given by Christoffel ([9], 272). See also Frobenius ([18], 11–12).

15·5. The Cayley transform first appears in [6]; it is there written in the form $(I+T)^{-1}(I-T)$, where T is a real skew symmetric matrix, and Cayley proves by computation that it is an orthogonal matrix when $n=4$. In [27] Hermite gives a generalization of the Cayley transform for $n=3$ in the form $W=(S+T)^{-1}(S-T)$, where S is a real symmetric matrix of rank n and T, as before, is a real skew symmetric matrix such that $S+T$ is also of rank n. He proves that $W^*SW=S$ and deduces that $(SWx, Wy)=(Sx, y)$, i.e. that the L.T. $x'=Wx, y'=Wy$ leaves the bilinear form (Sx, y) invariant. Cayley returns to the transform in [7] by proving Hermite's result for general n. Frobenius proves Hermite's result as well as Cayley's ([18], 37, Satz I; and 50, Satz IV). For further references see ([VI], 79). See also ([III], 122–124).

§16. For Theorem **16·2** see ([III], 141, Theorem 1).

Theorem **16·3** and its converse Theorem **16·4** are found in a paper by Toeplitz ([50], 192), who remarks in a footnote that they have long been known to Schur. In 1909, Schur published a theorem of which they are simple corollaries ([41], 490–492, Satz I). For Schur's theorem see also ([V], 147–150) or ([VI], 75–76).

Theorem **16·6** for orthogonal L.T.'s is due to Brioschi ([2]). The proof given in **16·6** is essentially Weyr's ([56], 226, Art. 46).

16·63. Hermite proves in [27] the more general theorem for $n=3$ that if S is a real symmetric L.T. then every real L.T. W, such that $I+W$ is regular and $W^*SW=S$, can be written as

$$W=(S+T)^{-1}(S-T),$$

where T is a real skew symmetric L.T. Frobenius proves Hermite's theorem and Cayley's theorem (our Theorem **16·63**) for general n ([18], 37, Satz III; and 50, Satz V). See also ([III], 122–124).

16·83. See ([III], 141–142, Theorem 2).

CHAPTER IV

The process of reduction of a L.T. to Jordan's canonical form, one of the principal topics of Chapter IV, was first given in 1870 ([XII], 114–126). Jordan's approach shows the main feature of our method; the division of the argument into two distinct parts. The first part, given in our Theorems **17·4**, **17·41**, **18·3** and **18·51**, establishes the existence of a dissection of the space $\mathfrak{B}_n$ with reference to the L.T. A of such a kind that

(i) $\mathfrak{B}_n = \sum_{\mu=1}^{m} \mathfrak{P}_\mu \oplus$,

where each $\mathfrak{P}_\mu$ corresponds to one of the eigen-values λ_μ of A and is the null manifold of $(A-\lambda_\mu I)^\nu$ $(\nu \geqslant j_\mu)$, so that $A-\lambda_\mu I$ is nilpotent with regard to $\mathfrak{P}_\mu$, and

(ii) $\mathfrak{P}_\mu$ and $\mathfrak{Q}_\mu = \sum_{\kappa \neq \mu} \mathfrak{P}_\kappa \oplus$ reduce A completely.

The second part of the argument now becomes a discussion of the transformation of a nilpotent L.T. to Jordan's canonical form; it is given in our §§ **20** and **21**.

The result of the first part of the argument already appears in Grassmann's work ([II], 253–259, Art. 390); he constructs a basis for $\mathfrak{P}_\mu$. Buchheim starts from Grassmann's basis and then, by using a device of Jordan ([XII], 125), readily obtains a new basis which satisfies our equations (21·01·3) and hence leads to the canonical form for A ([3], 73–75, Art. 6; and 76). The methods developed in Weyr's papers [55] and [56] have still more in common with our presentation. He considers the nullities of the different powers $(A-\lambda_\mu I)^\kappa$ $(1 \leqslant \kappa \leqslant j_\mu)$, and uses these numbers as characteristic invariants of the L.T. A (the so-called Weyr characteristic), which, with the eigen-values of A, determine a canonical form for A; his canonical form, however, differs from the Jordan form. We may also mention the proof by general induction given by Jordan for his canonical form ([XIII], 184–186), which is familiar to students of linear differential equations. A very elegant way of obtaining the canonical form is due to Weyl ([XVI]). He discusses very fully the division of the argument and stresses the construction of the L.M.'s that reduce A. Julia develops Weyl's method in great detail ([V], 81–92). For further references see ([VI], 70).

§ **17.** For Theorem **17·01** see ([III], 166).

17·2. The phrase 'index of a L.T. corresponding to an eigen-value λ' is used in the sense of Definition **17·2** by Dunford ([16], 187, Definition 1·5). Other authors only speak of an index of a nilpotent L.T. (for example [VIII], 7; and [III], 161).

17·3. Weyr proves Theorem **17·3** for symmetric L.T.'s ([56], 225–226). An equivalent theorem for this case is given by Weierstrass ([53], 240–243 and [54], 42–44).

17·4. This theorem seems to have been first noticed by F. Riesz who proves it for completely continuous L.T.'s in Hilbert space ([39], 79–86). See also ([III], 166, Theorem 3).

18·1. Weyr's Lemma is stated in ([56], 178–180). It also appears in ([XV], II, 73, Satz 12*a*), and, by Dunford, in ([16], 187, Lemma 1·3).

18·3. The theory of the minimal equation is due to Frobenius. He proves its existence and gives its explicit form ([18], 11; and 26, Theorem VI). Other proofs are given by Buchheim ([3], 76–77, Art. 7) and Weyr ([56], 186–188, Art. 20). Sylvester gives examples of third-order matrices of which the minimal equation is of second degree ([47], 157); he calls such matrices, for which the characteristic equation and the minimal equation differ, 'matrices dérogatoires'. See also (XV, II, 65); ([VIII], 23, Theorem 3); ([V], 81–86) and ([III], 167, Theorem 4). For the proof of the existence of at least one eigen-value of A, without the use of determinants, see Hamburger ([23], 174–175). See also Dunford ([16], 187–188, Lemma 1·6).

18·31. The Cayley-Hamilton Theorem is established for $n = 3$ by Hamilton ([XI], 566–568). Cayley states the theorem for general n ([8], 483), but verifies it only for $n = 2$ and $n = 3$. See also Laguerre ([34], 229), who only deals with $n = 2$. The first general proof of the theorem is due to Frobenius ([18], 13).

19·0. Hermite ([29]) constructs the polynomial $p(\zeta)$ satisfying the conditions (19·0·1) as the sum of the residues of a certain expression,

$$p(\zeta) = \sum_{\mu=1}^{m} \operatorname*{Res.}_{z=\lambda_\mu} \frac{p(z)\,q(\zeta)}{(\zeta - z)\,q(z)} = \frac{q(\zeta)}{2\pi i}\int_{\mathfrak{c}} \frac{p(z)}{(\zeta - z)\,q(z)}\,dz,$$

where $\mathfrak{c}$ denotes a closed Jordan curve (or a set of closed Jordan curves) such that the points λ_μ are in the interior of the domain (or domains) enclosed by $\mathfrak{c}$ while ζ is outside $\mathfrak{c}$.

19·1. The possibility of constructing polynomials in a L.T. is implied by the elementary calculus of L.T.'s (see §**7**). Thus, Cayley expressly mentioned this possibility ([8], 482). Functions of a matrix were systematically used by Laguerre ([34], 228–233);

the main feature of his paper was the consideration of power series of matrices ([34], 251–258). An expression for a general function $f(A)$ was given in 1883 by Sylvester ([45]) for a L.T. A with simple eigen-values, and this formula was generalized in 1886 by Buchheim ([4]) for the case of multiple eigen-values. Although Buchheim's formula was essentially the same as (19·1·1) he did not obtain the simple form $(A-\lambda_\mu I)^\kappa Q_\mu$ for the coefficients of $f^{(\kappa)}(\lambda_\mu)$. In 1896, Frobenius stated that the general function $f(A)$ can be defined as the sum of the residues of $(\zeta I - A)^{-1} f(\zeta)$ with regard to all eigen-values of A ([19], 11). This corresponds to Hermite's method of constructing the polynomial $p(\zeta)$ referred to in the note to **19·0**. If we use the series (19·43·5), which Frobenius had established as early as 1878 (see the note to **19·43**) in the neighbourhood of a pole $\zeta = \lambda_\mu$ of $R_\zeta = (A - \zeta I)^{-1}$, we obtain at once the expression (19·1·1) for the sum of the residues of $(\zeta I - A)^{-1} f(\zeta)$. According to Frobenius (loc. cit.), this had been Stickelberger's method in 1881 ([43]) to determine an expression for the general exponential A^α, where α is not necessarily integral or rational. See also ([VIII], 29, formula (31)); for further references see ([VI], 97–101).

Our method of first defining $f(A)$ by (19·1·1) and then verifying that, when f is a polynomial p, the expression coincides with the expression for $p(A)$ obtained by the rules of §7, is used by Dunford ([16]).

19·1–19·3. See Dunford ([16], 188–189, Definition 1·8, Theorems 1·9–1·12).

19·22. The existence of a polynomial $p(A)$ representing Q_μ is asserted by Frobenius ([18], 55); for the method of determining $p(A)$ see Frobenius ([20], 608–610).

19·23. Cayley proves that every function $f(A)$ can be replaced by a polynomial $p(A)$ of degree $n-1$ at most ([8], 483).

19·41. See, for example, ([V], 99–100).

19·42–19·43. For the power series (19·42·1) see Christoffel ([9], 272) and Frobenius ([18], 11–12); for (19·43·5) see Frobenius ([18], 54–55).

19·5. See ([VIII], 29, formula (33)).

19·6. Frobenius states and proves that the spectrum of $f(A)$ coincides with the set of values $f(\lambda_\mu)$, ([18], 11, Satz III). Sylvester states this result, independently of Frobenius, first for the special function $f(A) = A^{p/q}$ ([44], 563), and later in full generality ([46], 133, footnote). See also ([VIII], 30, Theorem 5). For the refinement of 'Sylvester's Theorem' given in the statement of **19·6** see Dunford ([16], 206, Theorem 2·29). We may also mention a generalization by Frobenius ([20]) for the case when f is a function of s variables and $A_1, A_2, \ldots, A_s$ are L.T.'s commutative in pairs. Phillips simplifies Frobenius's proof ([38], 270–271), and gives an analytical expression for $f(A_1, A_2, \ldots, A_s)$ comparable with (19·1·1) ([38], 273, formula (27)). For further references see ([VI], 21–23).

§**20.** Weyr constructs canonical bases for the eigen-value zero ([56], 190–196); his method is modified by Weyl ([XVI], 97–99). See also ([V], 86–92) and ([III], 162–166).

20·0–20·02. The index of an element of $\mathfrak{P}$, as defined in **20·0**, coincides with the 'grade' of an element of $\mathfrak{P}$ with respect to a given L.T. as defined by Turnbull and Aitken ([VII], 47). Their definition, however, which refers to every element of $\mathfrak{B}_n$, differs from that given in **20·0**. The conceptions of descent and order of an element seem to be new; for these, as well as for the rest of §**20**, see Hamburger ([23], 175–178).

20·1. The Weyr characteristic is introduced in [55] and ([56], 186). The numbers ρ_κ are defined in [55] and [56] by writing $\sum_{\kappa=1}^{\nu} \rho_\kappa$ as the nullity of A^ν; this sum, by Lemma **20·22**, is the rank of $\mathfrak{X}^\nu$.

21·21. Frobenius remarks that A is irreducible in a L.M. spanned by a chain belonging to A ([18], 24, Theorem III).

21·3. See the notes to **23·01** and **23·02**.

21·32. See the notes to **23·04**.

21·4. See Weyr ([56], 196–199, Art. 27).

22·0. Weyr discusses the canonical basis belonging to a general L.T. A in ([56], 199–200, Art. 28).

22·2. Weierstrass defined elementary divisors ([54]) two years before Jordan obtained the canonical form with which they are intimately connected.

22·21. The Segre characteristic is defined in ([42], 137). The connection with the Weyr characteristic is clarified by Turnbull and Aitken ([VII], 79–80), who refer to the Ferrar diagram of partition numbers of the rank of $\mathfrak{P}_\mu$. In the equations

$$\sum_{\iota=1}^{s_\mu} j_{\mu\iota} = \sum_{\kappa=1}^{j_\mu} \rho_{\mu\kappa} = k_\mu, \quad j_\mu = j_{\mu 1}, \quad s_\mu = \rho_{\mu 1}$$

the two sets of numbers $\{j_{\mu\iota}\}$ and $\{\rho_{\mu\kappa}\}$ are 'conjugate partitions' of k_μ. (For the definition of the $\rho_{\mu\kappa}$ see (23·04·1).)

22·3. The theorem that A can be reduced to a diagonal matrix if, and only if, A has simple elementary divisors is due to Weierstrass ([54], 41–44).

22·31. The theorem is a special case of a theorem of Frobenius ([18], 25, Theorem V).

22·32. The theorem is given by Frobenius ([18], 26, Theorem VII).

22·4. The definition of similar L.T.'s is given by Frobenius ([18], 21).

22·41. In [54] Weierstrass proves a theorem slightly more general than Theorem **22·41.**

22·42. See Weyr ([56], 203).

23·0. See Voss ([51], 286–287).

23·01 and **23·02.** See Weyr ([56], 214–215). The formula $S = CB^{-1}$ for every matrix commutative with A is Weyr's formula (3) on p. 214. A different method of determining the most general matrix S commutative with A is due to Taber ([48]), who uses Weyr's canonical form for A.

23·04. Formula (23·04·2) is given without proof by Frobenius ([18], 29, Theorem XV). The first proof is due to Maurer ([37]); a simpler proof is given by Voss ([51], 289–294).

23·11. Clifford ([10], 339) outlines a proof that a L.T. S commutative with A can be written as a polynomial in A. He seems to have in mind the case when A has simple eigen-values. See Buchheim ([3], 80–82, Art. 13) and Weyr ([56], 216–218, Art. 40).

23·2 and **23·21.** Sylvester ([47], 158) states a theorem for 'matrices non-dérogatoires' (see the note to **18·3**) which is equivalent to our Theorem **23·21.** He indicates that he has verified it for $n = 3$. The first proof of Sylvester's theorem is given for general n by Taber ([49]). Frobenius, before Sylvester, states an equivalent theorem without proof ([18], 28, Theorem XIII). The first proof of the theorem in Frobenius's form is due to Landsberg ([35], 340–342). For further references see ([VI], 93–94).

23·4 and **23·41.** Hilton determines by direct computation for a special example of a matrix A the general form of a matrix commutative with all matrices commutative with A ([IV], Chapter 5, §3, 117–118). In ([VII], 150, Theorem 1) and ([VIII], 106, Theorem 2) we find the following theorem: *Any matrix S which is commutative not only with A but also with every matrix commutative with A is a polynomial in A.* The refinement in our alternative formulation of Theorem **23·4** that S, to be a polynomial in A, need only be commutative with A and with all projectors commutative with A does not seem to have been noticed before; nor does the first formulation of our Theorem **23·4** in terms of the complete reduction of A and S; see Hamburger [23 (*a*)].

23·43. Frobenius raises the question whether the relation $AB = BA$ implies the existence of C such that $A = p(C)$ and $B = q(C)$ ([20], 603–604). The negative answer is due to Phillips ([38], 275–276), who discusses the examples for A and B given in **23·43**. It is interesting to notice that Frobenius (loc. cit.) mentions the same examples for A and B and sees that

$$A^2 = B^2 = AB = BA = O,$$

but he apparently does not notice that they provide the answer to his question.

CHAPTER V

§§ **24** and **25.** The pencil $H - \lambda G$ was first considered by Lagrange ([XIV], 380–383). Jacobi carried the discussion further ([32], 247–255), and gave the spectral representation corresponding to our formula (25·21·3) for the case of simple eigen-values. Weierstrass, in 1858, first proved that this representation also holds in the general case of multiple eigen-values ([53]). See also ([XI(*a*)], 1564–1566) and ([X], 32–33).

27·0–27·02. The theory of small oscillations was first given in a famous chapter in the first volume of Lagrange's *Mécanique analytique*. The essential results were already in the first edition of 1788. In the second edition the theory was considerably enlarged (see [XIV], especially 369–390). Lagrange's faulty conclusion ([XIV], 383) that multiple eigen-values of $H - \lambda G$ imply an unstable position of equilibrium was corrected by Weierstrass ([53], 243–

246), who clarified the difficulty. In 1846, Dirichlet ([15]) proved, independently of Lagrange's method, that the position of equilibrium is stable if V has an isolated minimum. His method was simpler and more general and did not use the approximating equations (27·0·5). Dirichlet's proof is given by Appell (loc. cit. 331–332). Dirichlet's conditions of stability are more general than those of **27·01**, since V may have an isolated minimum for $q = 0$ and at the same time the form $(Hq, q) = \sum_{\mu,\nu=1}^{n} a_{\mu\nu} q_\mu q_\nu$ of (27·0·4) may be only positive semi-definite; the terms in V of order higher than the second then determine the sign of $V - V_0$ in the neighbourhood of $q = 0$.

The question arises whether the equilibrium position is stable or unstable when Dirichlet's minimum condition for V is not satisfied. (We use a definition for instability corresponding to that of **27·01** for stability. We say that the position $q = 0$ is unstable if there corresponds to any small positive number ϵ a particular system of integrals $\{q_\nu(t)\}$, defined by the original differential equations (27·0·2) and with initial values satisfying the inequalities

$$|q_\nu(0)| < \epsilon, \quad |\dot{q}_\nu(0)| < \epsilon \quad (1 \leqslant \nu \leqslant n),$$

such that at least one of the $q_\nu(t)$ satisfies the inequality $|q_\nu(t)| > C$ for some finite value of t and for a certain positive constant C independent of the initial values of $q_\nu(0)$ and $\dot{q}_\nu(0)$). The discussion of the integrals $\{q_\nu(t)\}$ of (27·0·2) is here complicated by the fact that when an integral $q(t)$ ceases to be small for some finite value of t the equation (27·0·5) also ceases to be an approximation to the Lagrange equations (27·0·2) for this integral. It has, nevertheless, been possible to prove the instability of the equilibrium position in a great number of cases. See the numerous references given by Appell (loc. cit. 333, Remarque II). We mention here the results of two papers only, which discuss what seem to be the most significant cases of instability. The first is Liapounoff's Theorem ([36]): *If at least one of the eigen-values* λ_ν that occur in (27·0·6) *is negative, then the position of equilibrium is unstable.* Liapounoff's proof depends essentially on Poincaré's theory of the asymptotic approximation to the integrals of systems of ordinary linear differential equations of first order. The second result that we mention is Hamel's ([24]). He discusses for $n = 2$ the case when $V = V_0$ along a curve passing through the origin with $V > V_0$ in the neighbourhood of this curve. Here the origin is a minimum of V, but not an isolated minimum as in Dirichlet's case. Hamel proves that the position of equilibrium is unstable if

$$\text{(i)}\quad T = a\dot{q}_1^2 + b\dot{q}_2^2,$$

where a and b are continuous positive functions of q_1 and q_2, and

$$\text{(ii)}\quad V = V_0 + g(q_1) . f(q_1, q_2),$$

where f and g are power series subject to the following conditions:

$$(\alpha)\ g(0) = 0, \quad g(q_1) > 0 \quad \text{for} \quad q_1 \neq 0,$$

$$(\beta)\ f(q_1, q_2) > 0 \quad \text{for} \quad q \neq 0.$$

We have quoted a simplified form of Hamel's conditions. He does not confine his argument to analytic functions, and he only needs the first-order derivatives of f and g with regard to q_1 subject to certain further restrictions.

For the inequalities of **27·02** see also [13].

REFERENCES

Publications dealing entirely with the theory of finite dimensional linear transformations

H. Grassmann.

I. *Die lineale Ausdehnungslehre* (Leipzig, 1844). [*Gesammelte mathematische und physikalische Werke*, I, Part 1.]

II. *Die Ausdehnungslehre, vollständig und in strenger Form* (Berlin, 1862). [*Gesammelte mathematische und physikalische Werke*, I, Part 2.]

P. R. Halmos.

III. *Finite dimensional vector spaces*, Annals of Mathematics Studies, 7 (Princeton, 1942).

H. Hilton.

IV. *Homogeneous linear substitutions* (Oxford, 1914).

G. Julia.

V. *Introduction mathématique aux théories quantiques*, Première partie (Paris, 1936).

C. C. MacDuffee.

VI. *The theory of Matrices*, Ergebnisse der Mathematik und ihrer Grenzgebiete, II, 5 (Berlin, 1933).

H. W. Turnbull and A. C. Aitken.

VII. *An introduction to the Theory of Canonical Matrices* (London and Glasgow, 1932).

J. H. M. Wedderburn.

VIII. *Lectures on Matrices*, American Mathematical Society Colloquium Publications, XVII (New York, 1934).

Publications dealing in part with the theory of finite dimensional linear transformations

G. Carathéodory.

IX. *Vorlesungen über reele Funktionen* (2nd ed., Leipzig and Berlin, 1927), 307–349.

R. Courant and D. Hilbert.

X. *Methoden der mathematischen Physik*, I (2nd ed., Berlin, 1931), 1–38.

W. R. Hamilton.

XI. *Lectures on Quaternions* (Dublin, 1853).

E. Hellinger and O. Toeplitz.

XI(*a*). Integralgleichungen und Gleichungen mit unendlich vielen Unbekannten, *Encyklopädie der mathematischen Wissenschaften*, II, 3.2, c. 13, 1335–1601.

C. Jordan.

XII. *Traité des substitutions et des équations algébriques* (Paris, 1870), 114–126.

XIII. *Cours d'analyse*, III (1st ed., Paris, 1887), 170–175.

J. L. Lagrange.

XIV. *Mécanique analytique*, I (1st ed., Paris, 1788; 2nd ed., Paris, 1811). [*Oeuvres*, XI, 369–444.]

O. Schreier and E. Sperner.

XV. *Einführung in die analytische Geometrie und Algebra*, I, Hamburger mathematische Einzelschriften 10 (Leipzig and Berlin, 1931), 1–50; II, Hamburger mathematische Einzelschriften 19 (Leipzig and Berlin, 1935), 35–131.

H. Weyl.

XVI. *Mathematische Analyse des Raumproblems* (Berlin, 1923), 88–100.

MEMOIRS

N. Aronszajn.

*1. Rayleigh-Ritz and A. Weinstein methods for approximation of eigenvalues. 1. Operators in a Hilbert space, *Proc. American Nat. Acad. Sci.* 34 (1948), 474–480.

L. Autonne.

1(*a*). Sur l'Hermitien, *Rend. di Palermo*, 16 (1902), 104–128.

F. Brioschi.

2. Note sur un théorème relatif aux déterminants gauches, *Journal de Math.* 19 (1854), 253–256. [*Opere Matematiche*, V, 160–164.]

A. Buchheim.

3. On the Theory of Matrices. *Proc. London Math. Soc.* 16 (1884–1885), 63–82.
4. An Extension of a Theorem of Professor Sylvester's relating to Matrices. *Phil. Mag.* (5), 22 (1886), 173–174.

A. Cauchy.

5. Sur l'équation à l'aide de laquelle on détermine les inégalités séculaires des mouvements des planètes (1829), *Oeuvres complètes*, IIe série, IX, 174–195.

A. Cayley.

6. Sur quelques propriétés des déterminants gauches, *Journal für Math.* 32 (1846), 119–123. [*Collected Mathematical Papers*, I, 332–336.]
7. Sur la transformation d'une fonction quadratique en elle même par des substitutions linéaires. *Journal für Math.* 50 (1855), 288–299. [*Collected Mathematical Papers*, II, 192–201.]
8. A memoir on the theory of matrices. *Phil. Trans. Royal Soc.* 148 (1858), 17–37. [*Collected Mathematical Papers*, II, 475–496.]

* The reference to Aronszajn's paper was added after the list of references had been compiled.

E. B. Christoffel.

9. Theorie der bilinearen Funktionen. *Journal für Math.* 68 (1868), 253–272.

W. K. Clifford.

10. A Fragment on Matrices (1875), *Mathematical Papers*, 337–341.

R. Courant.

11. Über die Abhängigkeit der Schwingungszahlen einer Membran von ihrer Begrenzung und über asymptotische Eigenwertsverteilung, *Göttinger Nachrichten* (1919), 255–264.
12. Über die Eigenwerte bei den Differentialgleichungen der mathematischen Physik, *Math. Zeitschrift*, 7 (1920), 1–57.
13. Zur Theorie der kleinen Schwingungen, *Zeitschrift für ang. Math. und Mech.* 2 (1922), 278–285.
14. Über die Anwendung der Variationsrechnung in der Theorie der Eigenschwingungen und über neue Klassen von Funktionalgleichungen, *Acta Math.* 49 (1926), 1–68.

G. Lejeune-Dirichlet.

15. Über die Stabilität des Gleichgewichts, *Journal für Math.* 32 (1846), 85–88. [*Werke*, II, 3–8.]

N. Dunford.

16. Spectral Theory I, Convergence to projectors, *Trans. American Math. Soc.* 54 (1943), 185–217.

E. Fischer.

17. Über quadratische Formen mit reellen Koefficienten, *Monatshefte für Math. und Phys.* 16 (1905), 234–249.

G. Frobenius.

18. Über lineare Substitutionen und bilineare Formen, *Journal für Math.* 84 (1878), 1–63.
19. Über die cogredienten Transformationen der bilinearen Formen, *Berliner Sitzungsberichte* (1896), 7–16.
20. Über vertauschbare Matrizen, *Berliner Sitzungsberichte* (1896), 601–614.

J. P. Gram.

21. Über die Entwicklung reeller Funktionen in Reihen, mittelst der Methode der kleinsten Quadrate, *Journal für Math.* 94 (1883), 41–73.

H. Grassmann.

22. *Geometrische Analyse geknüpft an die von Leibnitz erfundene geometrische Charakteristik.* Mit einer erläuternden Abhandlung von A. F. Möbius: *Die Grassmannsche Lehre von Punktgrössen und den davon abhängenden Grössenformen*, Preisschriften, gekrönt und herausgegeben von der fürstlich Jablonowskischen Gesellschaft zu Leipzig (Leipzig, 1847), 1–60, 61–79. [*Gesammelte mathematische und physikalische Werke*, I, Part 1.]

H. L. Hamburger.

23. Remarks on the reduction of a linear transformation to Jordan's canonical form, *Journal London Math. Soc.* 22 (1947), 173–179.

23 (*a*). A theorem on commutative matrices, *Journal London Math. Soc.* 24 (1949), 200–206.

G. Hamel.

24. Über die Instabilität der Gleichgewichtslage eines Systems von zwei Freiheitsgraden, *Math. Annalen*, 57 (1903), 541–553.

W. R. Hamilton.

25. Communications on the Theory of Quaternions, *Proc. Royal Irish Acad.* 2 (1843/44), 424–434; 3 (1844/45), 1–16, 273–292, 344–353, Appendix XXXI–LX.
26. On Quaternions or on a new system of Imaginaries in Algebra, *Phil. Mag.* (3) 25 (1844), 10–14, 241–246, 489–495; (3) 26 (1845), 220–244; (3) 29 (1846), 26–31, 113–122, 326–328.

C. Hermite.

27. Sur la théorie des formes quadratiques ternaires indéfinies, *Journal für Math.* 47 (1854), 307–312. [*Oeuvres*, I, 193–199.]
28. Sur la théorie des formes quadratiques, Second mémoire, *Journal für Math.* 47 (1854), 343–368. [*Oeuvres*, I, 234–263.]
29. Remarque sur un théorème de Cauchy, *Comptes rendus*, 41 (1855). [*Oeuvres*, I, 479–481.]
30. Sur la formule d'interpolation de Lagrange, *Journal für Math.* 84 (1878), 70–79. [*Oeuvres*, III, 432–443.]

D. Hilbert.

31. Grundzüge einer allgemeinen Theorie der linearen Integralgleichungen (1te Mitteilung), *Göttinger Nachrichten* (1904), 41–91; (2te Mitteilung), *Göttinger Nachrichten* (1904), 213–259; (4te Mitteilung), *Göttinger Nachrichten* (1906), 157–227; (5te Mitteilung), *Göttinger Nachrichten* (1906), 439–480. [Reprinted in a book with the same title (Leipzig and Berlin, 1924), 1–38, 39–81, 109–174, 174–212.]

C. G. J. Jacobi.

32. De binis quibuslibet functionibus homogeneis secundi ordinis per substitutiones lineares in alias binas transformandis quae solis quadratis variabilium constant, *Journal für Math.* 12 (1834), 1–69. [*Werke*, III, 191–268.]

J. L. Lagrange.

33. Nouvelle solution du problème du mouvement de rotation d'un corps quelconque qui n'est animé par aucune force accélératrice (1773), *Oeuvres*, III, 579–616.

E. N. Laguerre.

34. Sur le calcul des systèmes linéaires, *Journal de l'École Polytechnique*, Cahier, 42 (1867), 215–264. [*Oeuvres*, I, 221–267.]

G. Landsberg.

35. Über Fundamentalsysteme und bilineare Formen, *Journal für Math.* 116 (1896), 331–349.

A. Liapounoff.

36. Sur l'instabilité de l'équilibre dans certains cas où la fonction de forces n'est pas un maximum, *Journal de Math.* (5), 3 (1897), 81–94.

L. Maurer.

37. *Zur Theorie der linearen Substitutionen*, Dissertation (Strassburg, 1887).

H. B. Phillips.

38. Functions of matrices, *American J. of Math.* 41 (1918), 266–278.

F. Riesz.

39. Über lineare Funktionalgleichungen, *Acta Math.* 41 (1918), 71–98.

E. Schmidt.

40. Zur Theorie der linearen und nicht-linearen Integralgleichungen, I Teil, Entwicklung willkürlicher Funktionen nach Systemen vorgeschriebener, *Math. Annalen*, 63 (1907), 433–476.

I. Schur.

41. Über die charakteristischen Wurzeln einer linearen Substitution mit einer Anwendung auf die Theorie der Integralgleichungen, *Math. Annalen*, 66 (1909), 488–510.

C. Segre.

42. Sulla teoria e sulla classificazione delle omografie in uno spazio lineare ad un numero qualunque di dimensioni, *Atti Accad. dei Lincei, Memorie*, (3), 19 (1884), 127–148.

L. Stickelberger.

43. *Zur Theorie der linearen Differentialgleichungen*, Akademische Antrittschrift (Leipzig, 1881).

J. J. Sylvester.

44. Sur les puissances et les racines des substitutions linéaires, *Comptes rendus*, 94 (1882), 55–59. [*Collected Mathematical Papers*, III, 562–564.]
45. On the Equation to the Secular Inequalities in the Planetary Theory, *Phil. Mag.* (5), 16 (1883), 267–269. [*Collected Mathematical Papers*, IV, 110–111.]
46. On involutants and other allied species of invariants to matrix systems, *Johns Hopkins Univ. Circulars*, 3 (1884), 9–12, 34, 35. [*Collected Mathematical Papers*, IV, 133–145.]
47. Sur les quantités formant un groupe de nonions analogues aux quaternions de Hamilton, *Comptes rendus*, 98 (1884), 273–276, 471–475. [*Collected Mathematical Papers*, IV, 154–159.]

H. Taber.

48. On the Matrical Equation $\varphi\Omega = \Omega\varphi$, *Proc. American Acad. Boston*, 26 (1891), 64–66.
49. On a theorem of Sylvester's relating to Non-degenerate Matrices, *Proc. American Acad. Boston*, 27 (1893), 46–55.

O. Toeplitz.

50. Das algebraische Analogen zu einem Satz von Fejer, *Math. Zeitschrift*, 2 (1918), 187–197.

A. Voss.

51. Über die mit einer bilinearen Form vertauschbaren bilinearen Formen, *Münchener Sitzungsberichte*, 19 (1889), 283–300.

H. Weber.

52. Über die Integration der partialen Differentialgleichung

$$\frac{\partial^2 u}{\partial x^2} + \frac{\partial^2 u}{\partial y^2} + k^2 u = 0,$$

Math. Annalen, 1 (1869), 1–36.

K. Weierstrass.

53. Über ein die homogenen Functionen zweiten Grades betreffendes Theorem, nebst Anwendung desselben auf die Theorie der kleinen Schwingungen, *Monatsberichte d. Akad. zu Berlin* (1858), 207–220. [*Werke*, I, 233–246.]
54. Zur Theorie der bilinearen und quadratischen Formen, *Monatsberichte d. Akad. zu Berlin* (1868), 310–338. [*Werke*, II, 19–44.]

Ed. Weyr.

55. Repartition des matrices en espèces et formation de toutes les espèces, *Comptes rendus*, 100 (1885), 966–969.
56. *O theorii forem bilinearných*. Praze (1889). Translated under the title 'Zur Theorie der bilinearen Formen', *Monatshefte für Math. und Phys.* 1 (1890), 163–236.

INDEX OF AUTHORS

GENERAL INDEX

L.T. = Linear transformation   L.M. = Linear manifold
H.T. = Hermitian transformation